Applications
of Magnetism

APPLICATIONS OF MAGNETISM

J. K. WATSON

University of Florida

A WILEY-INTERSCIENCE PUBLICATION

JOHN WILEY & SONS

New York • Chichester • Brisbane • Toronto

Library of Congress Cataloging in Publication Data:

Watson, James Kenneth, 1929–
   Applications of magnetism.

   "A Wiley-Interscience publication."
   Includes bibliographies and index.
   1. Magnetics. I. Title.
TK153.W35   621.3   79-20882
ISBN 0-471-03540-8

Printed in the United States of America

10 9 8 7 6 5 4 3 2 1

To my wife Betty
and to
Rick, William, and Nancy

Preface

The goal of this book is to introduce the advanced undergraduate to electrical engineering applications of magnetism. Assuming a modest background of field theory and electric circuits, the book seeks the development of a foundation of insights and skills that span across representative applications of modern magnetism. It also aims to bridge a gap, to provide for the practicing electrical engineer an access to the wealth of specialized literature on magnetics.

I perceive two needs: the need for a pedagogical resource and the need for an electrical engineering introduction to applied magnetics. Pedagogically, the text provides for the development of student design skills, putting together elementary ideas from circuits, device modeling, electromagnetic fields, and materials physics. These topics are brought together in a wide range of practical applications, wide enough to interest most electrical engineers and deep enough to give a meaningful overview of magnetic phenomena.

As examples of the need for a general introduction to magnetism, consider the following recent advances that are related to design opportunities for engineers. New magnetic alloys and metallurgical processes, originally developed for magnetic amplifier technology, continue to be available for other innovative applications. The materials family of magnetic oxides—ferrites and garnets—has continued to flourish with new materials of a wide range of properties, available in a great variety of configurations. Technologies based on this general class of materials include the magnetic-core memory, microwave magnetics in many forms, linear low-loss ferrites for high-frequency inductors and transformers, permanent magnets, all types of magnetic tape recording, floppy disks for digital storage, and the new technology of magnetic bubble memory.

New applications for permanent magnets will open up, making use of a new material breakthrough. Permanent magnets now being produced have coercivity values that once were considered to be fundamentally unattainable. In the category of systems to produce magnetic fields, there are increasingly varied applications that require high magnetic fields of specified gradient. Examples include enormous field strengths for materials research, systems proposed for the magnetic confinement of plasmas for fusion energy, magnetic gradient separation processes for refining minerals or for separating solid wastes, and proposed tracks for high-speed ground transportation using magnetic levitation instead of wheels. Broadband magnetic circuits have had an impact on the design of radio circuits. D-c to d-c converters, ferroresonant transformers, and switching regulators have revolutionized power supply design. Sensitive magnetometers chart geomagnetic and lunar fields. Magnetic plated wire continues to be a viable random-access digital storage technology for harsh environments. Thin-film technology is being widely adapted to new applications, including magnetic heads for high-density data recording and reproduction. Domain magnetics has emerged from laboratory obscurity to become an integrated circuit memory technology in which domains are moved, stretched, shrunk, or split with high reliability. Archival memory technology continues to be dominated by magnetic recording on tapes and disks.

Even though the list above is not exhaustive, it is evident that modern applied magnetism possesses a breadth and scope that cuts across the entire discipline of electrical engineering. This book seeks to meet the electrical engineer's need for a comprehensive introduction to the field, a need not met by any other book. The presentation is at the bachelor's level, intended to be suitable for senior undergraduates or graduate students, as well as for self-study by the practicing engineer. The subject is developed in a self-contained and elementary manner, with a central emphasis on the relation of material properties to circuit applications. A prior exposure to field theory is assumed as well as a background in electric circuits. No quantum mechanics is required, although some results from it are cited.

The subject matter is organized into eight chapters. Chapter 1 discusses notation and units, then introduces the concept that magnetic parameters translate into device volt-ampere characteristics. Using the notion of an ideal core shape, an approximate piecewise-linear circuit model is derived using four material parameters: saturation, coercivity, permeability, and dynamic loss. Each of the following chapters focuses on one of the four items in more detail to discuss the physics of the process, mathematical models, approximations, and typically an application that depends critically on that one particular parameter. Chapter 6 is a collection of applications for which several material parameters are important. These include the coincident-current core memory and about twenty more applications using inductors, transformers, and transformerlike circuits. Chapter 7 gives an introductory treatment of magnetic recording; Chapter 8 includes a more comprehensive synopsis of magnetic material physics, to sensibly describe domain wall and magnetic bubble applications.

Let me now explain my approach to four of the issues that face an author of this subject. First, the matter of units and notation. MKS (SI) units are used throughout, with CGS units carried along in a secondary role, since so much of the published literature on magnetic materials uses that system. The intrinsic magnetic material parameter is treated usually as a flux density, but both choices are shown and are considered to be equally fundamental. Second, the most prominent experimental properties of ferromagnetism are not only nonlinear but also double-valued. The general approach might be described as that of successive approximations, beginning with the simplest possible piecewise-linear model. I have not hesitated to make analyses based on conceptual models of ideal materials, since in this text I try to expose the concepts. Third, how is the theory of magnetism developed? My general guideline has been to give no more theory than is required for the immediate issue at hand. Thus Chapter 2 defines and uses the Bohr magneton to explain intrinsic material saturation; Chapter 4 invokes cooperative models as a requirement for high susceptibility and for remanence. Finally, to describe domain walls, Chapter 8 gives the Kittel-Galt model of exchange coupling.

The fourth matter for comment is the treatment of magnetostatics, perhaps the most interesting issue of all. The sequence of magnetostatic concepts and skills is covered in two major steps. Chapter 3 makes field calculations from currents and from specified distributions of magnetization, models the effect of short airgaps, introduces reluctance approximations, and considers design with permanent magnets. Chapter 8 deals more explicitly with demagnetization and self-consistency in the context of distributed magnetic systems.

I have agonized over the basic problem of trying to treat a breadth of topics accurately yet compactly, and in a manner accessible to electrical engineers. Where the criteria conflict, as they often do, I chose simple overviews of major concepts rather than detailed scientific accuracy. My rationale is that the book is introductory to the field, with its major aim being to communicate concepts of magnetism to nonmagneticians. I apologize to my colleagues whose work I have inadequately treated, either due to the above criteria or due to my other limitations.

Several types of courses can be designed by selecting topics to suit the needs of different universities. For instance, a course emphasizing materials and magnetic processes could be based on excerpts from Chapters 1, 2, 3, and 7 plus all of Chapters 4, 5, and 8, omitting Chapter 6. To emphasize only applications, one could cover all of Chapters 1, 3, 6, and 7 plus excerpts from 2 and 5. For a single-quarter course at Florida, a balanced emphasis uses Chapters 1, 2, 3, 4, and 7 with excerpts from 5, 6, and 8 introduced at appropriate points in the sequence of presentation. Homework problems are a major component of the course and are strongly encouraged for any course.

I would like to express my appreciation to the many colleagues from whom I have learned and to the decade of Florida students who have encouraged the assembling of this book. I am grateful for research support from the National Science Foundation which enabled me to gain an understanding of several ideas that underlie this tutorial treatment. I have learned by working with M. H. Graham, D. B. Dove, and L. J. Schwee; I appreciate the insights that have been generously given by V. J. Folen, F. B. Humphrey, F. B. Hagedorn and a host of others. Special thanks go to Henry C. Bourne, Jr. from whom I learned the piecewise-linear model used in Chapter 1, and who first exposed me to a systematic theory of magnetism. I thank Fritz J. Friedlaender for his encouragement and for his many suggestions, R. O. McCary for his advice and support, P. G. Frischman for his constructive critique; dozens of colleagues for permission to use figures from their research publications; and finally Mrs. Vita Zamorano who typed the manuscript. I appreciate the good advice that has led to several improvements. But I must accept sole responsibility for the advice I chose not to take, and for the remaining errors, shortcomings, and imbalances. Readers are eagerly invited to advise me of flaws that should be corrected in any future editions.

J. K. WATSON

Gainesville, Florida
January 1980

Contents

1.
Introduction

Electrical engineering applications of magnetism are built on a foundation of skills in circuits, electromagnetic field theory and the physics of materials. The term *application* of magnetism is used here to refer to a solution of an engineering problem, in particular a solution that depends on the innovative use of one or more magnetic material properties. An *electrical engineering* application of magnetism is based primarily on the use of known properties of existing materials. This text therefore emphasizes the electrical functions that can be realized from magnetic material properties, rather than emphasizing how material parameters can be achieved. Applications are used as the media for illustrating the meaning of basic magnetic parameters. The applications chosen for description are broad in scope but are not encyclopedic. Some were selected because they illustrate a particular magnetic property; others were chosen because of my interest or judgment of their importance. All motors and most motorlike devices are beyond the intended scope of this work.

Of the three foundation skills—circuits, fields, and materials—it is assumed that the typical reader at this point possesses greatest insights in circuits. For that reason the modeling process begins as a circuit-based model using magnetic cores. There are two broad classes of geometries of magnetic applications: applications that use cores of some sort wound with wire, and applications in which the magnetic material is otherwise distributed in space. Postponement of distributed geometries, and in fact the initial assumption of an ideal core geometry, permits the initial neglect of the demagnetizing field. In summary, it is suggested that any modeling of magnetic field devices is necessarily accompanied by special assumptions of device geometry, as in Section 1.3. Effects of airgaps on cores are taken into account in Chapter 3.

1.1 PERSPECTIVE

The first task of Chapter 1 is to define the values and dimensions of the magnetic units to be used, taken up in Section 1.2 for B and H and in Section 1.3.2 for the integral quantities.

The second topic of the chapter is to illustrate for a class of core geometries how magnetic material properties are related to the volt·ampere characteristics of the magnetic device made of that material. The integration procedures for magnetic materials are analogous to conductor and capacitor systems, however the solenoidal property of magnetism strongly suggests a fundamentally different geometrical dependence.

The third topic of Chapter 1 is to introduce a piecewise-linear model for magnetic materials, and for the associated electric circuit model. The present purpose is to illustrate the relation between magnetic models and their circuit representations. Each of the four components modeled in this simple way is the subject of a more detailed treatment in another chapter to follow. As the model is developed it is used to reveal the key ideas of a variety of applications.

1.2 EQUATIONS AND UNITS FOR *B* AND *H*

The symbols *B* and *H* are the magnetic field parameters at a point in space; *B* is magnetic flux density or magnetic induction, and *H* is magnetic field strength. Both quantities are actually vectors, with both magnitude and direction. In free space *B* and *H* are always parallel in direction and proportional in magnitude, but inside magnetic materials their relationship is more complicated. The value of the free-space constant of proportionality depends on the units being used.

Although there are at least six sets of units in existence, this text generally disregards all but two, the rationalized MKS or Georgi, and the CGS or Gaussian. Most calculations are done in MKS because of its wide acceptance as a subset of the international standard, the SI system. However in pragmatic recognition of the great continuing use of the CGS system, and of the considerable amount of existing literature in the materials area that uses the CGS system, values of newly introduced concepts are given also in CGS units. For ease of interpretation of material parameters, it is necessary to be able to translate with facility to and from CGS units.

1.2.1 MKS or SI Units

Inside magnetic materials the vector field quantities *B*, *H* are sometimes not parallel, so it is useful to represent the material contribution separately. In the SI system the equation for flux density is written in either of two ways:

$$B = \mu_0(H + M) \tag{1.1}$$

$$B = \mu_0 H + B_i \qquad \text{also written } B = \mu_0 H + J. \tag{1.2}$$

Each of the two equations is in units of tesla (T) or webers per square meter (Wb/m^2) and is the sum of a free-space component plus a component due to the presence of matter. In the absence of magnetic material the second term is zero, so that *B* and *H* are related by the magnetic constant μ_0. Another name* for μ_0 is the permeability of free space; its value is 4π 10^{-7} henry per meter (H/m). In (1.1) the material property is represented by the "magnetization" M, which has the same dimensions as H, amperes per meter (A/m). In (1.2) the material property is carried by the parameter B_i or J, which is called "intrinsic induction," "intrinsic flux density," or "magnetic polarization. From the form of the equation it is evident that B_i has the same units as B. The conceptual difference between M and B_i is that M is related to the strength of a magnetic pole, whereas B_i is the density of flux emanating from it. Of course the two quantities differ in numerical value by almost a million, since B_i includes the magnetic constant. For an ideal linear material with magnetization proportional to applied field intensity through the magnetic susceptibility χ,[†]

$$M = \chi H \qquad \text{and also} \qquad B_i = \mu_0 \chi H. \tag{1.3}$$

Thus either (1.1) or (1.2) reduces to the same result

$$B = \mu_0 H (1 + \chi) = \mu_0 \mu_r H = \mu H \tag{1.4}$$

In the last equation μ_r is the relative permeability and is the quantity referred to in a statement such as "the permeability of the iron sample is 1000." There are only a few special arrangements for which (1.3) is especially useful or accurate, because of nonlinear relationships between M and H. So a more realistic and general definition of the material parameter is obtained by subtracting the free-space component of flux density from the total, as

$$B_i = B - \mu_0 H \qquad \text{and} \qquad M = \frac{B}{\mu_0} - H. \tag{1.5}$$

1.2.2 CGS Units

When using CGS units, there are again two formats of the equation for flux density, where the analog to (1.1) is

$$B = H + 4\pi M. \tag{1.6}$$

The analog to (1.2) is unchanged from $B = \mu_0 H + B_i$. Flux density B now has the units of gauss (G), field intensity H has the units of oersteds (Oe), and the magnetic constant (permeability of space) has the value of unity and the units of G/Oe. The 4π factor of (1.6), characteristic of unrationalized systems of units, is a consequence of the historical

---

*Actually there is a conceptual distinction between the two, ignored here.

[†]χ_m is the standard symbol for magnetic susceptibility. The subscript is unnecessary here for clarity.

definition of magnetic poles in terms of forces. The term M is a pole density and $4\pi M$ is a density of lines of flux. For the same ideally linear condition given by (1.3) with magnetization proportional to H, the CGS analog to (1.4) is given as

$$B = H(1 + 4\pi\chi) = \mu H. \tag{1.7}$$

Although it is potentially confusing that the CGS and SI values for χ differ by 4π, it is convenient that the CGS value of μ is the same as the relative permeability in SI units. In a strict interpretation, the CGS μ is a numerical multiplier without units, as is μ_r in SI units. If so, the units of the right-hand side of (1.7) can be reconciled by an implicit magnetic constant, not written because its value is unity.

1.2.3 Conversion Between MKS and CGS Units

Having considered the SI and CGS units separately, we now address the minor problem of converting from one to the other. Conversion of B is simplest, merely involving a factor of 10^4. If a field has a flux density of 1 T, its value in CGS units is 10,000 G. Conversion of H is only slightly more complicated: a field strength of 4π Oe has a value of 10^3 A/m. That is, 1 Oe is the same field strength as 79.58 A/m $= 10^3/4\,\pi$.

EXAMPLE A

Earth's magnetic field has a flux density value of about $\frac{1}{2}$ G, including both horizontal and vertical components. Express the value in oersteds and in SI units.

ANSWER.   Since only free space is involved, it follows that the CGS value of H is $\frac{1}{2}$ Oe. The SI value of B is 5×10^{-5} T; the SI value of H is approximately 40 A/m. Incidentally, there exists a small unit for B called a gamma, used for describing terrestial and lunar magnetic fields (a gamma describes the same field as 10^{-9} T).

EXAMPLE B

Suppose a field strength of $H = 10^3$ A/m is applied to an ideal material of relative permeability $\mu_r = 50$, in a core configuration for which (1.1) through (1.7) are valid. For this case, find the values of all the magnetic parameters used in the equations.

ANSWER.   For SI units: $\chi = 49$, $\mu = 2\pi 10^{-5} = 6.28 \times 10^{-5}$ T·m/A, $B = 2\pi 10^{-2} = 0.0628$ T, $B_i = 196\pi 10^{-4} = 0.0616$ T, $M = 49,000$ A/m.

For CGS units: $H = 4\pi = 12.57$ Oe, $B = 200\pi = 628.3$ G, $4\pi M = B - H = B_i = 196\pi = 615.8$ G, $M = 49$, $\chi = 49/4\pi = 3.90$.

1.2.4 Some Points of Confusion

Perhaps the greatest source of confusion in the use of SI units is associated with the various symbols and names used by different authors to describe the material parameters in (1.1) and (1.2). The most common symbols found instead of B_i are J, I, or M. In (1.1) the symbol H_i is sometimes found instead of M. As a first step in resolving the confusion, it must be established whether SI units are in fact being used. Second, it should be determined whether the form of the flux density equation is like (1.1) or (1.2). To make this determination it may be necessary to compare the actual values of the parameters with other known values. Units for integral quantities are listed in Section 1.3.3 both for SI and CGS units.

There are several points of confusion about the use of CGS units, which are aggravated because there are at least four types of CGS systems. The reason for the existence of so many systems is historical— different systems were used for electricity and for magnetism before the two phenomena were unified. Appendices in the book by Jackson [1] give a careful treatment of units. He has tabulated a comparison of key formulas and parameter values that shows where constant parameters c and 4π occur, in five systems of units. Sometimes in the use of a CGS equation it is not clear whether the units are gauss or oersteds, as in (1.6). One can neatly sidestep this issue by referring to the result in electromagnetic units (emu), leaving it to the reader to choose between gauss (the emu for B) or oersted (the emu for H). Example B of Section 2.1.1 gives an example of this technique.

1.3 RELATING MATERIAL PROPERTIES TO DEVICE CHARACTERISTICS

Almost every application of a magnetic device imposes a constraint on the device current and voltage. A designer must be able to specify the volt·ampere properties of the magnetic device to meet the circuit requirements. This chapter suggests how magnetic processes are manifest as circuit parameters, indicating, for instance, how to achieve a required value of inductance. But to define the inductor losses or to identify the limitations of performance under extreme conditions of signal frequency or amplitude, a more detailed examination of the magnetic materials and processes is necessary.

Three distinct steps are common to the design of the wide class of devices that use magnetic cores, whether a pulse transformer or a magnetic recording head. The first two steps are the selection of the magnetic core material and the specification of core geometry. Properties of materials are modeled subsequently. Our immediate goal is to illustrate how the geometry of a core affects the translation of magnetic bulk properties into volt·ampere characteristics. A designer in magnetics must be adept in that simple skill, to be presented in an introductory manner. Typically, information about magnetic materials is available for bulk properties only, independent of geometrical considerations. Every change of core shape or size must be taken into account as part of the design process. Introductory comments about material properties are followed by three subsections that show the mechanics of the procedure, tabulate the units for magnetic integral quantities, and compare analogous integration procedures for conductive and capacitive material systems.

1.3.1 Magnetic Material Properties

The notation and symbols for describing magnetic materials are the ones used in (1.1) and (1.2), that is, B, H, B_i or M, χ, and μ. These parameters* and others have obtained from a history of experimental measurements on typical samples. The measured results are normalized for sample geometry and are listed as characteristic values for the material chemistry, sometimes with additional specifications for the metallurgical processes. A graph of B versus H gives the best overview of material properties, such a graph is called a magnetization curve, a B-H characteristic, or a hysteresis loop. It is understood that each such result actually is an average over a typical sample of the total response, which usually includes a variety of reversal processes. The character and shape of magnetization curves vary remarkably with the method of measurement, the initial conditions of the sample, and the sample geometry. For the time being it is assumed that the excitation is a slowly varying periodic signal of large amplitude, sufficient to drive the material from one saturation limit to the other. It is required that the sample geometry provide a closed flux path, such as a toroidal core with no

*Two main classes of material are of interest for core applications, ferromagnets and ferrites. For either material, susceptibility χ is greater than unity and may be as high as several thousand. The intrinsic induction B_i saturates in the range of 1 T (about 0.3 T for ferrites, 2.2 for iron); the B–H curve usually possesses hysteresis. By comparison, for paramagnetic and diamagnetic materials χ is of the order of only 10^{-4} and is negative for diamagnets.

airgaps. These constraints permit a quantitative translation of magnetic parameters into the corresponding electrical measurement.

1.3.2 Design Mechanics

The B–H characteristic is a point-form, or derivative property that must be put back into an integral form to be applicable to a particular core. The specific core is assumed to possess an ideal closed path for magnetic flux, for instance, as the doughnut shape of a toroidal core.

Two separate integrations are required, one for flux and the other for potential.

Although the total flux in the core is the vector area integral $\Phi = \int \bar{B} \cdot d\bar{s}$, in this chapter it is assumed that $\bar{B}$ is constant over and normal to the cross-sectional area of the core, therefore can be removed from under the integral. The result is the simpler form $\Phi = BS$. In the graphical interpretation of Fig. 1.1, this corresponds to a change of scale of the ordinate axis in going from Fig. 1.1a to 1.1b, multiplying by the area of the core S.

Similarly, the total potential drop around the core is the vector line integral $F = \int \bar{H} \cdot d\bar{l}$, where it is assumed that H is constant and parallel

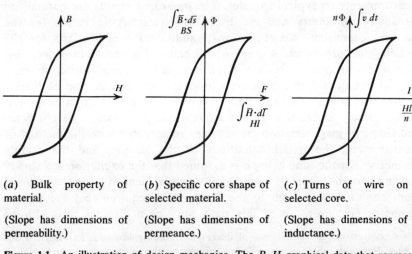

(a) Bulk property of material.

(b) Specific core shape of selected material.

(c) Turns of wire on selected core.

(Slope has dimensions of permeability.)

(Slope has dimensions of permeance.)

(Slope has dimensions of inductance.)

Figure 1.1 An illustration of design mechanics. The B–H graphical data that represent the intrinsic material property are very similar to the volt·second versus current data for the final device. As a first approximation, the only changes are the scale factors of the axes of the graphs. See text for explanation.

at every point along the flux path. Therefore H can be removed from under the integral, with the result $F = Hl$. As will be brought out subsequently, the physical requirement of this approximation is a homogeneous flux path. No airgaps are yet allowed. In Fig. 1.1a, the values on the abscissa axis are multiplied by the total path length "l" to give the values in Fig. 1.1b.

The simple pair of changes of scale factor just mentioned corresponds to a combination of the extrinsic design choice of the specific core geometry with the choice of intrinsic material properties specified by the $B–H$ loop. The final design step is the specification of the turns of wire to be wound upon the core. The number of turns n is depicted by a change of scale between the corresponding axes of Figs. 1.1b and 1.1c. The scale factors are defined by the equation $n\Phi = \int v \, dt$ along the ordinate and by $F/n = I$ along the abscissa, in order that the final result (Fig. 1.1c) will be represented in purely electrical units.

The remarkably simple integration of a nonlinear property that we have just accomplished deserves a few more comments. The approximation just described is useful and perhaps more accurate than might be expected from the mathematical requirements that B and H each be assumed constant over their respective regions of integration. The reasonable accuracy is because values for B and H are usually core averages, and averaging is a procedure that involves integration. Figure 1.1 deliberately was drawn with all three parts exactly alike, to emphasize the concept of keeping the same graph but changing the scale. In fact, the characteristic shape is changed slightly in going from Fig. 1.1a to 1.1b in a way that is brought out in the following two chapters.

In final reference to Fig. 1.1, consider the dimensions of *slope* on each of the three parts of the figure. In nonlinear circuits parameter values and measurement methods must have specific definitions to suit specific circuits. So at this occasion it is not our concern whether incremental slope or some sort of average slope is required. That is, a slope on Fig. 1.1a has the dimensions of magnetic permeability, μ; it is a separate question to find a specific value for a total $\mu = B/H$, or for an incremental $\mu = dB/dH$ at some specified operating point. In the same spirit, a slope on Fig. 1.1b has the dimensions of permeance $P = \mu S/l$, which is also the same as reciprocal reluctance, R^{-1}. And finally, a slope on Fig. 1.1c has the dimension of inductance. Dimensionally, inductance $L = \int v \, dt/I$ as well as $L = n^2 P$. Permeance is therefore a property of a specific core, which easily can be deduced from a measurement of inductance if the number of turns is known.

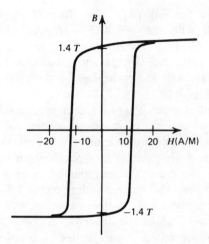

Figure 1.2 Static B–H loop for 50% Ni–Fe (Orthonol®). This alloy has been metallurgically processed to achieve a narrow B–H loop.

EXAMPLE C

Given the material data of Fig. 1.2, find the corresponding curve for a graph of $\int v\,dt$ versus I if 200 turns of wire are wound on commercial core no. 50004, a toroid of rectangular cross section (I.D. = 1.00, O.D. = 1.25, h = 0.25 in., nominal; section area S = 0.171 cm², mean path = l = $2\pi r_m$ = 8.97 cm). The core (Fig. 1.3) is a tape-wound core; that is, it is wound from a single, long continuous strip or tape of alloy, somewhat in the style of a clock spring. The given area is for tape thickness d = 2 mils. The purpose of the single-wound construction is to preserve the B–H loop squareness by avoiding airgap cuts through the core. Building up the core area by multiple layers of thin laminations is necessary if metal cores are to have good high-frequency response.

ANSWER. Using SI units and referring to Fig. 1.2, we tabulate the following required quantities: B has a well-defined region at the constant value B = 1.4 T; H has a constant region at the value 12 A/m; l(mean) = 8.97×10^{-2} m; S = 1.71×10^{-5} m²; n = 200 turns. The first pair of multiplications have the results: $\Phi = BS = 2.39 \times 10^{-5}$ Wb; $F = Hl = 1.08$ A for the constant regions. The final result is: $\int v\,dt = n\Phi = 4.78 \times 10^{-3}$ V·s; $I = F/n = 5.4$ mA. As a matter of interest, the area is estimated to be comprised of 57 layers of metallic tape. Note 1 in. is the same length as 2.54 cm; a mil is 10^{-3} in.

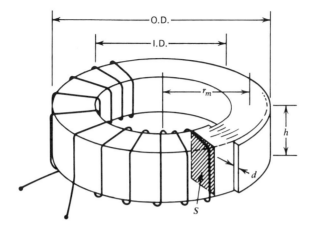

Figure 1.3 Tape-wound toroidal core with turns of wire. The effective cross section S may be less than overall core area $1/2(\text{O.D.} - \text{I.D.})h$ by an amount that depends on tape thickness, d.

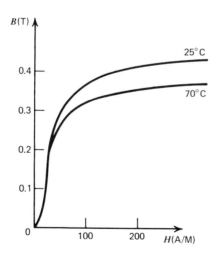

Initial relative permeability $\mu_i = 5000$ ($\pm 20\%$).

Frequency range $f \leq 10^6$ Hz.

Figure 1.4 Magnetization curve for a commercial Mn–Zn ferrite.

EXAMPLE D

Find the number of turns required to yield an inductance of 10 mH using the following core. The linear ferrite core material is specified in Fig. 1.4, which is an initial magnetization curve (of a previously demagnetized core). The core geometry is toroidal with the following nominal dimensions (inches): O.D. = 0.500, I.D. = 0.281, $h = 0.188$; path length $l = 3.03$ cm, effective area $S = 0.133$ cm^2. The manufacturing process involves the extrusion of a slurry of ferrite mixture, followed by high-temperature cure, somewhat similar to making doughnuts.

ANSWER. The required relation is $L = n^2 P$, where $P = \mu S/l$. The SI quantities are $\mu = \mu_r \mu_0 = 2\pi 10^{-3}$, $S = 1.33 \times 10^{-5}$ m^2, $l = 3.03 \times 10^{-2}$ m. Thus $P = 2.76$ ($\pm 20\%$) μH/$turn^2$, which allows us to solve for $n^2 = L/P = 10^{-2}/(2.76 \times 10^{-6})$. So $n = (10^4/2.76)^{1/2}$, or 60 turns to the nearest integer.

1.3.3 Design Units

Section 1.2 considered the units and dimensions of the point quantities B and H, with units of the integral quantities deferred until now. A major question is whether to account dimensionally for turns of wire. The USA Standards Committee [3] recommends against doing so by its definition of n as a simple numeric without dimensions. Despite the considerable merit in adhering closely to standard units, many designers find it useful to distinguish core parameters from device parameters (e.g., to have different units for Figs. 1.1b and 1.1c). For instance, it was useful in Example D to make a dimensional distinction between the permeance of a bare core (henry/$turn^2$), and the inductance of the coil wound upon it. But that distinction is apparently inconsistent with the units for permeability of space, henry/meter. The following compromise procedure is suggested as an adaptation of the usual SI units for magnetic cores with turns. We assign to n the units of *turns*, given in italics to indicate its optional use. When working on problems that involve turns of wire, we have the option of using *turns* as a valid unit. Yet on other problems, the italics remind us that *turns* can be disregarded, since the term is only a design aid, not a fundamentally required unit.

SI Units, Adapted for Turns. Table 1.1 shows the resulting SI units for magnetic quantities, adapted to the use of *turns*. The listed parameters were worked out systematically by reference to Fig. 1.1, starting with

Table 1.1 Summary of SI units, adapted for design with *turns*[a]

Symbol	Description	Units	Abbreviated Units
H	Field strength	ampere·*turn* per meter	A·*t*/m
B	Flux density	tesla per *turn*	T/*t*
		weber per square meter·*turn*	Wb/m²·*t*
μ	Permeability(B/H)	tesla·meter per ampere·*turn* squared	T·m/A·*t*²
		henry per meter·*turn* squared	H/m·*t*²
F	Magnetomotive force (mmf)	ampere·*turn*	A·*t*
Φ	Flux	weber per *turn*	Wb/*t*
		volt·second per *turn*	V·s/*t*
R	Reluctance(F/Φ)	ampere·*turn* squared per weber	A·*t*²/Wb
P	Permeance(Φ/F)	weber per ampere·*turn* squared	Wb/A·*t*²
		henry per *turn* squared	H/*t*²
I	Current	ampere	A
Λ	Flux linkage	weber	Wb
		volt·second	V·s
L	Inductance(Λ/I)	henry	H
		volt·second per ampere	V·s/A

[a]The italic notation means that *turn* is not a basic unit but is merely a design aid for optional use. Equivalent units for the same quantity are also given. The table was constructed using the convention that the units for the device quantities Λ, I, and L would not use *turn*. It follows that *turn* does appear in the units for each of the core quantities (F, Φ, R, P) and may be useful. For the sake of consistency, *turn* is included in the units for the field quantities (H, B, μ) but is usually omitted by convention.

the premise that flux-linkage, current, and inductance must have their units of volt·seconds, amperes, and henries, respectively.

CGS Units. The only CGS units for integral quantities that interest us are those for flux and for magnetomotive force (mmf). The international acceptance of the rationalized MKS system makes it unnecessary to identify odd cumbersome units such as the abampere and the abhenry. The CGS unit for Φ has the dimension of gauss·centimeter² and the special names of line or maxwell (Mx). This is a smaller unit by 10^8 than the weber; the units for B account for 10^4, with the other 10^4 due to the size of the unit area over which B is integrated. Thus 1 Wb describes the same flux as 10^8 Mx. The CGS unit for F has dimensions of oersted·centimeter and the name gilbert (Gb), which is a slightly smaller unit than the ampere·*turn*. A potential of 1 Gb is the same mmf as $10/4\pi = 0.7958$ A·t.

Mixed English Units. In the United States there has been widespread engineering use of a set of units adapted for use with length expressed in inches (1 in. equals 2.54 cm). In these mixed units total flux is given in lines, as in CGS units, thus flux density B is given in lines/in.^{2}.

(One weber is the same flux as 10^8 Mx or 10^8 lines; thus a flux density of 1 T may also be described as 1 Wb/m^2 or as 10^4 G or as 10^4 lines/cm^2 or finally as $10^4(2.54)^2$ lines/in.$^2 = 64.5$ kline/in^2.) Magnetomotive force is given in ampere·*turns*, as in MKS units, so that H is given in ampere·*turns*/inch. (A field strength of 1 Oe may also be described as $1000/4\pi = 79.58$ A·t/m, as approximately 0.8 A·t/cm, or as 2.02 A·t/in.) It follows that in mixed units the magnetic constant for free space, given as $\mu_0 = 4\pi 10^{-7}$ H/m in SI units, acquires the value 3.192 lines/A·in, which is equivalent to 1 G/Oe in CGS units. The use of mixed English units probably will diminish as SI units gain acceptance.

1.3.4 Device Analogs and Differences

Two philosophical matters are interesting to note before the discussion of device volt·ampere characteristics is concluded. The first item is an explicit reminder of a notion from elementary field theory: the procedure of integrating material properties over the geometry of a sample is fundamental to all classes of devices, and is not peculiar to magnetism. Second, the concept of an ideal core geometry is proposed.

This derivation is of the conductance of a resistor, $G = I/V$, using the material property σ, the electrical conductivity. Current density J and electric field strength E are related either by the equation $\bar{J} = \sigma\bar{E}$, or perhaps graphically by the slope σ on a plot of J versus E. Since J is a density of current flux, the total current is defined by its area integral over the cross section of the sample, $I = \int \bar{J} \cdot d\bar{s}$, in analogy with magnetic flux. In analogy with magnetic potential, the voltage across the conductor is given by the line integral of the electric field intensity, $V = \int \bar{E} \cdot d\bar{l}$ from one end of the sample to the other. The device conductance G, with units of reciprocal ohms (Ω^{-1}), is defined either graphically by a slope on a plot of I versus V, or more commonly by the ratio of the two integrals. The latter ratio simplifies to $G = \sigma S/l$ for uniformly shaped conductors, making it easy to forget the formal procedure behind that familiar equation.

The second derivation is of the equation for the capacitance of two parallel plates of large area S, separated by a small distance l, which is completely filled with dielectric material. The material property is specified by the dielectric constant ϵ, typically through the equation $\bar{D} = \epsilon\bar{E}$, but in principle by the slope on a graph of electric flux density D versus E. As in the usual derivation of a capacitance equation, an E field is postulated for the calculation of charge on the plates, and of voltage between the plates $V = \int \bar{E} \cdot d\bar{l} = El$. The charge is equal to the area integral of D, $Q = \int \bar{D} \cdot d\bar{s} = \epsilon ES$, where D is electric flux density in coulombs per square meter (C/m^2). Substitution into $C = Q/V$ gives the final result $C = \epsilon S/l$, after canceling E from numerator and denominator. The similarity to $G = \sigma S/l$ and to $P = \mu S/l$ is evident.

The procedures and principles were identical for each of the three derivations of permeance, conductance, and capacitance. In fact, the procedure is implied by the meaning of an intrinsic material property. However some differences are notable. First consider the possibility of a neglected component of flux, not confined to the sample but leaking through the nearby space. In contrast with the other two fluxes, fringing current through space is nearly always negligible, since for most conductors the conductivity is perhaps 10^{14} to 10^{19} of air. (For resistors of extremely low conductance, current leakage along surface contamination can be a problem.) The relative permeability of magnetic materials is usually in the range 10^2 to 10^5 of space; the relative permittivity of dielectric materials is usually less than 10. These numbers suggest that parallel leakage magnetic flux is often negligible. Chapter 2 takes up the matter of series airgaps, which do great impact on device function. In contrast with the following topic, the difference in leakage flux in the three systems is a difference in degree, but not a difference in principle.

An Ideal Geometry for Cores. The concept of an ideal core geometry was useful in conveying the essential features of design mechanics in an earlier subsection. The two field equations by Maxwell for the divergence of flux density are compared, to support the plausible idea that an ideal magnetic geometry may be basically different from an ideal geometry for electric fields.

The equation $\bar{\nabla} \cdot \bar{D} = \rho$ is a statement that D fields possess the vector property of divergence in regions where there exists a free volume-charge-density ρ. Generalizing from Cartesian coordinates where $\bar{\nabla} \cdot \bar{D} = dD_x/dx + dD_y/dy + dD_z/dz$, we note that divergence is the change in strength of a field as a function of distance in the same direction as the field. In other words, D-lines begin and end on free electric charges. In contrast, $\bar{\nabla} \cdot \bar{B} = 0$ is a statement that B-fields never possess the divergence property, thus no free magnetic "charge" exists where B may terminate. In other words, B-fields have no ends; they are called solenoidal, continuous, sourceless. Because of the inherent requirement that B-fields close on themselves, the simplest geometry of magnetic material should provide a homogeneous, closed flux path of uniform cross section. These requirements are met by the toroid of rectangular cross section, which is also a shape of commercial importance that lends itself to easy calculation in cylindrical coordinates.

It has been noted that $\bar{\nabla} \cdot \bar{B} = 0$ implies the absence of free magnetic charge, but since $B = \mu_0(H + M)$, it follows that

$$\bar{\nabla} \cdot \bar{H} = -\bar{\nabla} \cdot \bar{M}. \tag{1.8}$$

An interpretation of (1.8) is that a volume distribution of bound magnetic "charge," a magnetic pole density, is associated with the divergence of magnetization. Although B-fields possess the solenoidal property, such is not the case for H-fields, which can terminate on magnetic poles. It is convenient to use cylindrical coordinates notation to analyze a toroid, magnetized in the ϕ-coordinate direction. The general divergence for $\bar{M}$ in cylindrical coordinates is

$$\bar{\nabla} \cdot \bar{M} = \frac{1}{r} \frac{\partial}{\partial r} \left[rM_r \right] + \frac{1}{r} \frac{\partial}{\partial \phi} M_\phi + \frac{\partial}{\partial z} M_z. \tag{1.9}$$

But only M_ϕ exists for the toroid.

To achieve zero divergence, it is clear from (1.9) that M_ϕ must have no ϕ angular dependence. This condition requires a uniform flux path that crosses no airgap regions where $M = 0$. Chapter 3 considers air gaps.

1.4 A PIECEWISE-LINEAR MODEL FOR MAGNETICS

Section 1.3 gave a graphical procedure for calculating the volt·ampere characteristics of a magnetic device and pointed out than an analogous integration process is also applicable to conductive and dielectric devices. The "integration procedure" (actually a scale factor change) is now applied to a collection of magnetic properties that are defined analytically, rather than only graphically.

Four physical properties of magnetic materials are given plausible models. Each property is an identifiable component of a magnetization curve and each is modeled in the simplest way. The justification of each component of the model is postponed to a subsequent chapter that treats each specific property in more detail. The collection of four components is referred to as a piecewise-linear model, after the well-known technique for modeling nonlinear electric circuits. The model has two forms, magnetic and electric; the form selected depends on whether the integration procedure of Section 1.3 has been applied.

1.4.1 The Magnetic Model

Every magnetic material* is subject to saturation of intrinsic induction, the value of which is characteristic of the material composition. Until more details emerge in Chapter 2, we assume that B has a maximum allowable value called B_{sat} that cannot be exceeded even at extremely large values of H. Figure 1.5 represents saturation graphically, at plus and minus values of B_{sat}, by a pair of horizontal lines that intersect the other core features in an abrupt nonlinearity. Physically, saturation corresponds to the complete alignment of the elementary magnetic moments that constitute the intrinsic induction of the material. The saturation value B_{sat} is the first component of the piecewise-linear model.

The B–H curve of many magnetic materials possesses a hysteresis property, manifest as a curve that is double-valued in the H-direction. The width of the loop is the key parameter distinguishing easily reversed

*Diamagnetic materials are excluded from this statement.

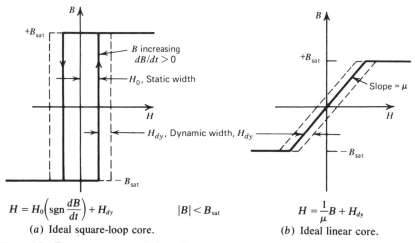

$$H = H_0\left(\text{sgn}\,\frac{dB}{dt}\right) + H_{dy} \qquad |B| < B_{sat} \qquad\qquad H = \frac{1}{\mu}B + H_{dy}$$

(a) Ideal square-loop core.   (b) Ideal linear core.

Figure 1.5 Four components of piecewise-linear model for magnetic materials: saturation flux density, B_{sat}; static width, H_0; slope, μ; dynamic width, H_{dy}.

or "soft" materials from "hard" materials used for permanent magnets. Depending mostly on the material composition and microstructure, an enormous range of width is available. Values of H range from less than $1 \text{ A} \cdot t/\text{m}$ to more than $10^5 \text{ A} \cdot t/\text{m}$. Extremely large values of width are a requirement for good permanent magnets; intermediate values are useful for magnetic recording or other memory applications; small or zero values of width are preferred for most inductors and transformers. The parameter of interest is the "static width" of the hysteresis loop, modeled in the simplest way as a square-loop parameter H_0. As shown in Fig. 1.5a, the total width of a square-loop material is $2H_0$, which ideally is constant and independent of B for any $|B| < B_{\text{sat}}$. For some materials (e.g., Fig. 1.2) H_0 is the dominant property. For other materials (Fig. 1.1) H_0 would be a rather crude description by itself. For materials such as in Fig. 1.4, parameter H_0 might be omitted entirely from the model, depending on the appearance of the entire characteristic. A $B-H$ loop with static width may imply that the physical process of flux change is by domain wall motion.

A third component of the model is a property of the slope of the magnetization curve, in which B is proportional to H. As shown earlier, the permeance of a core is proportional to the permeability parameter μ, thereby relating μ to inductance. In keeping with the philosophy of choosing the simplest tractable model, it is assumed that a component of H will be perfectly proportional to B as illustrated in Fig. 1.5b. For some materials (e.g., Fig. 1.4) the slope appears to be the dominant property, and a reasonable model by itself. For others, as in Fig. 1.1, even a crude model ought to include both a slope parameter and a static width H_0. For materials as in Fig. 1.2, the component of $H = (1/\mu)B$ appears to be negligible relative to H_0. For a gapless core, a linear $B-H$ curve may imply that the physical process of flux change is by rotation of local magnetic moments from their quiescent orientation.

The fourth component of the piecewise-linear model is a term that represents dynamic losses. Dynamic losses are not evident from a single $B-H$ loop; they require more data to describe, for instance, how the loop may become wider as the frequency of measurement increases. Dimensionally, it may be noted that the area inside a $B-H$ curve has units of joules per cubic meter (J/m^3) which is the same as watts per cubic meter per cycle per second of flux reversal. It follows that the wattage loss in a given core, due purely to hysteresis and associated with static width H_0, is expected to increase proportional to frequency. Actual measured losses exceed the expected hysteresis loss. For the present, the excess loss is modeled as due to a dynamic component of loop width $H_{dy} = g_e dB/dt$. This model is applicable to eddy current losses that accompany flux reversal of metal cores. Alternative models and loss mechanisms are reviewed in Chapter 5.

The last three components are now brought together into a single equation in H, with the assumption that $|B|$ is less than its saturation value. If $|H| \geq H_0$, the result is

$$H = H_0\left(\operatorname{sgn}\frac{dB}{dt}\right) + \frac{1}{\mu}B + g_e\frac{dB}{dt} \qquad |B| < B_{\text{sat}}. \qquad (1.10)$$

The multiplier of H_0 in the first term, sometimes called a signum function, is either plus or minus unity, depending on whether B is increasing or decreasing. The signum (sgn) function assures that the hysteresis loop is traversed in a generally counterclockwise direction as shown in Fig. 1.5a. The magnetic state at any instant is considered as a point on the graph that moves up the right-hand side and down the left of the $B-H$ loop. The second and third terms are of course the slope and the dynamic width components of H. Again for emphasis, having all three written in the same equation is not a requirement that all three components of H must have comparable values. Instead, the use of (1.10) to model a particular material recognizes that several physical processes require our further attention.

1.4.2 The Electrical Model

The piecewise-linear magnetic model of (1.10) is now given an electrical interpretation. The procedure of Section 1.3.2 converted a $B-H$ loop to a graph of $\int v\, dt$ versus I by multiplying H by l/n to give I, and by multiplying B by nS to give $\int v\, dt$. Since (1.10) is an equation in H, multiplication of each term by l/n gives an equation in I, ready for the next step

$$I = \frac{Hl}{n} = H_0\left(\operatorname{sgn}\frac{dB}{dt}\right)\frac{l}{n} + \frac{1}{\mu}\frac{Bl}{n} + g_e\frac{l}{n}\frac{dB}{dt}. \qquad (1.11)$$

Next, each B is multiplied by nS/nS, to fulfill the requirement above without changing the dimensions of the equation. After rearrangement, the result is

$$I = \frac{H_0 l}{n}\left(\operatorname{sgn} n\frac{d\Phi}{dt}\right) + \left(\frac{l}{n^2\mu S}\right)nBS + \frac{g_e l}{n^2 S}\frac{d(nBS)}{dt}. \qquad (1.12)$$

The final step involves the recognition of electrical quantities. The first term $H_0 l/n$ is a constant current I_0; $\operatorname{sgn} n\, d\Phi/dt$ is the polarity of a voltage v, independent of omitted amplitude multipliers l/nS. The second term is reciprocal inductance times $\int v\, dt$. The entire third term of (1.12) is the product of a conductance and voltage, simplified to $G_e v$. It is easy

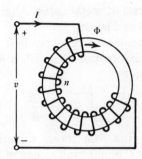

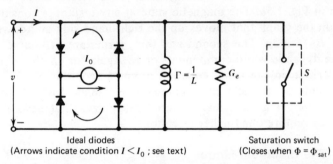

Ideal diodes   Saturation switch
(Arrows indicate condition $I < I_0$; see text)   (Closes when $\Phi = \Phi_{sat}$)

Figure 1.6 Piecewise-linear electrical model of the core of a magnetic device.

to confirm the dimensions of G_e as A/V, but further interpretation awaits
Chapter 5. The final result is the current equation, provided $I \geq I_0$,

$$I = I_0(\text{sgn } v) + \frac{1}{L} \int v \, dt + G_e v \qquad |\Phi| < \Phi_{sat}. \qquad (1.13)$$

Since the final result is a current equation, the corresponding circuit
consists of parallel components. Figure 1.6 shows the result, which is a
circuit model for a core with turns of wire. The four circuit elements—
inductance, conductance, shorting switch, and reversible current
source—are related to the four intrinsic material properties—slope,
dynamic width, saturation, and static width—as indicated by a term-by-
term comparison of (1.13) and (1.12). The shorting switch and the
current network need elucidation.

The "saturation switch" must be open for the normal functioning of
the other elements; this represents the condition that $|\Phi| < \Phi_{sat}$. If
saturation does occur, the switch closure simulates a short-circuit across

the elements to cause $v = 0$ regardless of the value of current. Since the voltage is proportional to $d\Phi/dt$, zero voltage is a condition of constant flux; core flux has reached its maximum allowable value. This important condition can be avoided, or it can be used in nonlinear design. Several examples appear at the end of Chapter 2.

The constant current source I_0 is a measure of the static width of a hysteresis loop. The associated ideal diode network, simulating (sgn v) causes the current direction to be controlled by the polarity of the input voltage. Since ideal diodes have zero voltage drop when conducting, the reversal network provides a short-circuit across the input terminal for the condition that $|I|$ is less than I_0, explained as follows. Under the condition that nI is an insufficient mmf for H to exceed H_0, the magnetic state of the core is unchanged. It can be deduced from Fig. 1.6 that the condition $I < I_0$ requires the internal current source I_0 to be partially shunted back to itself through the diodes. The shunting back requires the conduction of at least three diodes, thereby maintaining zero volts across the input. As noted above, $v = 0$ corresponds to $d\Phi/dt = 0$, as consistent with the condition that the input excitation current is insufficient to cause a flux change. However, if the input current exceeds I_0, an appropriate pair of diagonal diodes will become open circuits. The input voltage can then exist to cause excess current $(I - I_0)$ through the L and/or G elements.

Chapter 1 provides an electric circuit model for elementary magnetic phenomena, whether the magnetic data are given in graphical or analytical form. Within the approximations and limitations cited during the development, the results should be useful to applications, not yet considered, that do not demand extremes of performance.

Somewhat similar circuit models, called "equivalent circuits," were available a generation ago for the use of power transformer engineers. The model yielded by the present development is intended to be applicable to a wider class of magnetic materials as well as to a wider class of device applications. The components of the final circuit model were given as quantitative measures of magnetic processes during this development; subsequent chapters give more attention to basic phenomena that were necessarily glossed over during this introduction.

PROBLEMS

1 (Section 1.2). Suppose a field $H = 200\ A/m$ is applied to an ideally linear magnetic material with relative permeability $\mu_r = 1000$. Find MKS values for χ, μ, M, B_i and B.

2   **(Section 1.3).**   Find the dominant electrical parameters for a graph of
    $\int v\,dt$ versus I for the following device. The toroidal core, wound with
    250 turns of wire, has nominal dimensions I.D./O.D./ht = 4.0/6.0/2.0 in.
    with mean magnetic path length $l = 39.88$ cm and effective cross
    section of 10.968 cm^2 (commercial core no. 51426). The magnetic
    material is 0.002-in. tape wound of a special 50% cobalt-iron alloy called
    supermendur, which saturates at about 21,000 G and has $H_0 \approx 0.2$ Oe.
    This square-loop material is useful for high-temperature operation in
    the 300°C range.

3   **(Section 1.3).**   Find the dominant electrical parameters for a graph of
    $\int v\,dt$ versus I for the following device. The toroidal core, wound with
    150   turns   of   wire,   has   nominal   dimensions   I.D./O.D./ht =
    0.5/0.625/0.125 in. with mean magnetic path length $l = 4.49$ cm and
    effection cross section of 0.038 cm^2 (commercial core no. 50056). The
    magnetic material is 0.001-in. tape wound of a special 80% nickel-iron
    alloy called supermalloy, which begins to saturate at about 6 or 7 kG,
    $H_0 \approx 0.006$ Oe, and has a maximum permeability of about 3×10^5. This
    material is useful for applications that require high sensitivity without
    remarkable loop squareness.

4   **(Section 1.3).**   Find the number of turns required to yield an inductance
    of 0.05 H, using the following toroidal core. The nominal core dimen-
    sions are I.D./O.D./ht = 1.53/2.90/0.50 in. with a magnetic path length
    of 17.1 cm and effective area 2.21 cm^2. The linear ferrite material has an
    average permeability of about 3000 at 25°C.

5   **(Section 1.4).**
    a. Calculate the permeance in H/t^2 for the following commercial
       toroidal core, which is available in each of several different linear
       ferrites. The core has nominal dimensions I.D./O.D./ht =
       0.187/0.375/0.125 in. with magnetic path length $l = 2.16$ cm and
       effective area 0.076 cm^2. The available linear ferrite materials
       include type 3E3, which has exceptionally high permeability, type
       3B7, which has superior temperature stability, and type 4C4, which
       has high bandwidth. These materials are qualitatively similar to those
       of Fig. 1.4 except that the values of initial relative permeability are,
       respectively, 12,500, 2500, and 125.
    b. Find the inductance of a coil of 25 turns wound on each of the three
       cores.
    c. Find the approximate current at which each inductor will saturate.
       For this purpose you may assume that the materials saturate
       abruptly at values of $B \approx 0.38$, 0.38, and 0.3 T, respectively.

6   **(Section 1.4).**   calculate the rate of change of induction dB/dt for a
    square-loop, tape-wound core under the following conditions. The core

material has a static width $H_0 = 12$ A/m, but the applied drive field is a square-wave $H_a = \pm 24$ A/m, which drives the core outside the static magnetization curve. The value of the dynamic loss coefficient is assumed to be $g_e \approx 6 \times 10^{-4}$ m/Ω.

REFERENCES

1. D. J. Jackson, *Classical Electrodynamics*, Wiley New York, 1962. Has an appendix that compares five sets of units.

2. C. H. Page, "Relations Among Systems of Electromagnetic Equations," *Amer. J. Phys.*, **38**, 421–424 (April 1970). Clarifies the distinctions among several sets of units and the wording of statements that describe conversions between units.

3. "USA Standard Letter Symbols for Quantities Used in Electrical Science and Electrical Engineering," USAS Y10.5–(1968). Specifies names and symbols for (1.1) and (1.2).

4. "Letter Symbols for Units Used in Science and Technology," IEEE Standard No. 260 (1969); also ANSI Y10.19–1969. Particularly useful for standard abbreviations of units.

5. "Letter Symbols To Be Used in Electrical Technology," International Electrotechnical Commission, Publication 27–1 (1971). Justifies use of μ_0 for magnetic constant of free space.

6. *IEEE Standard Dictionary of Electrical and Electronic Terms* (IEEE Standard 100–1972) Institute of Electrical and Electronics Engineers, Inc., New York, 1972.

7. Henry C. Bourne, Jr., *Magnetic Circuits*, California Book Co., Berkeley, 1961. Considers several alternative forms of core functions and their application to transformers and to magnetic amplifiers.

2.
Flux Density, *B*

To study the subject of magnetic flux density, our interest turns to the intrinsic induction of magnetic materials, the second term in the equation $B = \mu_0 H + B_i$.

The total flux in a specimen involves the integration of B_i over the cross section of the specimen. If the specimen is demagnetized completely, the flux in any direction will be zero. A demagnetized sample consists magnetically of an array of individually magnetized regions or domains, arranged in some manner as in Fig. 2.1 so that the total net flux

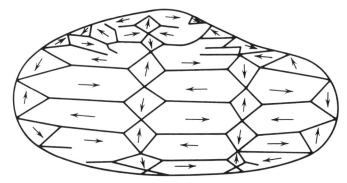

Figure 2.1 A plausible configuration of magnetic domains in a demagnetized ferromagnetic specimen. The intrinsic induction is saturated at its maximum value in each domain, yet the average induction of the entire sample is nearly zero.

in any direction is essentially zero. At any point within a domain the material is locally magnetized to its maximum saturated value, yet the total sample is described as demagnetized with $B \approx 0$.

But the study of domains is not our present goal. We do not care whether a single domain consists of a billion atoms of material or perhaps a thousand times greater or fewer. Rather than studying the general properties of domains, we shall concentrate on one specific property and explore its meaning. We want to know the saturation value of intrinsic induction of a single domain, the inferred value of magnetic moment at a typical atom of the same material, the value of total flux resulting from the integration over all domains, and finally the electrical interpretation in values for current, voltage, and time.

Section 2.1 points out that saturation values of intrinsic induction vary from one material to another. The saturation value and other physical parameters can be used to deduce the average magnetic moment per atom. The basic process of flux change involves the reorientation of atomic moments to a different direction.

Section 2.2 illustrates the integration of nonuniform intrinsic flux density over an area of interest using the piecewise-linear phenomenological models of Chapter 1. When the area of interest is a turn of wire around a core, the result is a contribution to the flux linkage for the device. Section 2.3 asserts that core saturation limits the area under the waveform of voltage at the core. Saturation thereby imposes a fundamental low-frequency limitation for core devices. The piecewise-linear electrical model in its simplest form is used to calculate voltage and current waveforms for saturating cores in simple circuits.

2.1 SATURATION OF *B* IN FERROMAGNETS

2.1.1 Bulk Material Property

This section deals with the saturation of intrinsic induction, a property of the composition of magnetic materials. In Chapter 1 saturation was represented by the value B_{sat}, the maximum possible magnitude of $B = \mu_0 H + B_i$. Although that model is excellent for soft magnetic materials, for many permanent magnet materials it is evident that saturation is described more accurately by its association with the material component B_i only, rather than with the total flux density, B. To avoid double subscripts, this section uses the notation $J = B_i$; thus the

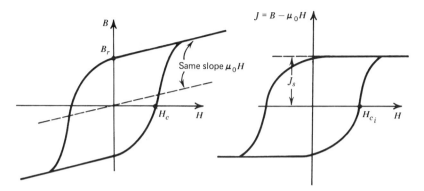

(a) B–H curve for permanent magnetic material.   (b) J–H curve for the same material.

Figure 2.2   Illustration of the concept that saturation of flux density $B = \mu_0 H + J$ is due to saturation of the intrinsic induction component J.

alternate form of the equation for B becomes

$$B = \mu_0 H + J, \tag{2.1}$$

where material saturation is designated by $J = J_s$. Figure 2.2 illustrates the same point. Total B never reaches a final value for large H, but continues to increase with incremental slope μ_0. On the other hand, $B_i = J$ does reach final saturation, with a value that is characteristic of the material.

To cause the reversal of a material modeled by a B–H width parameter H_0, a field must be applied such that $H > H_0$. A permanent magnet is characterized by a large value of H_0, with the result that $\mu_0 H$ is significant compared to J_s. The main idea that emerges is a basis for judging the accuracy of the approximation $B_{sat} \approx J_s$. The approximation is commonly and accurately used for easily reversed materials.

EXAMPLE A

Find the ratio $\mu_0 H_0 / J_s$ for the following two material models. (a) A permalloy with $H_0 = 1$ A·t/m, $J_s = 1$ T. (b) A permanent magnet similar to Alnico 8 with $H_0 = 1.3 \times 10^5$ A·t/m, $J_s = 0.8$ T.

ANSWER.

(a) 1.25×10^{-6}.
(b) 0.204.

Composition Dependence of J_s. It is now argued that the value of J_s is defined by the material composition. Table 2.1 gives a few values that are taken from the literature. Interestingly, the value of J_s varies with temperature and goes away completely above the Curie temperature. The Curie temperature is also characteristic of the material composition, and can be thought of as a measure of the strength of coupling within the system of elementary magnetic moments that comprise J. Our immediate interest is the value of J_s. Section 2.1.2 interprets J as a density of atomic magnetic moments. Models for the coupling between magnetic moments are in Chapter 4.

A quick scan of Table 2.1 reveals the fairly narrow range of values for J_s, from 0.3 to 2.45, for the materials shown. The top three entries in the table, iron, cobalt, and nickel, are the only existing elements that are ferromagnetic at room temperature. These few elements and their many alloys represent our total resource of ferromagnetic materials. Continuing from the table we see silicon iron, which has been an important commercial material since about 1900. The addition of a few percent of silicon to iron results in higher permeability, lower losses, and less aging. The two listed permalloys and others have been readily available commercially since the late 1940s, an outgrowth of investigations over the prior 30 years. It is interesting that J_s for permendur exceeds that of

Table 2.1 Saturation value of intrinsic flux density at room temperature for a few common magnetic materials, in MKS units. Most of the data are adapted from Bozorth.

Name	Composition (%)	Saturation J_s (T) at 20°C
Iron (pure)	Fe	2.158
Cobalt	Co	1.787
Nickel	Ni	0.608
Silicon iron	3 Si, 97 Fe	2.00
Supermalloy	79 Ni, 16 Fe, 5 Mo	0.80
Orthonol®[a]	50 Ni, 50 Fe	1.3–1.5
Permendur	50 Co, 50 Fe	2.45
Alnico 5	24 Co, 13.5 Ni, 8 Al 3 Cu, 51 Fe	1.34 (B_r)
Ferrite (Mn–Zn)	Various percentages of $MnFe_2O_4$ with $ZnFe_2O_4$	0.3–0.5 (varies with mix)

[a] A commercial permalloy also sold as Deltamax®, HCR, Orthonik, Hipernik 5, Permenorm 5000Z.

either of its two constituent elements. Alnico is an important permanent magnetic material; the definition of B_r is illustrated in Fig. 2.2a. All table entries except ferrites are classified as ferromagnetic materials.

Ferrites are a broad class of materials, and only one family is shown. The chemical composition is typically a variation of Fe_3O_4, with some other metal atom substituted for one of the iron atoms. Ferrites are important because their high electrical resistivity permits high-frequency applications with low losses. They are magnetic ceramics, classified as ferrimagnetic and also described as similar to antiferromagnets. Many of the modern innovative applications of magnetism use ferrites or garnets.

EXAMPLE B

A reference book gives the saturation flux density for iron as 218 emu/g at 20°C. How does that compare with data in Table 2.1?

ANSWER. If 218 is multiplied by the density of iron, 7.87 g/cc, the result is 1715.7 emu/cc, which is the value of M in (1.6), Section 1.2.2. The corresponding CGS value for $B_i = 4\pi M$ is 21,560 G, or 2.156 T in SI units, in good agreement with the Table 2.1 entry for iron. The question arose from a mass density of magnetic moment, rather than the usual volume density.

2.1.2 Magnetic Moment

The basic magnetic element is the magnetic moment, and indeed the SI unit for flux density is magnetic moment per unit of volume. The unit of $B_i = J$ is tesla (Wb/m²), which is the same as weber·meter per cubic meter. The latter form is significant because magnetic dipole moment has dimensions of Wb·m. In other words, flux density has units of magnetic moment per unit volume, even for a very small volume. The significance is that the saturation density, after minor manipulation, gives the average magnetic moment possessed by an atom of the material in question.

The concept of magnetic moment is important enough to merit some observations from several points of view. Consider first the analogous electrostatic equation in electric flux density,

$$D = \epsilon_0 E + P, \tag{2.2}$$

in which electric polarization P has units of C/m² and the interpretation of electric dipole moment/volume. A finite electric dipole $p = Ql$ arises from charges of plus and minus Q separated by a distance l. The P is a volume density of the vector summation of p's over all the atoms of the material in question. That is, $P = (1/V)\Sigma_i p_i = Np$ where N is the number of atoms per volume and where p is the average dipole moment per atom, in units of coulomb·meter (C·m).

In close analogy with P, the intrinsic induction J in (2.1) is sometimes called the magnetic polarization, with the interpretation of magnetic moment per cubic meter. As in the electrostatic case, $J = Nj$, where N is the volume density of atoms in atoms/m^3 and j is the average magnetic dipole moment per atom. It may be observed that in (2.2) the vector divergence of P, $\bar{\nabla} \cdot \bar{P}$, defines a volume density of bound electric charge, analogous to the volume density of magnetic pole defined by $\bar{\nabla} \cdot \bar{J}$ of (2.1).

The electric and magnetic cases differ in several important respects. The electric atomic dipole moment p can be induced by an applied electric field that causes a relative displacement of atomic charge components, whereas a magnetic dipole moment j exists even in zero applied H field. Furthermore the divergence of D in (2.2) can exist because free electric charge exists, whereas the divergence of B is zero.

Magnetic moment is a useful concept for macroscopic specimens as well as for atoms. Let us suppose a volume of area S and length l, $V = Sl$, has been oriented axially in a strong H-field sufficient to magnetize it to saturation parallel to its length. Under these conditions, magnetic flux $\Phi = J_sS$ will enter one end and leave the other. Each end will develop a magnetic pole, or polarization "charge" $Q_m = J_sS$ Wb, of opposite polarity such that the total magnetic moment is $Q_ml = J_sSl = J_sV = j$ Wb·m. Thus the magnetic moment j is constant for a given volume, independent of the shape. If the specimen above is an ideal permanent magnet, capable of retaining its magnetic moment $\bar{j}$ when the $\bar{H}$-field is reoriented, the reorientation will give rise to a restoring torque. The vector definition of the torque is

$$\bar{T} = \bar{j} \times \bar{H} = jH \sin\theta \text{ newton·meter,} \qquad (2.3)$$

where the direction of $\bar{j}$ is from $-Q_m$ to $+Q_m$ as shown in Fig. 2.3a. No net translational force acts on j unless H has unequal values at the two ends of the magnet.

There exists an alternative definition of magnetic moment called "area moment" to distinguish it from the above. The units of area moment are amperes·meter^2, as

$$m = IS, \qquad (2.4)$$

where I is a current around the periphery of an area S, Fig. 2.3b. The torque equation analgous to (2.3)

$$\bar{T} = \bar{m} \times \mu_0\bar{H} \text{ newton·meter} \qquad (2.5)$$

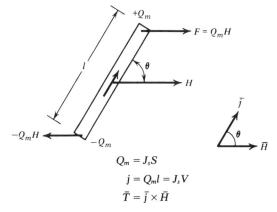

$$Q_m = J_s S$$
$$j = Q_m l = J_s V$$
$$\bar{T} = \bar{j} \times \bar{H}$$

(*a*) Pole representation of magnetic moment $\bar{j} = J_s V = Q_m l$.

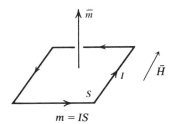

$$m = IS$$

$$\bar{T} = \bar{m} \times \mu_0 \bar{H}$$

(*b*) Magnetic area moment for a current-carrying coil.

Figure 2.3   Two representations of magnetic moment. In each case the torque acts on the moment to align it with the applied field.

is useful in the analysis of torque coils, for instance, as in meter movements. It is to be noted that μ_0, the magnetic constant, is part of the field term of (2.5) but is included in the magnetic moment in (2.3).

The two perspectives of magnetic moment, the pole model and the current model, are implicit in the two forms for $B = \mu_0 H + J = \mu_0(H + M)$. Each term J and M carries one of the interpretations of magnetic moment per volume. At the atomic level

$$J = Nj \quad \text{and} \quad M = Nm, \tag{2.6}$$

where N is the number of atoms per volume. It follows that the magnetic moment per atom is

$$j = \mu_0 m \tag{2.7}$$

and $(1/N)$ is the volume per atom. The following section defines a useful unit for specifying atomic values of magnetic moment.

2.1.3 Bohr Magneton

The present discussion is directed specifically to the magnitude of the saturation value $J_s = Nj$, when each contribution of magnitude j is aligned parallel. Since N is the number of atoms per cubic meter, its reciprocal is the volume per atom, confirming j as the magnetic dipole moment per atom. The magnetic moment per atom has a special unit of Bohr magneton. That is, $j = J_s/N = n_{\text{eff}}j_B$, where n_{eff} is the effective or average number of Bohr magnetons of value j_B. It will be shown that

$$j_B = 1.16528 \times 10^{-29} \text{ Wb·m},\tag{2.8a}$$

$$m_B = \frac{j_B}{\mu_0} = 9.273 \times 10^{-24} \text{ J/T}\tag{2.8b}$$

The Bohr magneton is within 0.1% of the magnetic moment possessed by an electron, so that the number n_{eff} essentially tells the average number of electrons per atom that contribute uncompensated magnetic moments.

It is important to note that our discussion is of a typical atom of a magnetic crystal, not of a single isolated atom. The most important property distinguishing ferromagnetic materials from the more common paramagnetic metals depends critically on the interaction between many atoms. However for pedagogical reasons, the discussion of the coupling energy that tends to align the moments of adjacent atoms is postponed. Instead our task is to establish the value of the moment and to discuss physical processes that produce magnetic moments at the atomic level. There follows a derivation of the value of a Bohr magneton, as the magnetic moment of the single electron in classical orbital motion about a simple atom. Electron spin possesses the same magnetic moment but only half the angular momentum of orbital motion.

The derivation starts with the definition of area moment $m = IS$ (2.4), where current $I = -e\omega/2\pi$ is implied by the orbital motion of a charge $-e$. The units of current are coulomb/second = coulomb/revolution × revolution/second. Area $S = \pi r^2$, where r is the classical radius of the Bohr orbit of the electron. The intermediate result is therefore

$$j_B = \mu_0 IS = \frac{-\mu_0 e\omega\pi r^2}{2\pi} = \frac{-\mu_0 e\omega r^2}{2}.\tag{2.9}$$

Quantum mechanical considerations require that the foregoing classical result be modified to indicate quantization of angular momentum in units of $\hbar = h/2\pi$, where Planck's constant $h = 6.62 \times 10^{-34}$ J·s and $\hbar = 1.0545 \times 10^{-34}$ J·s. Classical angular momentum is the cross-product $\bar{l} =$

Table 2.2 Magnetic data for the three ferromagnetic elements: Saturation intrinsic induction, ferromagnetic Curie temperature T_c, and n_{eff} the calculated effective number of Bohr magnetons per atom.

	J_s (T)			Density	
Substance	Room Temperature	0° K	n_{eff} at 0° K	(g/cc)	T_c(°K)
Iron	2.145	2.202	2.221	7.86	1043
Cobalt	1.759	1.817	1.716	8.8	1388
Nickel	0.609	0.641	0.606	8.85	631

Adapted from Kittel and Galt [3], with permission.

$\bar{r} \times \bar{p} = mr^2\bar{\omega}$, where r is the radius and linear momentum $p = mv = mr\omega$. After manipulation for replacement of the classical angular momentum by the quantized, the result is

$$j_B = -\mu_0 \frac{e}{2m} mr^2\omega = -\mu_0 \frac{e}{2m} l = -\mu_0 \frac{e}{2m} \hbar. \qquad (2.10)$$

In this MKS equation, the charge of the electron is $e = 1.602 \times 10^{-19}$ C; the rest mass of the electron is $m = 9.108 \times 10^{-31}$ kg. The values of (2.8) result.

We are now in a position to deduce the number of Bohr magnetons per atom for ferromagnets, certainly a fundamental atomic property. Table 2.2 gives values adapted from an important review paper of a few years ago by Kittel and Galt [3]. The experimental values for J_s are in good agreement with Table 2.1.

EXERCISE A

Given that Avogadro's number is 6.02×10^{23} atoms/g·mole, that the atomic weight for average iron is 55.85 g/g·mole, and the data in Table 2.2 for iron, do the following.

(a) Find the magnetic moment j and the volume $1/N$ for a typical iron atom at room temperature.
(b) Use the result from (a) to determine n_{eff}.

2.1.4 Spin, g-Factor, and Gyromagnetic Ratio

At this point we have not discussed the physical mechanisms that cause ferromagnetic moments, although it may have seemed so because the derivation of the Bohr magneton unit began with the assumption of orbital motion. For most true ferromagnetic materials (ferrites are a notable exception), the physical array of magnetic moments that comprise J_s are due not to orbital motion but rather to the electron property of spin. Spin is the intrinsic angular momentum possessed by a partiele, in this case by an electron. Although the spin quantum mechanical operator has no classical analog, many find intuitive comfort in the notion of an electron spinning on its own axis. Interestingly, the magnetic dipole moment possessed by one electron spin is one Bohr magneton, the same as orbital motion. Yet the angular momentum $\hbar/2$ of spin is only half as much, corresponding to the quantum number for spin of $S = \frac{1}{2}$. In other words, electron spin and electron orbital motion differ by a factor of 2 in the ratio magnetic moment to angular momentum, described generally by the gyromagnetic ratio

$$\gamma = -g\mu_0 \frac{e}{2m} = -g\ 1.105 \times 10^5 \frac{\text{radians/s}}{\text{A/m}} \qquad (2.11)$$

The g-factor is 2 for a system of pure spins and 1 for purely orbital. It is possible to determine the value of g experimentally, thereby to determine the relative contribution of each mechanism,* by measuring magnetic resonance or by gyromagnetic measurements such as the Einstein–de Haas experiment.

For the three common ferromagnetic elements (iron, cobalt, and nickel) the g-factor is close to 2; the magnetic moments are caused by spins with most of the orbital contribution described as "quenched." For these three materials, the values for n_{eff} in Table 2.2 are interpreted as the net unbalance or difference of electron occupancy of the two states "spin up" versus "spin down" in the unfilled 3-d shell of the atom.

The CGS equation for the Bohr magneton is $m_B = -e\hbar/2mc = -9.273 \times 10^{-21}$ erg/G. The CGS equation for the gyromagnetic ratio is $\gamma = -ge/2mc$, which for spins has the value 1.76×10^7 rad/s·Oe or 2.8 MHz/Oe. The values that give this result are m $= 9.1 \times 10^{-28}$ g; e $= 4.803 \times 10^{-10}$ esu; c $= 3 \times 10^{10}$ cm/s; thus $e/c = 1.6 \times 10^{-20}$ emu of charge.

EXERCISE B

Equation 2.11 defines a fundamental constant that gives the angular frequency of electron spin resonance as $\omega = \gamma H$, where $\gamma = 2.21 \times 10^5$

---

*Actually, the two classes of experiments give slightly differing results attributed to coupling between spin and orbital moments. Resonance g, the spectroscopic splitting factor, usually exceeds 2 by about the same amount that g', the magnetomechanical factor is less than 2. See Chikazumi [4], pp. 47–51.

(rad/s)/(A/m). Convert the units of H from amperes per meter to oersteds and show the ratio f/H is 2.8 MHz/Oe.

2.1.5 Resonance and Precession

Although this is a digression from the central theme of saturation, the gyromagnetic ratio γ is such an important parameter that some introductory comments on its use are justified. The basic mechanism for change of magnetization is that magnetic moments precess from one orientation to another. How rapidly the reorientation can occur depends on the inertia of the magnetic system. More precisely, (2.11) suggests that the elemental magnetic moment and the elemental angular momentum are fundamentally related to each other, and oppositely directed as indicated by the minus sign. Simply understated, a form of inertia is basically linked to the magnetization of materials. Not only does the inertia prevent an absolutely instantaneous reversal of magnetization, it also raises the possibility of a magnetic resonance under appropriate conditions of potential energy. A relevant analogy is the mechanical resonance of a spring-mass system.

Consider a model of the lossless precession of the magnetic polarization $\bar{J}$ about an applied field $\bar{H}$. In rotating inertial systems, the applied torque is equal to the rate of change of angular momentum, $\bar{T} = d\bar{l}/dt$, as in the analogous rectilinear case in which force equals the time derivative of linear momentum, $\bar{F} = d\bar{p}/dt$. It follows from (2.3) that a torque density τ results from the interaction of J with an effective field H, as

$$\bar{\tau} = \bar{J} \times \bar{H} = \frac{d\bar{L}}{dt}. \tag{2.12}$$

But (2.11) states that an angular momentum density $\bar{L}$ is related to $\bar{J}$ through the negative constant γ

$$\gamma\bar{L} = \bar{J}. \tag{2.13}$$

Multiplication of (2.12) by γ yields

$$\gamma\bar{\tau} = \gamma(\bar{J} \times \bar{H}) = \frac{d\bar{J}}{dt}. \tag{2.14}$$

The middle term is of the form $\bar{\omega} \times \bar{J}$, with

$$\omega = -\gamma H$$

so that (2.14) represents the lossless precession of $\bar{J}$ about $\bar{H}$ at the Larmor frequency ω. Figure 2.4a shows the result.

The concept of $\bar{J}$ precessing about $\bar{H}$ is similar to the mechanical

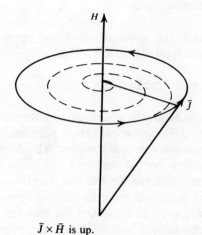

$\bar{J} \times \bar{H}$ is up.

$\gamma \bar{J} \times \bar{H}$ is down into the paper.

(a) Lossless precession of $\bar{J}$ about $\bar{H}$. Losses will introduce an extra torque that causes $\bar{J}$ to spiral into alignment with $\bar{H}$ (dashed line).

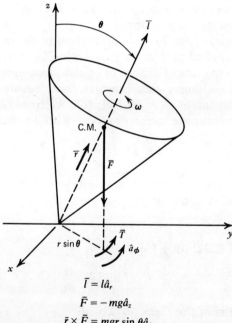

$$\bar{l} = l\hat{a}_r$$

$$\bar{F} = -mg\hat{a}_z$$

$$\bar{r} \times \bar{F} = mgr \sin\theta\, \hat{a}_\phi$$

(b) A heavy top precesses about the gravitational force F because the torque acts in the ϕ-coordinate direction.

Figure 2.4 Two examples of precession of an angular-momentum system due to applied torque.

system of a spinning top, inclined from vertical and acted on by gravity (Fig. 2.4b). Although a force $F = mg$ acts downward through the center of mass, the top is presumed not to fall because of its large angular momentum $\bar{l}$, which changes according to the torque equation

$$\frac{d\bar{l}}{dt} = \bar{T} = \bar{r} \times \bar{F}. \tag{2.15}$$

The vectoral change of angular momentum of the top amounts to a precession about the gravitational field.

We return to these ideas in subsequent chapters, with a slight modification of (2.11) by the addition of a lossy component of torque. Although the detailed description is usually not required, lossy precession is thought to be the basic dynamic process by which changes occur in the magnetization of materials.

2.2 INTEGRATION OF NONUNIFORM B

Section 1.3 gave the flux as the integral $\Phi = \int \bar{B} \cdot d\bar{s} \approx BS$, assuming that $\bar{B}$ not only was perpendicular to the incremental cross-sectional area of the core $d\bar{s}$, eliminating the dot product, but also assuming that B had a constant value over the area S of the core. We now remove the second restriction, to permit B to vary in some manner over the area of integration. The nonuniform B is a consequence of the nonuniform H-field that is found to be inherent even in an ideal configuration of core and coil. Partial flux saturation is examined for two different B–H material relationships.

Mathematically, the "flux" of any vector field $\bar{F}$ is defined as the integral over some surface of the function $\bar{F} \cdot \hat{a}_s$, which is the dot product of $\bar{F}$ with the unit normal to the surface. In the present case, the vector field is $\bar{B}$, which carries the name of magnetic flux density. The surface in question is the cross-sectional area of a toroidal core (Fig. 2.5), which is readily described using the cylindrical coordinate system (r, ϕ, z). The incremental area of the core is defined by

$$d\bar{s} = d\bar{z} \times d\bar{r} = dz\, dr\, \hat{a}_\phi, \tag{2.16}$$

where $\hat{a}_\phi$ is the unit vector in the ϕ-direction, normal to the incremental surface in the usual convention. It is assumed that the magnitude of $\bar{B}$ is allowed to vary but the direction is fixed

$$\bar{B} = B\hat{a}_\phi. \tag{2.17}$$

The vector dot product $\bar{B} \cdot d\bar{s}$ eliminates the unit vectors, yielding the

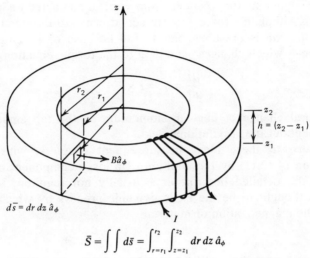

$$\bar{S} = \int\int d\bar{s} = \int_{r=r_1}^{r_2}\int_{z=z_1}^{z_2} dr\, dz\, \hat{a}_\phi$$

Figure 2.5 Geometry of an ideal toroidal core. A vector definition of the rectangular cross-sectional area is $\bar{S} = \hat{a}_\phi (r_2 - r_1)(z_2 - z_1)$, where $\hat{a}_\phi$ is the unit normal to the area. For an ideal coil, more turns should be added to extend the windings completely around the core.

increment of flux
$$d\Phi = B\, ds = B\, dr\, dz. \tag{2.18}$$

The total flux in the core is thus
$$\Phi_c = \int\int d\Phi = \int_{z=z_1}^{z_2}\int_{r=r_1}^{r_2} B\, dr\, dz. \tag{2.19}$$

In the event of saturation of the entire core at $B = B_{\text{sat}}$, the integral reaches the limiting value of
$$\Phi_{\text{sat}} = B_{\text{sat}}(r_2 - r_1)(z_2 - z_1) = B_{\text{sat}}h(r_2 - r_1). \tag{2.20}$$

Applied H-Field. The evaluation of (2.19) is undertaken for two special cases of nonuniform B, following a definition of winding geometry that is applicable to both cases. The following restrictions are made solely for the sake of mathematical tractability of the calculations. First, it is assumed that additional turns of wire are continued in the same manner as the few current-carrying turns shown in Fig. 2.5, to assure no variation of H with the ϕ-coordinate. Furthermore, if the n turns are closely spaced to approximate a toroidal sheet of current nI, there is no variation of H with the z-direction. With these restrictions, the elementary methods of Chapter 3 show that H has only a ϕ-component that varies as a function of radius. The result (Fig. 2.6) is

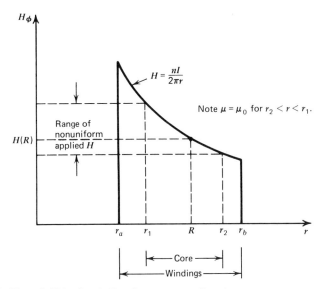

Figure 2.6 Plot of *H* in the ϕ-direction versus radius, for a current *I* in an ideal coil around a toroidal core (Fig. 2.5). The current-carrying coil has radii r_a, r_b enclosing the magnetic core of radii r_1, r_2 and is inherently more intense at the inside radius r_1.

$$H = \frac{nI}{2\pi r} \tag{2.21}$$

for the range of *r* inside the windings, $r_a < r < r_b$. Two points about this result: first, no discontinuity of *H* is observed at the core radii r_1 and r_2, as is consistent with material boundary condition requirements. Tangential components of *H* are required to be equal at boundaries that carry no current. (The shielding effect of induced current along the surface of the core itself is neglected until Chapter 5.) That is, since the boundary of the core and the direction of *H* are both in the ϕ-coordinate direction, say at r_1, the value of *H* is the same just inside the core as just outside the core. The *H*-field outside the core and inside the wire is a source of leakage flux (see Section 2.2.3).

The second implication of (2.21) is even more interesting. Despite the foregoing restrictions on the placement of windings, the core material is still subjected to a nonuniform *H* in the radial direction, if $r_2 > r_1$. The constant magnetostatic potential *nI* is distributed along a path that is shortest at the inside radius of the core and longer elsewhere. The next two sections examine the effect of a nonuniform *H* on each of two static components of the piecewise-linear model.

2.2.1 Flux in Square-Loop Materials

To solve the general integration formula set up in (2.19) for the particular case of a square-loop material, it is convenient to use the ideal model proposed in Chapter 1 for a square-loop material, with $\mu \approx \infty$ and $g_e \approx 0$

$$H = H_0\left(\text{sgn}\,\frac{dB}{dt}\right) \qquad |B| < B_s, \tag{2.22}$$

and to examine the consequences of the nonuniform applied field (2.21) as shown in Fig. 2.6. If the value of applied current $I = I'$ generates a field of H_0 at some intermediate radius R,

$$H(R) = H_0 = \frac{nI'}{2\pi R} \qquad r_1 \le R \le r_2, \tag{2.23}$$

it logically follows from the model that two different magnetic states will occur within the same core, as suggested in Fig. 2.7. Figure 2.8 illustrates the expected result that $B = B_s$ for $r < R$ and $B = -B_s$ for $r > R$. Substitution into (2.19) yields

$$\Phi_c = B_s h[2R - (r_1 + r_2)], \tag{2.24}$$

where R is deduced from (2.23) as proportional to current over the range

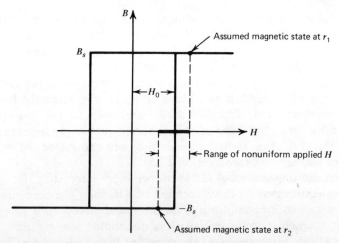

Figure 2.7 A B–H curve ideal square-loop magnetic material modeled by $H = H_0$ (sgn dB/dt). The nonuniform applied field (Fig. 2.6) is assumed to excite different magnetic states at different radii within the core. See also Fig. 2.8.

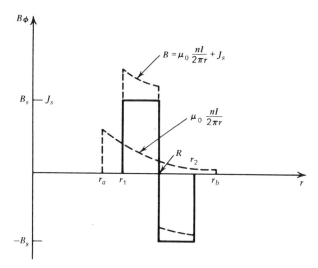

Figure 2.8 Variation of B_ϕ with radius for a core of square-loop material. The solid curve shows the two-state result of interest, deduced from Fig. 2.7. The dashed curve shows an exaggerated effect of applied field, in the form $B = \mu_0 H + J$, illustrating the tangential boundary condition for B_ϕ.

of interest,

$$R = \frac{nI}{2\pi H_0},$$
(2.25)

giving the flux curve of Fig. 2.9 as a final result.

It is interesting that a nonuniform field applied to a square-loop core has yielded a predicted result that strongly suggests the existence of magnetic domains (Fig. 2.10). It is even more interesting that the direction of saturated intrinsic induction J_s is parallel (or antiparallel) to the ϕ-direction of the applied field, suggesting that flux changes in the core take place by the process of domain wall motion. In general, these observations have been well documented experimentally. However for some materials it has been observed that the field strength required to create or nucleate a reversed domain often exceeds the field required merely to move an already existing domain wall. Since the simple parameter H_0 is an inadequate model of this process, the details above are expected to be applicable only qualitatively to such materials.

One may wonder what causes such a domain wall to move inasmuch as each of the domains possesses only $\pm\phi$-direction components of intrinsic induction. For either direction the torque density $\bar{J} \times \bar{H}$ is zero because $\bar{H}$ also possesses only ϕ-direction components. However

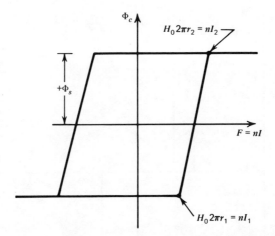

Figure 2.9 Flux curve calculated for an ideal square-loop magnetic material in the geometry of a toroid. The model assumes that the material will switch states at $H = H_0$, yielding slanted sides for the characteristic. See text for further discussion.

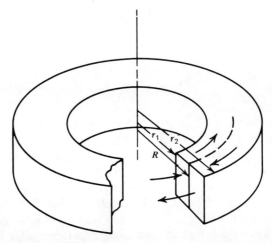

Figure 2.10 Cutaway of a square-loop core showing two saturated domains separated by a wall at R. The net flux in the positive-ϕ-direction increases as the wall moves outward.

within the wall that separates the two domains, the magnetic moments are oriented in a direction that couples to the applied field. The wall is a 180° wall; the direction of orientation of the intrinsic induction changes by 180° gradually across a finite wall width of perhaps a thousand atoms. We are not yet concerned with the ferromagnetic exchange coupling between magnetic moments that permits only a small angular change between neighbors. Nor are we yet concerned with the complex details of the wall precession. We merely observe with interest that the applied *H*-field can exert a torque on the domain wall itself, to cause the magnetic moments within the wall to precess as the wall moves.

2.2.2 Flux in Linear Materials

The integration formula of (2.19) is now to be solved for the case of a linear material, using the ideal model

$$B = \mu H \qquad |B| < B_s \tag{2.26}$$

with static width $H_0 = 0$ and ignoring dynamic losses so that $g_e = 0$. As in the previous subsection, the nonuniform *H*-field specified by (2.21) and Fig. 2.6 gives rise to a nonuniform distribution of *B* within the toroidal core. Figures 2.11 and 2.12 illustrate the case for which the value of applied current *I* causes saturation of the inside portion of the core, $r < R$. In other words, the current causes a field strength $H = B_s/\mu$ at $r = R$. For this case, $B = B_s$ for $r \leq R$ but $B = \mu H$ for $r \geq R$ where $H = nI/2\pi r$ as in (2.21). Substitution of these values into the equation for core flux gives the intermediate result

$$\Phi_c = h \int_{r_i}^{r_2} B \, dr = h \left[B_s(R - r_1) + \int_R^{r_2} B \, dr \right]. \tag{2.27}$$

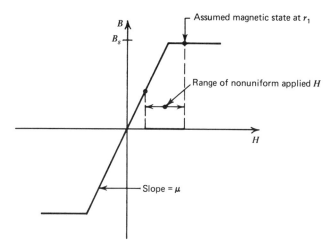

Figure 2.11 A *B–H* curve for ideal linear magnetic material modeled by $B = \mu H$. The nonuniform applied field (Fig. 2.6) may cause the inside of the core to saturate. See also Fig. 2.12.

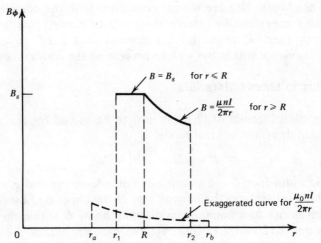

Figure 2.12 Variation of B_ϕ with radius for an ideal linear core. The solid curve, deduced from Fig. 2.11, shows the result of interest.

When the integral has been completed, we have

$$\Phi_c = h\left[B_s(R - r_1) + \frac{\mu n I}{2\pi} \ln \frac{r_2}{R}\right].$$ (2.28)

When the current is small enough to cause no partial saturation, $I < I_1$ as in Fig. 2.13, the leading term is omitted from each of the brackets. In the linear region of no saturation, the permeance is defined as $P = \Phi/F$ or

$$P = \frac{\Phi_c}{nI} = \frac{\mu h}{2\pi} \ln \frac{r_2}{r_1}.$$ (2.29)

EXERCISE C

(a) Use (2.29) to find the permeance of a core if $\mu_r = 10^3$ and $r_2/r_1/h = 2/1/1$ cm. What percentage error results from the approximation $P = \mu S/l$, where $l = \pi(r_1 + r_2)$.

(b) Repeat the calculations for $r_2/r_1/h = 3/2/1$ cm.

ANSWER

(a) 1.39 $\mu H/t^2$, 4% low.
(b) 0.81 $\mu H/t^2$, 1% low.

What physical processes can cause a linear B–H relationship as in Fig. 2.11? A plausible answer is a domain configuration constructed from saturated regions of intrinsic induction that are oriented to lie statically

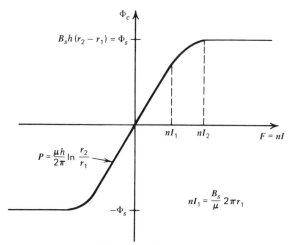

Figure 2.13 Flux curve calculated for a toroidal core of ideally linear magnetic material (Fig. 2.11). The rounded corner corresponds to partial saturation of the core.

either in the radial direction or in the z-direction, but not in the ϕ-direction. Figure 2.14 shows a simple example of a possible configuration of domains that satisfy the requirements of zero B_i for zero H. When a field is applied in the ϕ-direction, the orientation of the induction of each domain will be turned so as to project a component into the same ϕ-direction. When the field is removed, the orientation returns to the static orientation as though by a spring. The springlike quality is described by the "anisotropy constants" of the material. A stiff spring requires a large field, thus corresponds to a low value of permeability.

2.2.3 Leakage Flux and Flux Linkage

Actually, the flux linkage of the magnetic device $\Lambda = n\Phi$ is the sum of the flux enclosed by each turn of wire wound around the core. Even in the case considered above, where the windings are ideally distributed, it is clear that the total flux enclosed by the windings must include not only the flux in the core but also an additional component of flux outside the core. Figures 2.6, 2.8, and 2.12 demonstrate the existence of an air flux enclosed by the windings but outside the core.

In principle, the total flux linking each turn of the winding on a core can be calculated by increasing the range of integration in (2.19) from the core area to include the entire area of the turn of wire. The result is the addition to the existing (2.19) of a component of air flux $\Phi_a =$

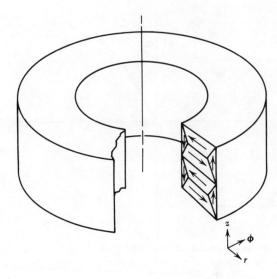

Figure 2.14 Cutaway of a linear core, illustrating a plausible domain configuration at zero induction. The r, z components of B_i rotate into the ϕ-direction when a field is applied.

$B_a(S_t - S_c)$, where S_t and S_c are the turn and core areas, respectively, and B_a is the average flux density over that specific region. If H is known, as in Fig. 2.4, the relation $B = \mu_0 H$ permits B_a to be estimated or even calculated if the winding shape is tractable.

EXERCISE D

On a particular core, the area enclosed by a typical turn is 1.5 cm², of which 1.0 cm² is the core of permeability $\mu_r = 100$. Assuming the value of average H is the same for the winding as for the core, find the fraction of flux linkage carried by the core.

ANSWER. 99.5%.

The air flux is often negligible for a tightly wound, nonsaturated, high-permeability core. However we shall see that the estimates above are somewhat too optimistic. Chapter 3 reveals that the H-field near sparsely spaced wires is much larger than the average field in the center of the turn. These concepts are particularly important when it is necessary that a transformer have low leakage inductance. Even in such cases, precise calculations of leakage flux are seldom necessary inasmuch as transformer coupling coefficients are easily measured.

2.3 SATURATION OF FLUX LINKAGES

We now examine the electrical consequences of magnetic saturation, having considered the saturation of B and of its area integral Φ. The present discussion uses the language of currents and voltages to develop a foundation for applications. The "saturation switch" of the piecewise-linear model is the electrical component of interest. The two states of the switch lead to two circuit models with initial conditions that must be reconciled at the instant the switch is actuated.

Since the emphasis here is on applications and waveforms, it is appropriate to summarize briefly the most relevant key points from earlier sections of the chapter. In clarifying the meaning of B_{sat} it has been established that the saturating quantity is actually the intrinsic flux density B_i, and that the condition of saturation physically corresponds to the parallel alignment of elemental magnetic moments. It also follows that the incremental slope of a B–H characteristic, in the region of saturation, is not absolutely zero as implied in Chapter 1, but actually has the value μ_0, the magnetic constant of free space. A more detailed examination of the integrations that were done only approximately in Section 1.3 has revealed a few minor adjustments that were glossed over by the procedure of simple multiplication. For the case of idealized materials, we found that the transition to saturation was less abrupt for the Φ–F characteristic than for the corresponding B–H. Furthermore, the value of flux that links the winding was shown to be slightly larger than the flux in the core. These considerations represent limitations to the detailed accuracy of the "saturation switch" approximation.

The topic of flux linkages

$$\Lambda = n\Phi = nBS_c \tag{2.29}$$

ties together magnetic and electrical calculations. The concept of calculating magnetic flux has now been established. Our next task deals with some representative voltage integrals, since the flux linkages are equivalent to the integral of induced voltage $\Lambda = \int v \, dt$. Core saturation imposes an upper limit on the value of the volt·seconds product at the terminals of the winding on the core. The limitation is used in two ways: either as a condition to be avoided in linear applications, or alternatively as a design condition to be used in nonlinear magnetics.

2.3.1 Increment of Flux Linkage

One of the key concepts of magnetic design is that the area under the voltage waveform defines a vertical displacement on the $\Lambda - I$ curve.

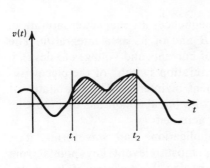

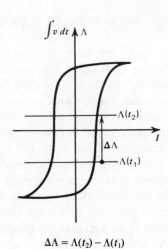

$$\Delta\Lambda = \int_{t_1}^{t_2} v \, dt = \Lambda(t)\Big|_{t_1}^{t_2}$$

$$\Delta\Lambda = \Lambda(t_2) - \Lambda(t_1)$$

(a) Area under voltage waveform.

(b) Vertical displacement on a
$\Lambda - I$ curve.

Figure 2.15 An increment of area under a voltage waveform corresponds to an increment of flux linkage. The positive area of (a) is equal to the positive increment of (b).

For example, consider the change in flux linkage in Fig. 2.15a during the time interval from t_1 to t_2 (cross-hatched area). That is,

$$\Delta\Lambda = \int_{t_1}^{t_2} v \, dt = \Lambda(t)\Big|_{t_1}^{t_2} = \Lambda(t_2) - \Lambda(t_1) \tag{2.30}$$

has the same numerical value as the increment $\Delta\Lambda$ in Fig. 2.15b.

EXAMPLE C

A rectangular pulse of 10 V amplitude and 2 μs duration is applied to a step-up transformer wound on a core modeled by $B = \mu H$. Specify the saturation value Λ_s for the core to avoid saturation, assuming initial conditions at the origin of $\Lambda - I$.

ANSWER. $\Lambda_s = nB_sS_c \geq \int v \, dt = 2 \times 10^{-5}$ V·s. See Fig. 2.16.

2.3.2 Flux Linkage of Periodic Functions

The integration of a symmetrical waveform of alternating polarity yields a resulting waveform with peak-to-peak amplitude increment given by the maximum area in a half-period, $\Delta\Lambda = \int_0^{T/2} v(t) \, dt$. For example, in Fig. 2.17 $v(t)$ is a square wave of alternating amplitude V and of period

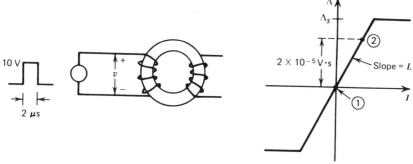

(a) A single voltage pulse of 10 V amplitude and 2 μs duration is applied.

(b) Initial condition is at origin: $\Lambda_s = nB_sS_c$ must exceed 2×10^{-5} V·s.

Figure 2.16 Answer to Example C.

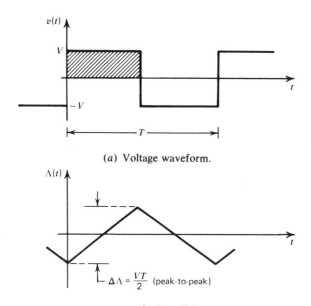

(a) Voltage waveform.

(b) Flux linkage.

Figure 2.17 The area under one half-cycle of the voltage waveform defines the peak-to-peak excursion of $\Delta\Lambda$.

T; thus the increment of flux linkage during each half-cycle is $VT/2$. The waveform for the voltage integral is a triangular waveform of peak-to-peak amplitude $VT/2$. If a square wave of voltage is applied to a core, the voltage waveform integral cannot exceed the magnetic saturation Λ_s for either polarity, if core saturation is to be avoided. Since the maximum positive change of Λ is from $-\Lambda_s$ to $+\Lambda_s$ of the core, it follows that

$$\frac{VT}{2} \leq \Delta\Lambda_{\max} = 2\Lambda_s = 2nB_sS_c, \qquad (2.31)$$

assuming a symmetrical flux excursion. This is a major result. A review of Figs. 2.15 and 2.17 may help clarify the important concept, exposed by (2.31), that core saturation imposes a limit on the volt·second product that can be applied to a core device. The limit can be interpreted either as a low-frequency limit or as a voltage-amplitude limitation.

Whether the periodic voltage waveform is sinusoidal or square, qualitatively similar statements are relevant to the excursion of the area under the waveform.

If $v(t) = A \sin \omega t$, the periodic portion of its integral is

$$\int^t v \, dt = \frac{A}{\omega} \int^t \sin \omega t \, \omega \, dt = -\frac{A}{\omega} \cos \omega t. \qquad (2.32)$$

The peak-to-peak amplitude $2A/\omega$ would result from use of integration limits $\omega t = 0$ to π.

EXAMPLE D

A useful design trick that often simplifies saturation calculations, uses the approximation of a sinusoidal waveform by the area-equivalent square wave. Given that $v(t) = A \sin \omega t$, find the amplitude V of a square wave such that V equals the half-cycle average of the sine wave.

ANSWER. $V = \langle v \rangle = \int_0^{\pi/\omega} v \, dt / \int_0^{\pi/\omega} dt = 2A/\pi.$

For the sake of simplicity, neither of the cases above has explicitly considered the initial conditions of the core or the initial condition of voltage integration. The above assumption of symmetrical flux excursion is not necessarily automatically achieved in practice. For some power circuits, it may be advisable to give some attention to transients of turning the voltage on/off.

Transformer Equation.   The well-known transformer design equation is developed directly from (2.31) and (2.32). From (2.31) the square-wave maximum voltage rating of a wound core is

$$V = 4f\Lambda_s = 4fnB_sS_c, \qquad (2.33)$$

where $f = 1/T$. From (2.32), the area-equivalent sinusoid has a peak amplitude of $A = V\pi/2$, thus a root-mean-square value of $A_{\rm rms} = A/\sqrt{2}$.

After substitution

$$A_{rms} = \sqrt{2}\pi \, fnS_cB_s = 4.44 \, fnS_cB_s. \qquad (2.34)$$

EXERCISE E

Find the voltage rating of a transformer for use at $f = 60$ Hz if the transformer was originally designed for use at 120 V, 400 Hz.

ANSWER.   18 V.

2.3.3 Voltage and Current Waveforms

Several examples listed below use the piecewise-linear model of Section 1.4 to illustrate effects of core saturation. The piecewise-linear method is a time-segmentation approach in which the circuit model for the magnetic device may change from one time interval to the next. In some cases the square-wave input voltage may force a change of circuit model. In other cases the circuit model changes as the core enters or leaves saturation. The dynamic width component of the model is omitted in all examples. At this point the waveforms will be highly idealized, since there has been no discussion of stray inductance or capacitance, or of the resistance of windings. Winding resistance is considered as external to the core model. In other words, the examples to follow assume that during saturation (when the saturation switch is closed) the current is limited by the winding resistance because the induced core-voltage is zero.

EXAMPLE E

A 5-V, 400-Hz square wave is applied to a coil on a square-loop core with $I_0 = 5$ mA, $\Lambda_s = 5 \times 10^{-3}$ V·s ($\Gamma = 1/L = 0$) (approximately the same as the core of Example C of 1.3).

(a) Correlate the voltage and current waveforms with the path on the $\Lambda - I$ plot of the piecewise-linear model.
(b) Find the lowest frequency 5-V square wave that can be applied to this core without saturation.
(c) Sketch the voltage and current waveforms to be expected if the frequency is $\frac{2}{3}$ the value from (b). Assume that the current is limited by a series resistance of $R = 1\,\Omega$ between source and winding; a combination of source impedance and winding resistance.

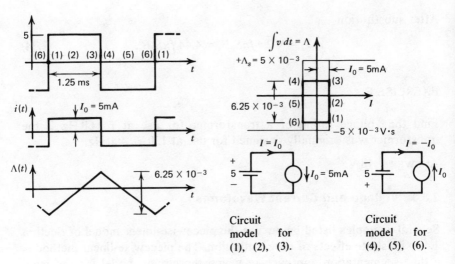

Part of answer (a) for Example E.

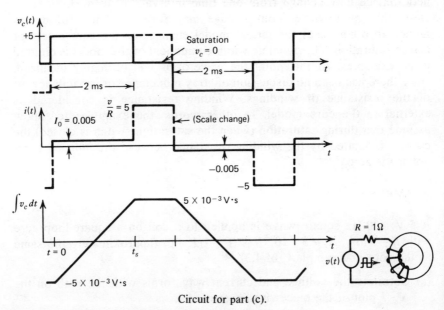

Figure 2.18 Answers for Example E.

ANSWER

(a) $\int_0^{T/2} v \, dt = VT/2 = 6.25 \times 10^{-3}$V·s. The circuit model is merely a 5-V battery connected to a current source of 5 mA, reversing polarity each half-cycle. Figure 2.18 shows waveforms $v(t)$, $i(t)$, and $\Lambda(t)$; six points of the time scale are also indicated on the $\Lambda - I$ loop. Note that the integral of $v(t)$ is not necessarily symmetrical about zero.

(b) $VT/2 = 2\Lambda_s$ at $T/2 = 2$ ms. Thus $f = V/4\Lambda_s = 250$ Hz.

(c) As indicated in the waveform sketches, the core voltage becomes zero at saturation; thus the current is limited only by the small external resistance and the flux linkage is constant at its saturated value.

EXAMPLE F

A 5-V, 5 kHz square wave is applied to the 10-mH inductor of Example D, Section 1.3. Choose an appropriate circuit model and answer (a), (b), and (c) as in Example E.

ANSWER. Using $S_c = 1.33 \times 10^{-5}$ m², $n = 60$, $B_s = 0.375 \pm 10\%$; then $\Lambda_s = 3 \times 10^{-4}$ V·s, where the saturation switch actuates. On the $\Lambda - I$ plane it is noted that the core saturates at $I = 30$ mA $= \Lambda_s/L$. An estimate of the saturation inductance of the coil as $L \approx 2 \mu H$ results from the assumption of an abrupt change in μ_r (from 5000 to 1) at saturation, an alternative to the "saturation switch" model. See Fig. 2.19.

(a) $VT/2 = 5 \times 10^{-4}$ V·s. In contrast with the square-loop core, the waveforms for $i(t)$ and $\Lambda(t)$ are identical in the linear range where $\Lambda = LI$. A steady-state condition of symmetry about the origin is assumed.

(b) Using $\Lambda_s = 3 \times 10^{-4}$ V·s yields $f = 4.17$ kHz.

(c) The waveforms for $v(t)$ and $\Lambda(t)$ are similar to the example for the square-loop core. The current waveform for an actual circuit may differ from the result shown, which assumes a single-valued $\Lambda - I$ characteristic, thus omits effects of dynamic losses.

EXAMPLE G

This example, similar to Example E, uses the same square-loop core driven by a sinusoid of peak amplitude $A = 2.5\pi = 7.854$ V, area-equivalent to a 5-V square wave.

(a) Draw the current waveform for $f = 400$ Hz.

(b) Find the lowest frequency, f_L, of the given amplitude input at which the core just saturates.

(c) Sketch $v(t)$, $i(t)$, and $\Lambda(t)$ for the case of $f = \frac{2}{3}f_L$, having first calculated the phase angle for core saturation.

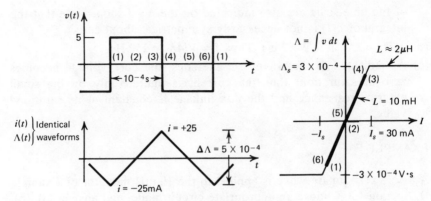

Part of answer (a) of Example F.

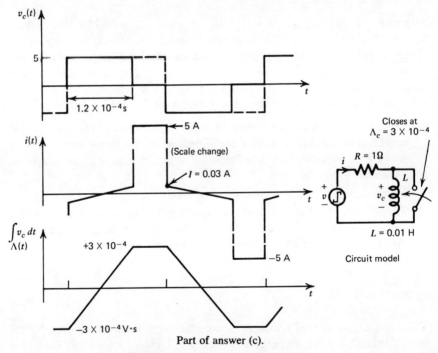

Part of answer (c).

Figure 2.19   Answers for Example F.

ANSWER

(a) An interesting question arises near the waveform zero crossing, in the region where $i = v_s/R$ is less than I_0. Since the core voltage is zero, this is a condition of waveform distortion (lasting for a phase angle θ_1 or time t_1). From Fig. 2.20b it is easily deduced that $0.005 = 2.5\pi \sin \omega t_1$, so that $\theta_1 = \omega t_1 = 0.036°$, hence $t_1 = 0.25 \ \mu s$.

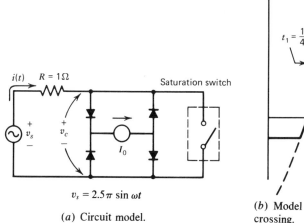

$$v_s = 2.5\pi \sin \omega t$$

(a) Circuit model.

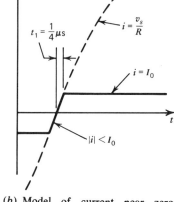

(b) Model of current near zero crossing.

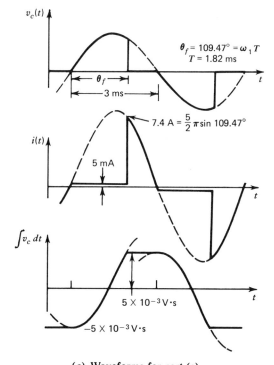

(c) Waveforms for part (c).

Figure 2.20 Solution to Example G.

(b) From the definition of area-equivalence, the frequency should be the same as Example E. From (2.32) it follows that the area under a half-cycle sine wave is

$$\frac{2A}{\omega} = 2\Lambda_s. \tag{2.35}$$

Given $2\Lambda_s = 10^{-2}\,\text{V}\cdot\text{s}$ and $A = 2.5\pi\,\text{V}$, it follows that $f = 250\,\text{Hz}$, as expected.

(c) For a lower frequency $\omega_1 = 2\omega/3$ the time of saturation T defines the actuation of the shorting switch, thus T is shown as a limit on the area integral of the voltage

$$\int_{t=0}^{T} A \sin \omega_1 t \, dt = 2\Lambda_s = \frac{A}{\omega_1}(1 - \cos \omega_1 T). \tag{2.36}$$

It follows from (2.35) that $(1 - \cos \omega_1 T) = \frac{4}{3}$, thus yielding the firing angle $\theta_f = \omega_1 T = 109.47°$. The waveform details of Fig. 2.20c show how time intervals of sinusoidal waveform segments are pieced together, according to circuit rules for matching initial conditions.

Examples E through G were intended to establish the meaning of the piecewise-linear model, in particular to show how saturation affects voltage and current waveforms in elementary circuits. An elementary circuit is one in which either core current or voltage is specified.

In each of the foregoing examples the core is connected to an ideal voltage source through a very small resistor to limit the current at saturation. Except during core saturation there is negligible voltage drop across the resistor; thus the core voltage is equal to the known source voltage. In a voltage-driven elementary circuit the current at any instant is found as follows. If the core is saturated, the current is determined by the voltage source and series impedance, independent of the core. If the core is nonsaturated and the voltage drop across the series impedance is negligible, the current is determined from the core characteristics and voltage source. For an ideal square-loop coil the current is almost independent of the voltage waveform, whereas for an inductive coil the current is proportional to the integral waveform of the core voltage.

In Example H the core is driven by a sinusoidal current source and the voltage is to be determined. A waveform segmentation method is used again, in preparation for the analysis of less elementary circuits. Example H, and others below, illustrate the further concept that the integral of the inductive voltage $v = L\,di/dt$ can specify the value of current i only within an additive constant. For that reason, special attention is given to the initial conditions.

EXAMPLE H

A 5-kHz sinusoidal current source drives an inductor, modeled as $L = 10$ mH below $\Lambda_s = 3 \times 10^{-4}$ V·s as in Example F. Find the waveforms for $i(t)$, $v(t)$, $\Lambda(t)$ predicted by the piecewise-linear model for two values of current amplitude.

(a) $I_{max} = 10$ mA.
(b) $I_{max} = 50$ mA.

ANSWER

(a) The core does not saturate, since $i \leq I_s$, where $I_s = \Lambda_s/L = 30$ mA. Given $i(t) = 10 \sin \omega t$ mA, where $\omega = 10^4 \pi$ rad/s, then $V_c(t) = L\,di/dt = j\omega\,LI = \pi \cos \omega t$.

(b) Figure 2.21c shows that $i(t)$ and $\Lambda(t)$ have the same waveform until Λ saturates as i passes through 30 mA. The fundamental definition of $v = d\Lambda/dt$ avoids the possible confusion that would arise from the definition $v = d(Li)/dt$, since both L and i are time varying. The voltage waveform is thus found to be the center segment of a cosine wave, a consequence of the abrupt saturation of the idealized core $\Lambda - I$ model of Fig. 2.21b. The voltage waveform of an actual core has a more rounded shape but has the same constraint on the area under it.

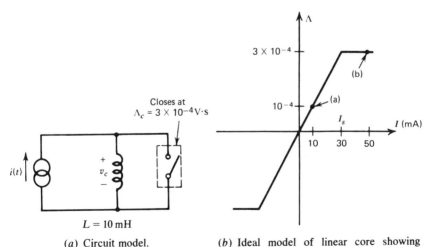

(a) Circuit model.

(b) Ideal model of linear core showing peak amplitudes for (a), (b).

Figure 2.21 Solution to Example H.

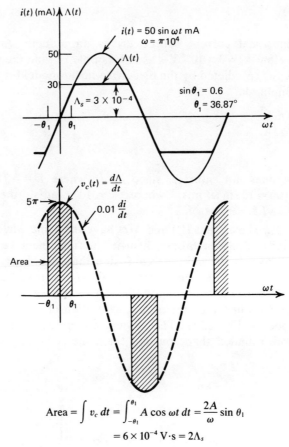

$$\text{Area} = \int v_c \, dt = \int_{-\theta_1}^{\theta_1} A \cos \omega t \, dt = \frac{2A}{\omega} \sin \theta_1$$

$$= 6 \times 10^{-4} \text{ V·s} = 2\Lambda_s$$

(c) Waveforms of $i(t)$, $v_c(t)$, and $\Lambda(t)$ for part (b).

Figure 2.21 (Continued)

EXAMPLE I

A series $R - L$ circuit is driven by a sinusoidal voltage of 9 V peak, $f = 750$ Hz. Find the current and coil voltage waveforms if $R = 150 \, \Omega$ and $L = 10$ mH with $\Lambda_s = 3 \times 10^{-4}$.

ANSWER. Since neither current nor voltage is specified for the coil, the network must be solved first to determine whether saturation will occur. Assuming nonsaturation, $Z = R + j\omega L = 150 + j47.12 = 157.22 \angle \theta_1$, where $\theta_1 = 17.44°$. Hence current i_1 lags the applied voltage by θ_1 and would reach a peak amplitude $|I| = 9 \text{ V}/157.22 = 57.2$ mA, a sufficient value to saturate the core. The coil voltage peak amplitude would be

$9(47.12/157.22) = 2.70 \, \text{V}$ without saturation. After coil saturation the current i_2 will reach the peak value $I = V_s/R = 60 \, \text{mA}$. Figure 2.22$b$ shows both component current waveforms, and the composite current that results from the saturation switch closing (1) and opening (2) at the phase angle of $\theta_2 = 31.6°$, relative to i_1. The coil voltage and the flux linkage have waveforms similar to those of Example H.

The examples above demonstrate the potential usefulness of the piece-wise-linear model to the analysis of nonlinear magnetic circuits driven by periodic signals. The method of waveform segmentation in these

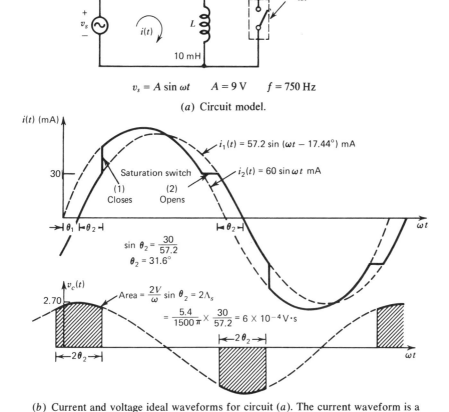

$R = 150\Omega$

$\Lambda_{sat} = 3 \times 10^{-4} \text{V} \cdot \text{s}$

$v_s = A \sin \omega t \qquad A = 9 \, \text{V} \qquad f = 750 \, \text{Hz}$

(a) Circuit model.

$i(t)$ (mA)

$i_1(t) = 57.2 \sin (\omega t - 17.44°)$ mA

30

$i_2(t) = 60 \sin \omega t$ mA

Saturation switch

(1) Closes   (2) Opens

$\sin \theta_2 = \dfrac{30}{57.2}$

$\theta_2 = 31.6°$

$v_c(t)$

2.70

Area $= \dfrac{2V}{\omega} \sin \theta_2 = 2\Lambda_s$

$= \dfrac{5.4}{1500\,\pi} \times \dfrac{30}{57.2} = 6 \times 10^{-4} \text{V} \cdot \text{s}$

(b) Current and voltage ideal waveforms for circuit (a). The current waveform is a piecewise construction of two components.

Figure 2.22 Illustrations for Example I. Neither current nor voltage is specified directly; the circuit must be solved before it can be determined whether the core saturates. See text for details.

examples appears to require the current to have a discontinuity. In an inductive circuit the current cannot jump from one value to another instantaneously because an infinite rate of change of current requires a large voltage $L\,di/dt$. The incremental inductance always exceeds zero even for a saturated core because the relative permeability of free space is unity. Example J reviews a well-known R–L circuit transient problem to expose the principle of current continuity, then extends the problem to the case of coil saturation to a small but finite inductance.

EXAMPLE J

A square pulse of amplitude V and duration $T = 5$ ms is applied to an initially quiescent, series $R - L$ circuit with $R = 20\,\Omega$ and $L = 10$ mH. It is assumed that for $I \geq 30$ mA, the saturation incremental inductance is $2\,\mu$H.

(a) Find the maximum value of V for linear operation of the circuit. Sketch the transient waveforms of coil current and voltage.

(b) Sketch the waveforms if V is twice the value found in (a).

ANSWER

(a) Waveforms are shown in Fig. 2.23. During the pulse the circuit equation to be solved is

$$V = i_1R + L\frac{di_1}{dt} \quad \text{for} \quad 0 \leq t \leq T.$$

Conventional methods yield the result $i_1(t) = [1 - e^{-t/\tau}]V/R$, $\tau = L/R = 0.5$ ms, thus $i_1(T) = [1 - e^{-10}]V/R \approx V/R$. The problem requirement $V/R = 30$ mA yields the result $V = 0.6$ V. The circuit equation after the pulse

$$0 = i_2R + L\frac{di_2}{dT} \quad \text{for} \quad t \geq T$$

has a solution of the form $i_2(t) = I_0e^{-(t-T)/\tau}$, which is a decaying

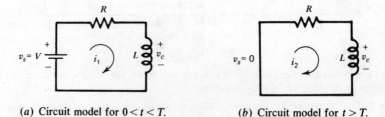

(*a*) Circuit model for $0 < t < T$.   (*b*) Circuit model for $t > T$.

Figure 2.23 Solution to Example J.

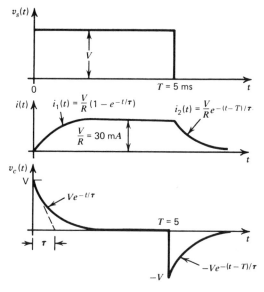

(c) Solution to part (a).

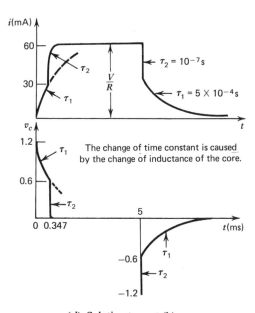

The change of time constant is caused by the change of inductance of the core.

(d) Solution to part (b).

Figure 2.23 (continued)

exponential that begins at $t = T$. Since the current cannot change instantaneously, $i_2(T) = i_1(T)$; thus $I_0 = V/R$ to satisfy the initial conditions of i_2. The equality above is a requirement of current continuity between two equations at an instant of time.

The coil voltage is

$$v_c = L\, di/dt = Ve^{-t/\tau} \qquad \text{for} \quad 0 \le t \le T$$
$$= -V e^{-(t-T)/\tau}, \qquad\qquad t \ge T;$$

also

$$\Lambda(t) = V\tau[1 - e^{-t/\tau}] \qquad 0 \le t \le T$$
$$= V\tau e^{-(t-T)/\tau} \qquad t > T,$$

noting that $V\tau = 0.6 \times 0.5 \times 10^{-3} = 3 \times 10^{-4} = \Lambda_s$ from the problem requirement. The back-kick of voltage for $t > T$ represents the collapse of coil current, to restore the quiescent condition of $i = 0$. The self-resetting action with the decay of an uni-directional (unipolar) current represents a collapse of stored magnetic energy that does not occur in a coil if the static width H_0 is the dominant property of the core.

(b) The current equation is $i_1(t) = 60\,(1 - e^{-t/\tau_1})\ mA$, but when the current reaches the value $i_1 = 30\ mA$ at $t = \tau_1 \ln 2 = 347\ \mu s$, the time constant suddenly becomes $\tau_2 = 10^{-7}$ s for the remainder of the transient. The waveforms in Fig. 2.23d illustrate continuity of current for the condition of inductance change at an instant of time.

2.3.4 Suggestions for Waveform Observations

Applied magnetism is ultimately experimental. To design ingenious magnetic circuits often requires laboratory skills in addition to analytical skills and theoretical understanding. The piecewise-linear model—and analyses using the model—are only approximations to actual device performance; furthermore, the analysis is always a simpler approximation.

A meaningful set of experiments may be drawn from the examples of Section 2.3.3. Qualitatively, the experiments consist of making oscilloscope observations of current and voltage waveforms that result from applying signals to coils that are wound onto cores. The signals may be sinusoids, square waves, or possibly pulses. For ease of interpretation, it would be preferable to have the cores of either extreme type: either a square-loop core or a linear core. Quantitatively, the experiments may include detailed comparisons of experimental observation with calculated values. It is suggested that any tutorial experiments that are quantitative should use cores with known parameters: magnetic path length, area, saturation induction, coercivity or permeability, and preferably with no airgap. The observation of waveforms versus time may also be extended slightly to show a hysteresis loop.

Hysteresis Loop Measurement. The following comments are introductory, intended for the student who has not previously measured a hysteresis loop by oscilloscope. It is assumed that the cores are small, with a few tens of turns wound by hand. The test circuit of Fig. 2.24 is described, in which $y - y$ is ultimately connected to the y-axis input of the scope, and $x - x$ to the x-axis input. The voltage across $x - x$ is proportional to magnetizing current ($v_x = i_1 r$), and v_3 is intended to be proportional to $\int v_2 \, dt$. Experience has shown that most measurement problems arise because of one or more of the three problem areas, which motivates the following three suggestions.

1. Estimate the current and voltage required by the core, and use these values in deciding how to set up the supply circuit. In Fig. 2.24 v_s must be an adequate voltage to cause core saturation at the frequency of measurement,

$$\langle v_s \rangle \geq 4\Lambda_s f. \tag{2.37}$$

Furthermore, v_s/r must be capable of exceeding the drive current requirements of the core,

$$v_s/r > \frac{1}{n_1} \oint \bar{H} \cdot d\bar{l}. \tag{2.38}$$

In the circuit shown, the filament transformer can supply 1 or 2 A if r is not too big.

2. Be careful about ground problems. In the circuit shown (Fig. 2.24) either side of resistor r can be connected to scope ground because the filament transformer provides ground isolation. Alternatively, if v_s is from a grounded signal generator, scope ground must also be con-

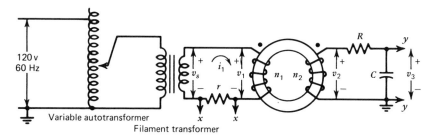

Figure 2.24 A test circuit for measuring the hysteresis loop of small toroidal cores.

nected to the left side of *r* so as to not short out *r*. In Fig. 2.24 output winding n_2 is optional as far as grounding is concerned and the *RC* integration circuit could just as well be connected to the primary winding. However it should be noted that v_1 includes a winding resistance component that can be significant

$$v_1 = i_1 R_w + n_1 \frac{d\phi}{dt}, \tag{2.39}$$

whereas v_2 senses only the flux change

$$v_2 = n_2 \frac{d\phi}{dt}. \tag{2.40}$$

3. Design the *RC* integrator. Two requirements are that *R* should be large enough to have negligible effect on the primary current, and that $\omega RC \gg 1$ is necessary for good integration. The latter requirement can be deduced from the transfer function

$$\frac{V_3}{V_2}(s) = \frac{1}{RCs + 1} \approx \frac{1}{RCs} \tag{2.41}$$

in order to obtain the integral of v_2

$$\frac{V_2}{s} = RC\, V_3 \quad \text{or} \quad \int v_2 \, dt = RCv_3(t). \tag{2.42}$$

The effect of too small an *RC* product is shown in Fig. 2.25.

As a final suggestion, take the opportunity to look at all the waveforms versus time, as well as ∫ *v dt* versus *i*. Examine every subtle nuance of each waveform to see whether it is what you had expected. Look at $i_1(t)$, $v_s(t)$, $v_1(t)$, $v_2(t)$, and $v_3(t)$. Finally, you are urged to compare v_3 versus i_1 quantitatively with calculations for the core under test.

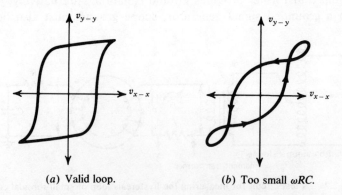

(*a*) Valid loop.   (*b*) Too small *ωRC*.

Figure 2.25   Effect of too short an integrator time constant.

PROBLEMS

1 (**Section 2.1**). Given that the atomic weight of average nickel is 58.71, use the data in Table 2.2 for nickel to do the following.
   a. Find the magnetic moment j and the volume $(1/N)$ for a typical nickel atom at room temperature.
   b. Use the result of (a) to determine the effective number of Bohr magnetons per atom.

2 (**Section 2.1**). Carry out the elementary cross-product and the time derivative of (2.14) for $\bar{H} = H\hat{a}_z$ and for $\bar{J}$ at a constant angle θ from the positive z-axis. The cylindrical coordinate system is suggested. The result should show that the precession frequency $\omega = d\phi/dt$ is independent of angle θ.

3 (**Section 2.2**). Carry out the integration of (2.19) for a square-loop material as in Fig. 2.8, to yield the result of (2.24).

4 (**Section 2.2**). Calculate numerical values for all parameters in Fig. 2.13 for a toroidal core of O.D./I.D./ht = 1.27/0.714/0.478 cm assuming a linear ferrite of $\mu_r = 5000$ and $B_s \approx 0.4$ T.

5 (**Section 2.3**). Specify the number of primary turns to be wound on a transformer core of cross section 2×3 cm, to assure that the core will not saturate under steady-state conditions. The core material is conventional silicon-iron transformer material, which saturates at $B_s = 2.0$ T. The transformer is intended for use on line voltage, 115 V_{rms} at 60 Hz.

6 (**Section 2.3**).
   a. Find the time duration Δt of the voltage-pulse waveform in Example H, part b, in which a 10-mH inductor (which saturates at $\Lambda_s = 3 \times 10^{-4}$ V·s) is driven by a 50-mA sinusoidal current at $f = 5$ kHz.
   b. Repeat the example to find v, θ_1, and Δt if $f = 15$ kHz.

7 (**Section 2.3**). Suppose in the $R - L$ circuit of Fig. 2.22a the voltage source v_s is a periodic train of rectangular pulses of amplitude V and duration T_1, separated by zero amplitude for time T_2 such that the period of the waveform is $(T_1 + T_2)$. Find and carefully sketch the waveforms of inductor current and voltage for the following conditions.
   a. $V = 3v$, $T_1 = 400 \mu$s, $T_2 = 800 \mu$s.
   b. $V = 6v$ with times as in (a).
   c. $V = 6v$, $T_1 = 40 \mu$s, $T_2 = 80 \mu$s.
   d. $V = 15 v$ with times as in (c).

(*Hint.* In (c) note that the unknown peak voltage amplitudes v_a, v_b

can be found from the two equations $v_a e^{-T_1/\tau} - V = v_b$ and $v_b e^{-T_2/\tau} + V = v_a$).

8 **(Section 2.3).** Wind a small inductor using a linear ferrite core of known properties, such as toroid no. 768T188/3E2A which is described in Example D, Section 1.3.2.

     a. Measure L and Q using an audiofrequency impedance bridge.

     b. Calculate the approximate saturation value of Λ in volt·seconds from the known core properties.

     c. Set up an experiment and quantitatively interpret the scope waveforms for voltage and current under conditions in which the core is driven to saturation. Compare the actual waveforms with the highly idealized model (Fig. 2.22). Estimate $\int v\, dt$ for the voltage pulse for comparison with (b).

9 **(Section 2.3.4).** Make the measurements requested below on a square-loop core (tapewound, nickel-iron alloy) that has been wound with an appropriate number of turns.

     a. Examine scope waveforms of current, voltage, and $\int v\, dt$ and make a quantitative comparison with the predictions of a piecewise-linear model for your device.

     b. Display on the scope the hysteresis loop $\int v\, dt$ versus i, with the core driven into saturation. Compare your amplitude measurements with calculated values for B_{sat} and H_0.

REFERENCES

1. R. M. Bozorth, *Ferromagnetism*, D. Van Nostrand, New York, 1951. The most comprehensive and systematic collection of its time of experimental data, especially for ferromagnetic alloys, composition, and processing. Also includes a compilation of magnetic theories.

2. R. S. Tebble and D. J. Craik, *Magnetic Materials*, Wiley-Interscience, New York, 1969. A handbook of information on magnetic materials including ferrites and garnets as well as ferromagnets.

3. C. Kittel and J. K. Galt, "Ferromagnetic Domains," *Solid State Phys.* 3, 437 (1956). A classical paper of fundamentals in the theory of magnetism.

4. S. Chikazumi, *Physics of Magnetism*, Wiley New York, 1964. See Chapter 3 for further information on orbital motion, spin, gyromagnetic effects, ferromagnetic resonance, and atomic models. See Section 4.3 for theory of alloys, and Chapter 5 for theory of ferrites.

5. R. M. Fano, L. J. Chu, and R. B. Adler, *Electromagnetic Fields, Energy and Forces*, Wiley New York, 1960. Fundamental relationships for forces in matter are presented from the view that $\mu_0 H$ is the fundamental parameter, rather than B. For instance, the Lorentz force on a moving charge is given as $\bar{F} = Q\bar{v} \times \mu_0 \bar{H}$ rather than $\bar{F} = Q\bar{v} \times \bar{B}$.

3.
Field Strength, *H*

This book considers that H is the field strength companion to magnetic flux density B, as the analogous E is the field strength companion to electric flux density D. The analogous quantities E and H can exist in two different forms, depending on the type of source from which the field arises. For instance, an E-field is solenoidal if it is caused by time-varying B, in addition E possesses curl in the region where dB/dt exists. By contrast, an electric field caused by charges is not solenoidal, possessing divergence in the region where charge exists, and furthermore it possesses the property that E is the gradient of a single-valued potential. In a similar manner an H-field is solenoidal if it is caused by current and in addition possesses curl in the region where current flows. By contrast, a magnetic field attributed to magnetic poles will diverge in the region where the poles occur, and H will be the gradient of a single-valued magnetic potential. The two forms of H are treated separately in this chapter.

Although the subject is too complex to be considered in Chapter 3, the gradient of other forms of potential energy can be considered under certain conditions as effective H-fields within a magnetic material. The vector sum of the components of H and H_{eff} then can be treated as the total field of the system.

Section 3.1 takes up the design of H-fields due to current flowing in conductors that are suitably arranged in free space (i.e., air-core coils). Readers with skills in the basic principles of field calculations should skim quickly to Section 3.1.3 for the application to coil design, including considerations of current density.

Section 3.2 considers H-fields that arise from nonuniformities of magnetic material, in the context of permanent magnet applications. Basic principles of field calculations emphasize the pole model of magnetic material, with the alternative Amperian model shown for comparison. Design principles for permanent magnet (PM) systems, including both static and dynamic design criteria, are followed by data for PM materials.

Section 3.3 draws on ideas from the previous two sections in modeling the effect of an airgap in the magnetic core of a current-carrying coil.

Section 3.4 presents three topics of design interest. First, the design of a commercial electromagnet is summarized; next, the application of super-conducting coils to high-field generation is pointed out. Finally, a type of vacuum pump based on the use of a magnetic field is described.

This chapter seeks to establish valid engineering design skills based on the broad applicability of a minimum set of principles of vector calculus. This perspective has led to the omission of certain elegant concepts that are particularly useful for field calculations. For instance, the solid angle subtended at a point by a sheet of current or of magnetic poles is a useful concept for calculating the field at that point due to either sheet source. As another example, the magnetic vector potential $\bar{A}$, the curl of which is $\bar{\nabla} \times \bar{A} = \bar{B}$, is useful in more general geometries than are considered here. The reader with insights or needs that are beyond the elementary skills of Section 3.1 may wish to pursue these topics from other sources.

3.1 FIELDS FROM CURRENTS

This section seeks to establish the basic concepts that are relevant to the general subject of magnetic fields caused by the flow of current along conductors. We start with the assumption of an infinitesimal conductor surrounded by free space and review two basic equations, the Biot-Savart equation and Ampere's circuital law. These two equations are used to calculate H and its line integral, respectively. Our emphasis is on their application to field coil design, to create a region of H in space.

3.1.1 Applying the Biot-Savart Equation to Calculate H-Fields

The design of coils for producing H-fields is based on two steps: a mathematical description of coil geometry, and physical considerations of currents in the conductors. This section deals with the mathematical formulation of H-fields assuming current-carrying conductors of infinitesimal cross section. The equations that result are used in Section 3.1.3 to realize practical coils.

The Point-Form B–S Equation. Our main tool for the derivation of equations for H, for a few special configurations, will be the point-form Biot-Savart (B–S) equation, in derivative form;

$$d\bar{H}(\bar{r}_2) = \frac{I}{4\pi}\, d\bar{l}_1 \times \frac{\hat{a}_R}{R^2} = \frac{I}{4\pi}\, d\bar{l}_1 \times \frac{\bar{R}}{R^3}. \tag{3.1}$$

As illustrated in Fig. 3.1, this is an equation for an incremental vector field contribution $d\bar{H}$ at the "field point," coordinate location $\bar{r}_2$, caused by a point source $I\, d\bar{l}_1$ in which the direction of I is indicated by the increment of circuit l_1 located at $\bar{r}_1$. The vector $\bar{R} = \bar{r}_2 - \bar{r}_1$ is the distance from the "source point" to the "field point." The middle form of (3.1) illustrates the inverse square law distance dependence that is characteristic of a point source. The cross-product of $d\bar{l}_1$ with the unit vector $\hat{a}_R = \bar{R}/R$ has the function of assuring that $d\bar{H}$ is perpendicular both to

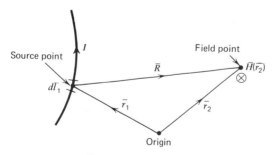

$I\, d\bar{l}_1$ is in the direction of $I.$

$\bar{R} = \bar{r}_2 - \bar{r}_1$

Figure 3.1 Illustration of geometry for (3.1), the B–S equation in point form.

$d\bar{l}_1$ and to $\bar{R}$. The procedure for finding the total field at r_2 due to current in the entire circuit l_1 requires the vector addition of all contributions $d\bar{H}(r_2)$ due to each increment of l_1; in other words (3.1) is integrated over all l_1.

Equation 3.1 leads to tractable closed solutions for a few special geometries. In our examples of applying (3.1), the following procedure is used. First, define for the geometry of interest each term $d\bar{l}_1$, $\bar{r}_1$, $\bar{r}_2$, and $\bar{R}$; second, execute the cross-product and determine the limits for integration of l_1. The integration is a mathematical operation that may or may not be straightforward.

The first series of examples reviews a basic notion from elementary field theory. If the source geometry is a point source, line source, or sheet source, the field dependence is $1/R^2$, $1/R$, or invariant, respectively. The point source relation is given by (3.1). Example A illustrates the use of this equation to find the field due to a line source.

Line Source

EXAMPLE A

Find the H-field at $(x_0, 0, 0)$ due to a current I in the positive direction along the z-axis, see Fig. 3.2.

(a) Find the contribution due to the segment of conductor between the limits $-z_1 \le z \le z_2$.
(b) Find the field if the conductor is infinitely long, $-\infty < z < \infty$.

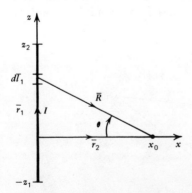

$\bar{r}_1 = z\hat{a}_z, \qquad \bar{r}_2 = x_0\hat{a}_x, \qquad d\bar{l}_1 = dz\hat{a}_z$

$$\tan \theta = \frac{z}{x_0}$$

Figure 3.2 Geometry for calculating the field at x_0 due to a current I along the z-axis. See Example A.

ANSWER. $d\bar{l}_1 = \hat{a}_z\, dz$, $\bar{r}_1 = z\hat{a}_z$, which is the distance from the origin to a general $d\bar{l}_1$, $\bar{r}_2 = x_0\hat{a}_x$, so $\bar{R} = x_0\hat{a}_x - z\hat{a}_z$ and $d\bar{l}_1 \times \bar{R} = x_0 dz\, \hat{a}_y$.

(a) The required integral is thus $\bar{H}(x_0) = \hat{a}_y(Ix_0/4\pi) \int_{z=-z_1}^{z_2} dz/(x_0^2 + z^2)^{3/2}$. We can either seek the help of integral tables or make the substitution $z = x_0 \tan\theta$, which leads to $\bar{H}(x_0) = \hat{a}_y(I/4\pi x_0) \int_{\theta=-\theta_1}^{\theta_2} \cos\theta\, d\theta$ and the final result

$$\bar{H}(x_0) = \hat{a}_y \frac{I}{4\pi x_0} (\sin\theta_2 + \sin\theta_1). \tag{3.2}$$

(b) As z_1 and z_2 increase to $\pm\infty$, the angles increase to $90°$ to yield the result for an infinite line

$$\bar{H}(x_0) = \hat{a}_y \frac{I}{2\pi x_0}. \tag{3.3}$$

EXAMPLE B

Find the value of H-field 2 cm from a long straight wire that carries a current of 30 A.

ANSWER. From (3.3) $|H| = 30/0.04\pi = 238.7$ A·t/m.

Sheet Current. The concept of sheet current is important, not only to the design of coils, but also in Chapter 5 to the modeling of the shielding effect of induced surface current. It is thus convenient to use three representations for current: I is the total current in a conductor, J is current density (A/m²), and K is sheet current density (A/m). It is to be noted that both J^* and K can be given a vector notation to indicate the direction of current. Figure 3.3 shows two ways to describe sheet current K. Example C uses the relation

$$dI = J\, dx\, dy = K\, dy. \tag{3.4}$$

EXAMPLE C

Integrate (3.3) to find the field at a distance x_0 from a sheet current of density $K\hat{a}_z$.

ANSWER. A more general vector form of (3.3) can be written as $\bar{H} = (I/2\pi R)\hat{a}_l \times \hat{a}_R$, where $\hat{a}_l$ is the unit vector of the line current and $\bar{R}$ is the vector to x_0 from the line source at general point y (Fig. 3.4). The

---

*In this chapter the symbol J is used to designate current density (A/m²) and intrinsic induction is designated as B_i.

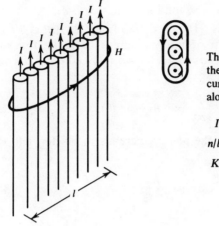

The direction of the H-field is given by the "right-hand rule" (align thumb with current, $\hat{a}_z$; then curved fingers point along H, $\hat{a}_\phi$).

I = current/turn

n/l = turns/meter

$K = nI/l$ (A/m)

(a) Model of discrete turns of wire as a sheet current.

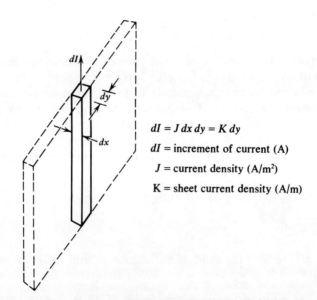

$dI = J\,dx\,dy = K\,dy$

dI = increment of current (A)

J = current density (A/m^2)

K = sheet current density (A/m)

(b) Comparison of three models of current in an incremental area.

Figure 3.3 Two representations of sheet current: (a) is useful for coil design; (b) is a useful way to describe current in a surface layer of thickness dx.

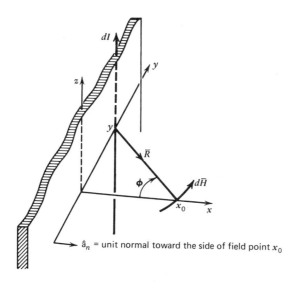

From (3.3);

$$d\bar{H}(x_0) = \frac{dI}{2\pi R}\, \hat{a}_z \times \hat{a}_R$$

$$\tan \phi = \frac{y}{x_0}$$

$$\cos \phi = \frac{x_0}{R}$$

$$dI = J\, dx\, dy$$

Figure 3.4 Geometry for the generalization of (3.3) for use as an increment of sheet current $K\hat{a}_z$ in the $y - z$ plane, Example C.

problem asks for I (3.3) to be regarded as one increment dI of a current sheet in the $y - z$ plane, causing an increment $dH = dI/2\pi R$. Using (3.4) and the definitions $\hat{a}_l = \hat{a}_z$, $\hat{a}_R = \hat{a}_x \cos \phi - \hat{a}_y \sin \phi$, $R = x_0/\cos \phi$ and $y = x_0 \tan \phi$, hence $dy = x_0 \sec^2 \phi\, d\phi$, it follows that

$$d\bar{H} = \frac{K}{2\pi}\left(\hat{a}_y + \hat{a}_x \frac{\sin \phi}{\cos \phi}\right) d\phi,$$

which is to be integrated from $-\phi_1$ to ϕ_1, where ϕ_1 goes to the limit $\pi/2$. Noting that the x-component integrates out to zero because of symmetry, the result for positive x_0 is

$$\bar{H} = \hat{a}_y \frac{K}{2} \qquad \text{for} \quad x_0 > 0, \tag{3.5a}$$

which is independent of distance. The direction of H is opposite for negative x, shown as a more general

$$\bar{H} = \hat{a}_y \frac{K}{2}(\text{sgn } x) \qquad \text{or} \qquad \frac{\bar{K} \times \hat{a}_n}{2} \qquad (3.5b)$$

The interpretation of these results to practical geometry is that a sheet current K A/m causes a discontinuity of tangential H across the current sheets of

$$\Delta H = K \qquad \text{A/m} \qquad (3.6)$$

Examples A and C have served to illustrate the mechanics of applying the B–S equation, while demonstrating the well-known distance dependence from ideal source shapes. Two useful source elements, the finite wire segment and the current sheet, have also been defined. The next two examples give closed equations for practical coil geometries for the field on the axis of symmetry. The off-axis fields are omitted because they are too cumbersome for an introductory treatment.

Circular Coil

EXAMPLE D

A circular coil of radius r carries a current I in the positive ϕ-coordinate direction. Find the expression for the field at a general point z on its axis.

ANSWER.   Figure 3.5 shows the geometry to define the components of (3.1) in cylindrical coordinates. Since the intermediate results $d\bar{l}_1 \times \bar{R} = rd\phi(z\hat{a}_r + r\hat{a}_z)$, the surviving z-component of $\bar{H}$ becomes

$$\bar{H}(z) = \hat{a}_z \frac{I}{4\pi} \int_0^{2\pi} r^2 \frac{d\phi}{R^3},$$

which easily is integrated to the final result

$$\bar{H}(z) = \hat{a}_z \frac{I}{2r}\left(1 + \frac{z^2}{r^2}\right)^{-3/2} = \hat{a}_z \frac{I}{2r}\sin^3\theta. \qquad (3.7)$$

A key point in the derivation is that the radial component of $d\bar{H}$, the first term of the cross-product, will integrate out to zero physical value. That can be deduced from a symmetry argument, or mathematically examining the physical projection by making the substitution $\hat{a}_r = \cos\phi\ \hat{a}_x + \sin\phi\ \hat{a}_y$ and carrying out the required integration of ϕ from zero to 2π.

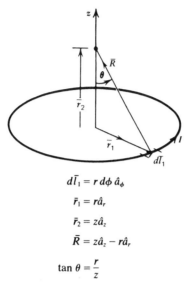

$$d\bar{l}_1 = r\,d\phi\,\hat{a}_\phi$$

$$\bar{r}_1 = r\hat{a}_r$$

$$\bar{r}_2 = z\hat{a}_z$$

$$\bar{R} = z\hat{a}_z - r\hat{a}_r$$

$$\tan\theta = \frac{r}{z}$$

Figure 3.5 Geometry for calculating the field at a general point z on the axis of a circular coil, Example D.

EXAMPLE E

Use (3.7) to find an expression for the field at any point z on the axis of a solenoidal coil of radius r, height $2h$, and sheet current density $K\hat{a}_\phi$.

ANSWER.   Referring to Fig. 3.6, consider the contribution $d\bar{H}(z)$ due to a circular coil at z' carrying a current $dI = K\,dz'$. Since $dz' = r\csc^2\theta\,d\theta$, it follows from (3.7) that

$$\bar{H}(z) = \hat{a}_z\,\frac{K}{2}\int_{\theta_1}^{\theta_2}\sin\theta\,d\theta. \tag{3.8}$$

With the definition $-\cos\theta_2 = \cos(\pi - \theta_2) = \cos\alpha$, the final result can be written

$$\bar{H}(z) = \hat{a}_z\,\frac{K}{2}(\cos\theta_1 + \cos\alpha), \tag{3.9}$$

where $\tan\theta_1 = r/(h+z)$ and $\tan\alpha = r/(h-z)$ for $|z| < h$.*

Solenoidal Coil.   The expression for H on a solenoid axis, (3.9), has the same geometrical dependence as the equation for B of an ideal permanent magnet of the same cylindrical geometry, as Section 3.2.1

*See (3.38), page 98, for a general definition of $\cos\theta$.

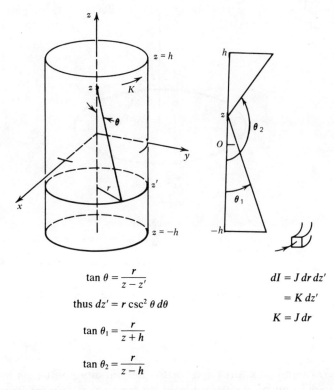

$$\tan \theta = \frac{r}{z - z'}$$

thus $dz' = r \csc^2 \theta \, d\theta$

$$\tan \theta_1 = \frac{r}{z + h}$$

$$\tan \theta_2 = \frac{r}{z - h}$$

$$dI = J \, dr \, dz'$$
$$= K \, dz'$$
$$K = J \, dr$$

Figure 3.6 Geometry for the derivation of the field at a general point on the axis of a solenoid, Example E.

explains. Several special cases of the equation are worthy of note. At the center of a very long coil $\bar{H} \approx \hat{a}_z K$, since $\theta_1 = \alpha \approx 0$; yet at one end of the coil $\bar{H} \approx \hat{a}_z K/2$, since $\theta_1 \approx 0$ and $\alpha = 90°$. One of the cosine terms changes polarity if the field point on the coil axis lies outside the end of the coil.

CGS Units. The B–S equation in Gaussian units is

$$d\bar{H} = \frac{(I/c)(d\bar{l} \times \hat{a}_R)}{R^2} \quad \text{Oe,}$$

where R is in centimeters and I is in statamperes, hence I/c is the definition of current in abamperes. In practical CGS units with I in amperes, the B–S equation is

$$d\bar{H} = \frac{(I/10)(d\bar{l} \times \hat{a}_R)}{R^2} \quad \text{Oe,}$$

which is the same form as (3.1) multiplied by 0.4π. The same multiplier of 0.4π is applicable to all the equations above that explicitly use current I. MKS equations with sheet current K require a multiplier of $4\pi10^{-3}$ to convert them to CGS practical units.

EXAMPLE F

Use practical CGS units to calculate the value of H-field 2 cm from a long straight wire that carries a current of 30 A. Compare the answer with Example B.

ANSWER. The practical CGS version of (3.3) is $H = 0.2\, I/r$, so $H = 0.2 \times 30/2 = 3$ Oe, which checks.

EXERCISE A

Use (3.2) to find the expression for the field on the axis of a square coil. If the coil lies in the $x - y$ plane, is centered on the z-axis, and has sides $2s \times 2s$, and current I, the problem is to show that for any point z,

$$\bar{H}(z) = \hat{a}_z \frac{2I}{\pi s} \left(1 + \frac{z^2}{s^2}\right)^{-1} \left(2 + \frac{z^2}{s^2}\right)^{-1/2}. \tag{3.10}$$

EXERCISE B

Use (3.2) to find the expression for the field on the axis of a rectangular coil of sides $2a \times 2b$. Test your result for the case $a = b = s$ by comparing with (3.10).

3.1.2 Applying Ampere's Circuital Law

After gaining some familiarity with the geometry of electric currents and the associated H-fields they cause, it is possible in a number of cases to deduce the H-field from the use of Ampere's circuital law, as a pleasant alternative to the vector calculus of the B–S equation. Some examples follow a review of Ampere's law.

Review of Curl H. Ampere's circuital law is the integral form of Maxwell's equation for curl H with displacement current omitted,

$$\bar{\nabla} \times \bar{H} = \bar{J} \qquad \text{A/m}^2. \tag{3.11}$$

The H-field possesses curl in a region where current exists. The simplest case to examine is a long round wire on the z-axis, carrying direct current of uniform density $J\hat{a}_z$. The general equation for curl $\bar{H}$ in cylindrical coordinates is

$$\bar{\nabla} \times \bar{H} = \hat{a}_r\left[(1/r)\frac{\partial H_z}{\partial \phi} - \frac{\partial H_\phi}{\partial z}\right] + \hat{a}_\phi\left[\frac{\partial H_r}{\partial z} - \frac{\partial H_z}{\partial r}\right] + \hat{a}_z\frac{1}{r}\left[\frac{\partial (rH_\phi)}{\partial r} - \frac{\partial H_r}{\partial \phi}\right].$$

$$(3.12)$$

For this problem assumptions of geometric symmetry and the centerline location of the z-axis (Fig. 3.7) cause all derivatives except one to be zero. The result is that (3.11) becomes

$$(1/r)\frac{d(rH_\phi)}{dr} = J_z,$$

$$(3.13)$$

with the solution

$$H_\phi = \frac{J_z r}{2}$$

$$(3.14)$$

for the magnetic field inside the wire itself. This result is for the d–c case of uniform J_z. Chapter 5 treats the a–c skin effect case in which H_ϕ has insufficient time to diffuse into the conductor, thus causing nonuniform J_z with larger values near the conductor surface.

Ampere's Circuital Law. Obtaining the integral form of (3.11) is a two-step process. First, take the dot product of each side with a surface

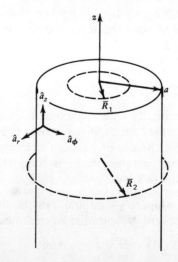

Figure 3.7 Cutaway view of long round conductor of radius a, centered on the z-axis and carrying current in the z-direction.

increment $d\bar{s}$ and integrate over the surface of interest, yielding

$$\int \int \bar{\nabla} \times \bar{H} \cdot d\bar{s} = \int \int \bar{J} \cdot d\bar{s}.$$

Next, by Stokes' theorem the left-hand side is replaced by a line integral around the periphery of the same surface, for the final result

$$\oint \bar{H} \cdot d\bar{l} = \int \int \bar{J} \cdot d\bar{s} = I_{\text{encl}}. \tag{3.15}$$

A key point in applying (3.15) is that the path of integration on the left side defines the perimeter of the area on the right side, hence the current enclosed by that perimeter. For instance in Fig. 3.7 let the perimeter be at $r = R_1 < a$, inside the conductor. Using $\bar{H} = H\hat{a}_\phi$, $d\bar{l} = R_1 d\phi \hat{a}_\phi$, $\bar{J} = J\hat{a}_z$, $d\bar{s} = \hat{a}_z 2\pi r\, dr$ in (3.15) yields

$$\int_{\phi=0}^{2\pi} HR_1 \, d\phi = \int_{r=0}^{R_1} J 2\pi r \, dr. \tag{3.16}$$

After integration the result is

$$2\pi R_1 H = J\pi R_1^2,$$

which can be solved for the unknown $H = JR_1/2$ in agreement with (3.14).

An interesting subtlety is illustrated for $r = R_2 > a$, outside the conductor, which yields the result

$$2\pi R_2 H = 2\pi \int_{r=0}^{R_2} Jr \, dr = J\pi a^2, \tag{3.17}$$

since $J = 0$ for $r > a$. Solving (3.17) for the unknown, we have $H = I/2\pi R_2$, which agrees with (3.3). Both components of the solution for H_ϕ appear in Fig. 3.8. The loci of constant $|H|$ are closed paths, hence H is solenoidal both inside and outside the conductor. However H possesses nonzero curl only inside the conductor as required by (3.11).

In summary, (3.15) is a statement that the total potential drop around a closed path, $F = \oint \bar{H} \cdot d\bar{l}$, is equal to the net current enclosed by that path. To use (3.15) to solve for H, it is necessary to eliminate the dot product and to remove H from under the integral. To eliminate the dot product implies choosing a path of integration parallel to the direction of H. The second point implies choosing a path of integration along which the value of H is constant. Ampere's circuital law is an elegant way to solve for the value H, almost by inspection, when the vector direction of H can be deduced from the symmetry of the conductors.

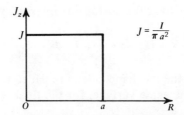

(*a*) The d–c current is distributed uniformly for $R \leq a$.

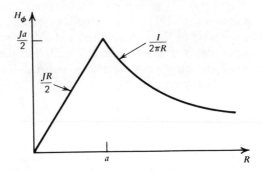

(*b*) Calculated results for *H* inside and outside the conductor.

Figure 3.8 Illustration of Ampere's circuital law, applied to the calculation of *H* due to a long current-carrying conductor, see Fig. 3.7.

Toroidal Current Sheet. The field inside a uniformly wound toroidal coil is readily found by the method above. A toroidal form of inside radius r_a, outside radius r_b, and height *h* is uniformly wound with *n* turns of *I* amperes (Fig. 3.9). The conductor symmetry assures uniform H_ϕ along a constant radius *R*, thus the left side of (3.15) yields $H_\phi 2\pi R$. In the region of interest $r_a < R < r_b$, the right-hand side of (3.15) is $I_{encl} = nI$ or $K_1 2\pi r_a$ using sheet current notation, so

$$H_\phi = \frac{nI}{2\pi R}. \tag{3.18}$$

The remainder of the solution, for $R < r_a$ and $R > r_b$, gives $H = 0$, since zero current is enclosed by the paths. The discontinuities $\Delta H = K$ at r_a, r_b are consistent with (3.6).

Magnetic Potential. It would be erroneous to conclude that Ampere's circuital law is useful only in ideal cases of perfect conductor symmetry. Let us now consider some examples for which *H* is not necessarily

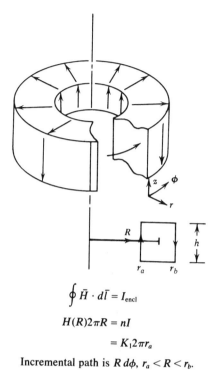

$$\oint \bar{H} \cdot d\bar{l} = I_{encl}$$

$$H(R)2\pi R = nI$$

$$= K_1 2\pi r_a$$

Incremental path is $R\,d\phi$, $r_a < R < r_b$.

(a) Cutaway sketch of toroidal coil to show integration path.

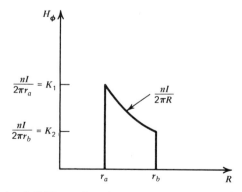

(b) Calculated $H(R)$ as a function of the radius R of integration path.

Figure 3.9 Geometry for calculation of H-field of a toroidal current distribution.

parallel or constant on the path of integration, noting that the line integral is a magnetic potential.

EXAMPLE G

An infinitely long straight wire carries a current I parallel to the positive z-direction, but offset from the z-axis at $x = 0$, $y = y_0$ (Fig. 3.10).

(a) Find the x-component of the field strength at a general point on the x-axis.
(b) Use result (a) to find the magnetic potential difference along the x-axis by evaluating the line integral $\Delta F = \int_{-\infty}^{\infty} \bar{H} \cdot d\bar{l}$, where $d\bar{l} = dx\, \hat{a}_x$.

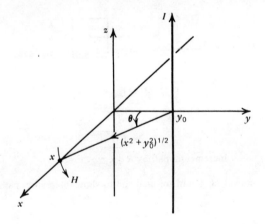

Figure 3.10   Geometry of offset conductor, Example G.

ANSWER

(a) The total magnitude of $H = I/2\pi(y_0^2 + x^2)^{1/2}$, from (3.3). Its projection onto the x-axis can be expressed as $H_x = (I/2\pi r)\cos\theta$, where θ is defined by $x = y_0 \tan\theta$.
(b) With help from integral tables, the resulting potential is found to be $I/2$, as would be anticipated from Ampere's law.

EXAMPLE H

Without actually carrying out the integration, use Ampere's law to determine the qualitative features of $H_\phi(\phi)$ on the periphery of a circle of radius r around the z-axis of Fig. 3.10.

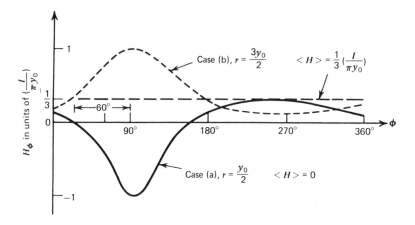

Figure 3.11 Qualitative trend of the ϕ-component of field at a point on a circle of radius r centered on the origin of Fig. 3.10, Example H.

(a) Let $r = y_0/2$ so the offset conductor is not inside the path of integration.
(b) Let $r = 3y_0/2$ to enclose the conductor.

ANSWER. The approximate value of H is sketched in Fig. 3.11 as a function of angle ϕ from the x-axis. The total H is tangent to the integration path only for $\phi = 90°$ and $270°$, where the source-to-field vector R is at extremum.

(a) $H_\phi(90°) = -I/\pi y_0$, $H_\phi(270°) = I/3\pi y_0$, the average value is required to be zero.
(b) $H_\phi(90°) = I/\pi y_0$, $H_\phi(270°) = I/5\pi y_0$, the average value of $I/2\pi r$ is $I/3\pi y_0$.

EXAMPLE I

Without actually carrying out the integration, use Ampere's law to determine the qualitative features of the field of a one-turn coil as follows. One rectangular turn of wire is wrapped around a plastic coil form of toroidal shape (Fig. 3.12a), and we want to find H_ϕ along the axis of the toroid. Let the coil geometry be in the ratio inside radius to outside radius to height $= 2:3:1$, so the single turn is square, permitting use of (3.10).

ANSWER. For $\phi = 90°$, $z = 0$ in (3.10) so $H = \sqrt{2}I/\pi s$ for a square coil $2s \times 2s$. The average H_ϕ along the axis of the coil form, from Ampere's law, is $\langle h_\phi \rangle = I/2\pi r$, where $r = 5s$. The general features are as sketched in

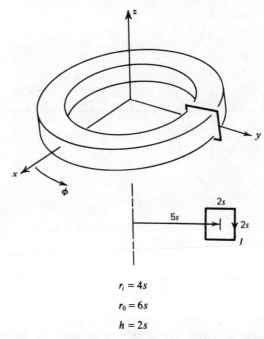

$$r_i = 4s$$
$$r_0 = 6s$$
$$h = 2s$$

(*a*) A one-turn square coil is wound on a toroidal coil form.

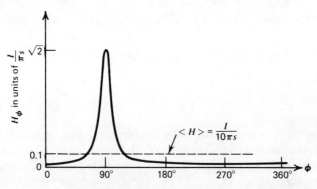

(*b*) Approximate solution for the ϕ-component of H along the centerline of the coil form in (*a*).

Figure 3.12 Geometry and approximate field of a one-turn coil on a toroidal form, Example I.

Fig. 3.12*b*. A more detailed calculation can be made for various angles, derived from repeated use of (3.2) for each segment of the turn.

Examples G through I illustrate the application of Ampere's circuital law to nonuniform fields. In such cases a detailed line integral of the local field is required to calculate the potential. Use of Ampere's law in such cases yields the average field, which may differ substantially from the local field.

3.1.3 Design Considerations for Field Coils

Three general topics need attention in the design of a coil to produce a magnetic field. First of course is the value of field strength required, but in addition the spatial distribution of the field must be considered. Should the field vary with position or should its value be uniform? How uniform should it be, and over what volume must the uniformity be maintained? Then come the questions of number of turns of wire and the allowable current in the wire. Particular attention is given to the current density as the limiting design parameter.

Spatial Distribution of H-Fields. An enormous variety of coil and field geometries have been developed by ingenious designers, to meet a variety of requirements too numerous to list completely. A very common requirement is for a coil to generate a specified field in a region. Another application may require the field polarity to alternate with position, or for the field to be very localized in extent. One coil design for plasma experiments has the conductors arranged like the seam of a baseball.

The parameter of field gradient is often of special interest. A requirement for field uniformity requires the gradient to be zero. But another application may require a specified gradient. A uniform field exerts no translational force on a magnetic dipole, so gradient fields are required to separate magnetic particles or to cause magnetic bubble domains to be moved along their propagation paths.

Helmholtz Coils. A well-known configuration for uniform fields consists of two circular coils on the same axis, separated a distance equal to the radius. When the coils are connected to aid, the field at the midpoint between the coils possesses not only zero gradient but also zero second derivative. The value of field at the midpoint is easily obtained from the equation for the field on the axis of a circular coil, (3.7) repeated below. The value of z at the midpoint is $|z| = r/2$ for each coil, then the equation is multiplied by 2 to account for two coils. The final result at the midpoint is

$$H = \frac{I}{r} \left(\frac{5}{4}\right)^{-3/2} \qquad \text{A/m}, \tag{3.19}$$

where I is the ampere·turn rating of each of the two coils.

For a circular coil in the plane $z = 0$, centered on the z-axis, the field at a point on the axis has been derived as

$$\bar{H}(z) = \hat{a}_z \frac{I}{2r} \left(1 + \frac{z^2}{r^2}\right)^{-3/2} \tag{3.7}$$

with even symmetry in z. For a coil of unit radius the first derivative of the magnitude is

$$\frac{dH}{dz} = -\frac{(3I/2)z}{(1 + z^2)^{5/2}}, \tag{3.20}$$

which possesses odd symmetry. It is interesting that the second derivative $d^2H/dz^2 = 0$ at the field point $z = \pm\frac{1}{2}$. So it turns out that the second derivative property of the Helmholtz pair is actually a property of each coil positioned at $z = r/2$ on either side of the field point.

Concepts and References for Uniform Fields. In principle the Helmholtz criterion can be applied to coil shapes other than circular, but the algebra gets messy. For instance, the derivative of (3.10) for the field on the axis of a $2s \times 2s$ square coil, for $s = 1$, is

$$\frac{dH}{dz} = -\frac{2I}{\pi} z \, (5 + 3z^2) \, (1 + z^2)^{-2} (2 + z^2)^{-3/2}. \tag{3.21}$$

Computer calculations of this function show its magnitude to be maximum near $z = 0.5448s$, thus defining the field point where the second derivative is null.

One approach for achieving higher uniformity for small fields is to build ever larger coil-pairs. Another approach is to add additional windings. A five-winding cube coil by Rubens [3] has been widely used in industrial labs. Garrett [9] has studied the field uniformity question theoretically. Franzen [10] has extended Garrett's theory to include effects of finite coil geometry.

Wire Size and Current Density. The theoretical design of a field coil yields a result in the form $H = kI$, where k is a geometrical factor with units of reciprocal meters (m^{-1}). Our interest now is in the total current I ampere·*turns* with the interpretation $I = ni$, that is, n-turns of i amperes each. It then becomes necessary to choose a wire size adequate to carry the current.

Choosing wire size means choosing the area of the conductor. Clearly larger wire has lower resistance for a given length, thus the voltage drop and power loss are less. The upper limit on wire size does not concern us, since it is usually dictated by the expense of buying oversize wire, or perhaps by the weight or volume or inconvenience of winding. Our greater interest is the *lower* limit of wire size, generally determined by excessive heating of the wire. For routine applications, a rule of thumb is to specify some nominal value of current density J such as 1000 A/in.^{2} or 1 mA/c.m.,* or 1.5 to 2 A/mm^2.

It is possible to choose wire size for a coil in a manner that not only meets a specification for current density, but also satisfies both the voltage across the coil and the field produced by the coil. The key to the design relation is as follows. If current density J is specified, it follows that the electric field strength is implied by $E = J\rho$, where ρ is resistivity of the conductor. Since the coil voltage is $V = El$, the total wire length l is found from

$$l = \frac{V}{E} = \frac{V}{J\rho}. \tag{3.22}$$

The required number of turns that comprise this total length can then be determined if the length of the mean turn is known.

EXAMPLE J

For a copper conductor, find the value of electric field in V/m that corresponds to current density $J = 1000$ A/in.^{2}.

ANSWER. 1000 A/in.^{2}, widely used in the United States, is the same current density as 155 A/cm^2 (1 in. = 2.54 cm). At 20°C the resistivity of copper is $\rho = 1.7241 \times 10^{-6}$ Ω·cm, so $E = J\rho = 2.672 \times 10^{-2}$ V/m. It should also be noted that ρ will increase nearly 4% per 10°C rise in temperature.

EXAMPLE K

Specify the wire size and turns for a circular coil of $r = 0.1$ m in order that 20 V d–c will produce a field of 25 Oe at the center. Use $J = 1.55$ A/mm^2.

ANSWER. From (3.22) $l = 20/2.6724 \times 10^{-2} = 748.4$ m, hence $n = l/0.2\pi \approx 1191$ t to the nearest integer. Since 25 Oe is the same H as

---

*Circular mil; see definition below.

1.989×10^3 A·t/m = ni/0.2 from (3.7), $i = 0.334$ A. It follows that the resistance is $R = V/i \approx 60\,\Omega$ and the wire area $a_w = 0.215\,\text{mm}^2$ follows from $a_w = i/J$. The power dissipated is 6.68 W. The nearest standard wire sizes in metric or American Wire Gauge (AWG) differ slightly from the area just given. The nearest metric gauges are 5 or 6 with diameter 0.5 and 0.6 mm, respectively. The nearest AWG is no. 24 with diameter 0.0201 in. = 0.5106 mm. Therefore some of the values above for V, J, R, n, i, H, and P will change slightly after the wire has been specified.

Circular Mils. In the United States wire area is sometimes given in units of circular mils, (c.m.) defined as follows. If d is the wire diameter in mils, then d^2 is the area in circular mils. It is noted that 1 mil = 0.001 in., thus an area of 1 c.m. may also be described as $10^{-6}\,\pi/4 \approx 7.854 \times 10^{-7}$ in.^{2} or also as $5.067 \times 10^{-4}\,\text{mm}^2$. It follows that a current density of $J = 1$ mA/c.m. is the same current density as 1273 A/in.^{2} and as 1.97 A/mm^2. Table 3.1 is a copper wire table using AWG values.

Extending the Rule of Thumb for Current Density. A closer look at current density in conductors suggests an alternative to the rule-of-thumb of constant current density. Here we allow the current density to vary in a way that limits the maximum operating temperature of the conductor. The following comments do not necessarily apply to general magnetic devices such as transformers with core losses, but are restricted to the case in which all the power dissipation in the system is due to I^2R power loss in the conductor. Common practice at high wattages is to use a cooling fluid such as water to carry away the heat. For low-wattage applications higher values of J may be possible if permitted by the thermal design of the system.

For instance, it is possible to increase current density for smaller geometry and still not exceed the maximum conductor temperature. Joule heat is evolved within a wire in proportion to wire volume V, as

$$I^2R = J^2\rho V = J^2\rho\pi r^2 h. \tag{3.23}$$

Yet heat is carried away from a long isolated single conductor in proportion to wire surface area $2\pi rh$, so the temperature rise above ambient is proportional to the ratio of volume to surface as

$$\Delta T \propto \frac{J^2\rho\pi r^2 h}{2\pi rh} = \frac{J^2\rho r}{2}. \tag{3.24}$$

It follows that if the temperature rise ΔT is specified as some constant upper limit, the right-hand side of (3.24) is a constant, hence its square root is also a constant. In conclusion, rather than the rule of thumb of constant J, an alternative criterion is

$$J\sqrt{r} = \text{constant}, \tag{3.25}$$

where r is defined as the radius of a bundle of conductors. The definition of r as applicable to the wire bundle, rather than to a single wire within the bundle, is an important point in the heat flow analysis.

EXAMPLE L

Use (3.25) to find the allowable current density in a single copper wire of radius $r = 4 \times 10^{-3}$ cm, scaled from an assumed allowable value of $J = 200$ A/cm^2 in conductors tied together in a bundle of $r = 1$ cm.

ANSWER. $J(4 \times 10^{-3})^{1/2} = 200(1)^{1/2}$, hence $J = 3163$ A/cm^2 and the total current is 159 mA. The small wire would be approximately AWG no. 40 with a current rating of only about 10 mA if the 200 A/cm^2 rule of thumb were applied. More than an order of magnitude difference.

Some Upper Limits for Current Density. High-field solenoids at the U.S. National Magnet Laboratory are capable of generating upward of 10^5 Oe. The solenoids are wound with flat geometry conductors of copper for high electrical conductivity, alloyed with other materials such as beryllium to help withstand the enormous magnetic forces. The flat conductor geometries are arranged various ways for improved flow of an enormous quantity of cooling water. Such designs permit current densities in the range of 5×10^4 A/cm^2.

The critical current at which a wire will melt can be calculated from handbook data using an equation of form similar to (3.25). It is interesting that the current density of Example L is about 9% of the value of current density at which the copper wire would fuse. Values of approximate fusing currents for various wire materials are tabulated in handbooks. The failure of a wire at high current normally occurs at a local spot by thermal runaway when a local defect causes a local increase in current density. This increase creates a hot spot because of the locally higher value of $J^2\rho$ heating. The hot spot leads to a still higher value of local resistivity because of the positive temperature coefficient of resistance. The failure mechanism is attributed to conductor melting, but it may be due partially to electromigration.

The form of (3.25) suggests that extremely large values of current density may be permitted if the conductor size is extremely small. For microelectronic applications the current density is limited by a failure mechanism called electromigration or electrotransport. The metal atoms of the conductor are actually transported away under conditions of high

Table 3.1 Wire table for annealed copper (AWG)

| AWG B&S Gauge | Diameter (mils) | Cross Section | | Ohms per 1000 ft at 20°C (68°F) | Pounds per 1000 ft | Feet per Pound | Feet per Ohm at 20°C (68°F) | Ohms per Pound at 20°C (68°F) |
		Circular Mils	Square Inches					
0000	460.0	211,600	0.1662	0.04901	640.5	1.561	20,400	0.00007652
000	409.6	167,800	0.1318	0.06180	507.9	1.968	16,180	0.0001217
00	364.8	133,100	0.1045	0.07793	402.8	2.482	12,830	0.0001935
0	324.9	105,500	0.08289	0.09827	319.5	3.130	10,180	0.0003076
1	289.3	83,690	0.06573	0.1239	253.3	3.947	8,070	0.0004891
2	257.6	66,370	0.05213	0.1563	200.9	4.977	6,400	0.0007778
3	229.4	52,640	0.04134	0.1970	159.3	6.276	5,075	0.001237
4	204.3	41,740	0.03278	0.2485	126.4	7.914	4,025	0.001966
5	181.9	33,100	0.02600	0.3133	100.2	9.980	3,192	0.003127
6	162.0	26,250	0.02062	0.3951	79.46	12.58	2,531	0.004972
7	144.3	20,820	0.01635	0.4982	63.02	15.87	2,007	0.007905
8	128.5	16,510	0.01297	0.6282	49.98	20.01	1,592	0.01257
9	114.4	13,090	0.01028	0.7921	39.63	25.23	1,262	0.01999
10	101.9	10,380	0.008155	0.9989	31.43	31.82	1,001	0.03178
11	90.74	8,234	0.006467	1.260	24.92	40.12	794	0.05053
12	80.81	6,530	0.005129	1.588	19.77	50.59	629.6	0.08035
13	71.96	5,178	0.004067	2.003	15.68	63.80	499.3	0.1278
14	64.08	4,107	0.003225	2.525	12.43	80.44	396.0	0.2032
15	57.07	3,257	0.002558	3.184	9.858	101.4	314.0	0.3230
16	50.82	2,588	0.002028	4.016	7.818	127.9	249.0	0.5136
17	45.26	2,048	0.001609	5.064	6.200	161.3	197.5	0.8167

18	40.30	1,624	0.001276	6.385	4.917	203.4	156.6	1.299
19	35.89	1,288	0.001012	8.051	3.899	256.5	124.2	2.065
20	31.96	1,022	0.0008023	10.15	3.092	323.4	98.50	3.283
21	28.46	810.1	0.0006363	12.80	2.452	407.8	78.11	5.221
22	25.35	642.4	0.0005046	16.14	1.945	514.2	61.95	8.301
23	22.57	509.5	0.0004002	20.36	1.542	648.4	49.13	13.20
24	20.10	404.0	0.0003173	25.67	1.223	817.7	38.96	20.99
25	17.90	320.4	0.0002517	32.37	0.9699	1,031.0	30.90	33.37
26	15.94	254.1	0.0001996	40.81	0.7692	1,300	24.50	53.06
27	14.20	201.5	0.0001583	51.47	0.6100	1,639	19.43	84.37
28	12.64	159.8	0.0001255	64.90	0.4837	2,067	15.41	134.2
29	11.26	126.7	0.00009953	81.83	0.3836	2,607	12.22	213.3
30	10.03	100.5	0.00007894	103.2	0.3042	3,287	9.691	339.2
31	8.928	79.70	0.00006260	130.1	0.2413	4,145	7.685	539.3
32	7.950	63.21	0.00004964	164.1	0.1913	5,227	6.095	857.6
33	7.080	50.13	0.00003937	206.9	0.1517	6,591	4.833	1,364
34	6.305	39.75	0.00003122	260.9	0.1203	8,310	3.833	2,168
35	5.615	31.52	0.00002476	329.0	0.009542	10,480	3.040	3,448
36	5.000	25.00	0.00001964	414.8	0.07568	13,210	2.411	5,482
37	4.453	19.83	0.00001557	523.1	0.06001	16,660	1.912	8,717
38	3.965	15.72	0.00001235	659.6	0.04759	21,010	1.516	13,860
39	3.531	12.47	0.000009793	831.8	0.03774	26,500	1.202	22,040
40	3.145	9.888	0.000007766	1049.0	0.02993	33,410	0.9534	35,040

From *Reference Data for Radio Engineers*, 6th ed., 1975. Reprinted by permission of Howard W. Sams, Inc., Indianapolis, Ind., a subsidiary of ITT.

current density, particularly if high temperatures and high temperature gradients also exist. Electromigration exhibits a thermal runaway similar to wire fusing, and in fact may be the same physical process. Gold and gold-copper alloys evidently can tolerate higher current density. Values of J in excess of 10^6 A/cm^2 are routinely used in magnetic micro-electronics, for instance, with a $1\,\mu$m $\times 6\,\mu$m gold conductor in a magnetic bubble circuit.

3.2 FIELDS FROM MAGNETIC MATERIALS

In contrast with Section 3.1, which has dealt with H-fields caused by current-carrying conductors, this section introduces the very important concept that fields can arise from magnetized materials even in the absence of electric current. Although a general magnetostatic analysis is a formidable problem, the central ideas are easy to show from a simplified example. The first objective is to develop magnetostatic models for magnetic materials, then to illustrate the concepts with models for an ideal permanent magnet. The second objective is to demonstrate the principles of design with permanent magnets.

There are two common techniques for modeling magnetic materials. The first method uses the concept of magnetic poles, or magnetic "charge" in which the volume density of poles is given by the divergence of intrinsic induction. Field strength H is derived from the pole density by the magnetostatic version of Coulomb's law. The second method uses the vector operation of curl, with the interpretation that $\bar{\nabla} \times \bar{M}$ produces the same $\bar{B}$ as an equivalent electric current density. The same cylindrical permanent magnet is modeled with each approach to illustrate the equivalence of the two methods, although each method yields a different part of the total solution.

One peculiarity of the derivation deserves some prior comment. For simplicity, the ideal magnetic sample is assumed to be uniformly magnetized throughout its interior. As a result of the uniformity, all spatial derivatives are zero inside the sample, with the result that the distributions of poles or of Amperian currents are confined to the sample surfaces.

The pole model and the Amperian current model are given in Sections 3.2.1 and 3.2.2, respectively. Section 3.2.3 presents the elementary design of static fields with permanent magnets. Section 3.2.4 deals with properties and applications of new permanent magnet materials that are now becoming important.

3.2.1 H-Fields from Magnetic Poles

One of the most important effects in magnetic design is the field due to magnetic material as a source. In everyday experience the most common example is the field produced by a permanent magnet, but in general any divergence of magnetization can give rise to a field. The present discussion describes the field as due to a distribution of magnetic poles, the density of which is equal to the negative of the divergence of intrinsic induction,

$$\rho = -\bar{\nabla} \cdot \bar{B}_i \qquad \text{Wb/m}^3. \qquad (3.26)$$

In principle if $\bar{B}_i$ is known, the pole density can be found from (3.26), leading to the determination of $\bar{H}$ as described below. However the total H that acts on a material is the sum of the applied field plus the calculated field, with the result that $\bar{B}_i$ may not be known with precision if it responds to the total H. For the time being the self-consistency part of the problem is omitted for the sake of simplicity.

The Magnetostatic Coulomb's Law. The fundamental equation in magnetostatics is taken to be [6]

$$d\bar{H}(\bar{r}_2) = \frac{\hat{a}_R dQ_m}{4\pi\mu_0 R^2}, \qquad (3.27)$$

where $d\bar{H}$ is the increment of field at location $\bar{r}_2$ due to an incremental pole or magnetic charge dQ_m located at $\bar{r}_1$, where $\bar{R} = \bar{r}_2 - \bar{r}_1$ in the usual manner. In analogy with electrostatics the source dQ_m can be due to an incremental volume distribution from (3.26)

$$dQ_m = \rho \, dv \qquad (3.28a)$$

or to a surface pole distribution

$$dQ_m = \bar{B}_i \cdot d\bar{s}. \qquad (3.28b)$$

In either case the total H results from integrating (3.27) over all source poles (i.e., over all values of $\bar{r}_1$). It is understood that the integration will include both polarities of pole, since the divergence (3.26) is of intrinsic induction.

This static treatment assumes that currents are zero, thus H no longer possesses the solenoidal property but instead begins and ends on poles. It follows that H is the gradient of a magnetostatic potential F, as

$$\bar{H} = -\bar{\nabla}F \qquad \text{where} \qquad F = \frac{1}{4\pi\mu_0} \int \frac{dQ_m}{R}. \qquad (3.29)$$

Either of two valid procedures can be used to find *H*, by integration of (3.27), or by finding *F* and taking its gradient as indicated in (3.29). The direct method is demonstrated below; the potential method is deferred to Chapter 8.

Pole Model for Cylindrical Magnet. We now want to calculate the *H*-field on the axis of a cylindrical magnet of height $2h$ and radius $\imath$, magnetized ideally and uniformly to saturation so that

$$\bar{B}_i = B_{is}\hat{a}_z, \tag{3.30}$$

where the cylinder axis is the *z*-axis (Fig. 3.13*a*). For the sake of simplicity it is assumed that $\bar{B}_i$ will not be perturbed by the *H*-field that we will calculate, an assumption of an ideal permanent magnet property. The pole distribution is zero except on the ends of the cylinder where the surface pole density is B_{is} from (3.28*b*), positive polarity on the top end and negative on the lower. Each end of the cylinder is therefore a disk of uniform pole density for this ideal example.

Consider the calculation of $\bar{H}$ at a point z on the axis of the cylinder, due to only one disk of charge in the $x - y$ plane (Fig. 3.13*b*). The components of (3.27) in cylindrical coordinates are

$$dQ_m = B_{is}\,ds \qquad \text{where } ds = dr\,rd\phi$$
$$\bar{r}_1 = r\hat{a}_r$$
$$\bar{r}_2 = z\hat{a}_z$$
$$\bar{R} = z\hat{a}_z - r\hat{a}_r. \tag{3.31}$$

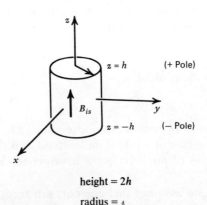

height $= 2h$

radius $= \imath$

(*a*) An ideal cylindrical permanent magnet.

Figure 3.13 Geometry used in the derivation of the *H*-field from the positive pole of an ideal cylindrical magnet.

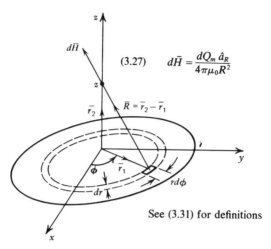

(3.27) $\qquad d\bar{H} = \dfrac{dQ_m \, \hat{a}_R}{4\pi\mu_0 R^2}$

$\bar{R} = \bar{r}_2 - \bar{r}_1$

See (3.31) for definitions

(b) The top surface of the cylindrical magnet is modeled as a disk of uniformly distributed magnetic charge.

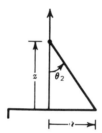

(c) Definition of angle θ_2 subtended by the radius of the disk of charge, $\cos \theta_2 = z/(z^2 + \imath^2)^{1/2}$ used in (3.34).

Figure 3.13 (*Cont'd*)

The field due to the top disk of poles is set up as

$$\bar{H}(z) = \frac{B_{is}}{4\pi\mu_0} \int_{\phi=0}^{2\pi} \int_{r=0}^{\imath} (z\hat{a}_z - r\hat{a}_r) r \frac{dr\,d\phi}{(z^2 + r^2)^{3/2}}. \tag{3.32}$$

Only the z-component survives the integration, as

$$\bar{H}(z) = \hat{a}_z \frac{B_{is}}{2\mu_0} \left[1 - \frac{z}{(z^2 + \imath^2)^{1/2}} \right], \tag{3.33}$$

which is the result for the field on the axis above a single disk of uniform pole density. It is observed that H approaches a limiting value as z

becomes small, and in fact H undergoes a discontinuity as the field point crosses the surface of magnetic charge. It is therefore convenient to rewrite (3.33) using the signum function

$$\bar{H}(z) = \hat{a}_z \left(\frac{B_{is}}{2\mu_0}\right) (\text{sgn } z - \cos \theta_2), \tag{3.34}$$

where θ_2 is defined in Fig. 3.13c. But the field of the total cylinder is due to positive poles at $z = h$ and negative poles at $z = -h$, as in Fig. 3.13a. In the notation of (3.34) the result is

$$H_z = \frac{B_{is}}{2\mu_0}[\text{sgn}(z - h) - \text{sgn}(z + h) + \cos \theta_1 - \cos \theta_2], \tag{3.35}$$

which can be rewritten into two separate equations:

$$H_z = \frac{B_{is}}{2\mu_0}(\cos \theta_1 - \cos \theta_2) \qquad \text{for} \quad |z| > h \tag{3.36a}$$

$$H_z = \frac{B_{is}}{2\mu_0}(\cos \theta_1 - \cos \theta_2 - 2) \qquad \text{for} \quad |z| < h. \tag{3.36b}$$

Figure 3.14 shows how the assumed B_i, when added to $\mu_0 H_z$ from (3.36), yields the sum

$$B_z = \frac{B_{is}}{2}(\cos \theta_1 - \cos \theta_2), \tag{3.37}$$

which is a smooth function with no discontinuities.* In (3.36) and (3.37), the angles should be defined by geometrical expressions such as

$$\cos \theta_1 = \frac{z + h}{[(z + h)^2 + \imath^2]^{1/2}},$$

$$\cos \theta_2 = \frac{z - h}{[(z - h)^2 + \imath^2]^{1/2}} \tag{3.38}$$

rather than by the restricted range of tangent functions noted below (3.9). The similarity of (3.37) to (3.9) for a solenoid is discussed further in Section 3.2.2.

Figure 3.15 gives more general sketches of the B- and H-fields for the ideal cylindrical magnet. The field lines for B are shown as sourceless,

---

*It is evident from Fig. 3.14 that the slope of B versus z is zero only at $z = 0$. Observing that dB_z/dz is generally nonzero raises the question whether (3.37) is a valid solution if it does not meet the criterion $\bar{\nabla} \cdot \bar{B} = 0$. The same question can be raised about (3.7) for the field on the axis of a single turn of wire. Indeed, neither equation is generally valid, being developed only for the special case of the field point on the axis of symmetry. Jackson gives the general solution for which (3.7) is a special case [1].

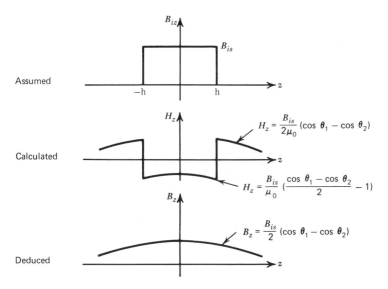

Figure 3.14 Three components on the axis of a cylindrical magnet. The assumption of intrinsic induction B_i implies a distribution of $\pm$ poles at $z = \pm h$, from which H_z is calculated. Finally, B is deduced from the sum $B = \mu_0 H + B_i$.

whereas the lines for H are seen to emanate from the north pole and to terminate on the south pole.* The equation $B = \mu_0 H + B_i$ is obeyed both inside and outside the magnet. Outside the magnet $B_i = 0$, so B and H are coincident in direction and proportional in magnitude. Inside the ideal magnet $\bar{B}_i = \hat{a}_z B_{is}$ everywhere by assumption, thus B and H differ from one another both in direction and magnitude.

The direction of H inside the magnet is generally opposite to the direction of magnetization, in a direction to demagnetize it. The combination of negative H and positive B_i corresponds to the second quadrant of the $B_i - H$ characteristic, the region of interest in permanent magnet design. A wide $B_i - H$ characteristic means a large static width H_0, which is a measure of quality for permanent magnet materials. A larger value of H_0 means greater immunity to demagnetizing fields.

Equation 3.36b defines the value of demagnetizing field as proportional to the saturation induction

$$H_d(z) = -\frac{B_{is} f}{\mu_0} \quad \text{A/m}, \tag{3.39}$$

---

*This convention means the north-seeking pole of a compass is indeed a north pole, but the geographically northerly pole of the earth possesses a south polarity.

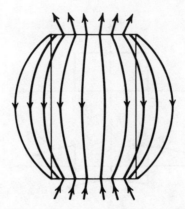

Top surface is north pole (+). (Also called the north-seeking pole for a compass.)
Bottom surface is south pole (−)

(a) H-Field lines begin and end on magnetic poles, if current is zero. Internally, H tends to demagnetize the sample, thus is called the "demagnetizing field."

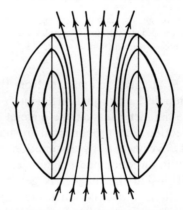

(b) B-Field lines are continuous, inside and out. Outside the magnet B and H are exactly proportional.

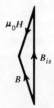

(c) Vector addition of $B = \mu_0 H + B_i$ inside the magnet near the upper pole. Inside the magnet B and H are dissimilar.

Figure 3.15 Qualitative comparison of B- and H-fields, for the ideally magnetized cylinder of Figs. 3.13 and 3.14.

where f is a geometrical factor. Materials developed for magnetic bubble applications are required to have a low value of B_{is} as a criterion for the existence of cylindrical magnetic domains. The geometrical factor f is smaller for longer or thinner magnet shapes, in support of the tendency of such shapes to stay magnetized to a greater degree. The f is somewhat similar to the demagnetizing factor of (8.3), Section 8.2.2.

EXAMPLE M

Aharoni and Gunders [7] have made measurements of the field from several Alnico 5 magnets including one of radius $r = 12.7$ mm and length $2h = 153$ mm (CGS data for Alnico 5: $B_r = 12$ kG, $H_c \approx 650$ Oe.)

(a) Test the applicability of (3.36a) by calculating the field at a point 50 mm from one end of the magnet for comparison with their measured value of about 100 Oe for a magnet that was not fully magnetized.

(b) Calculate the demagnetizing field at the center of the bar internally, using (3.36b) and compare H_d with the coercivity H_c.

ANSWER.   In metric units $B_{is} = 1.2$ T, $H_c = 517$ A/cm. The prefix* $B_i/2\mu_0$ A/m $\times 4\pi\,10^{-3}$ Oe/(A/m) = 6000 Oe.

(a) The geometric factor is $[\cos\tan^{-1}(12.7/203) - \cos\tan^{-1}(12.7/50)] = 0.0288253$, so the calculated $H_z = 172.95$ Oe.

(b) The geometric term is $[2\cos\tan^{-1}(12.7/76.5) - 2] = -0.0270$, so the calculated $H_d = -162$ Oe. Since the demagnetizing field at the center is only a fraction of H_c, we may suppose that the bar is magnetized in the center, but some partial demagnetization will surely occur near each end where $H_d \approx -6000$ Oe.

EXAMPLE N

A cylindrical magnet is removed from its circuit without being protected by a "keeper." Use (3.36b) to try to predict whether the magnet will demagnetize itself. The magnet is 2 diameters long and the material is Alnico 5 (see Example M for data).

ANSWER.   In metric units $B_{is} = 1.2$ T and $H_c = 517$ A/cm. If the magnet were magnetized to saturation, from (3.36b) the field just inside one end surface would be $H_d = (0.6/\mu_0)(0.97 - 2) \approx -4918$ A/cm $(-6180$ Oe), and

---

*In CGS units B_{is}/μ_0 is $4\pi M_s$ for (3.33) through (3.37). The geometrical factors for the equations are dimensionless.

the field at the center of the magnet would be $H_d = (0.6/\mu_0)(1.78885 - 2) \approx$ -1008 A/cm $(-1267$ Oe). Since the demagnetizing fields exceed the material coercivity even at the center of the magnet, we expect the magnet to demagnetize itself. Equations 3.36 are not applicable to demagnetized magnets. See Lai and Watson [8] for clarification.

Volume Poles. We have illustrated the pole model for a cylindrical magnet, based on the idealization that the cylinder was uniformly magnetized. The constraint of uniform magnetization is now relaxed to permit poles to exist throughout the material volume as well as on its surfaces. The volume density of poles may be calculated from the divergence of the nonuniform magnetization by using (3.26). There are two general classes of models of magnetization, depending on the manner of nonuniformity allowed by the model.

The so-called continuum model allows the magnitude of B_i to vary as a function of position. The smooth variations of pole density lend themselves well to analysis, and this general class of model has been widely used with considerable success.

But our present purpose is to give a physical explanation of pole existence, an explanation that involves magnetic domains. In the following models the magnitude of intrinsic induction B_i is assumed to be constant at its saturated value, but the direction is allowed to vary with position.

Consider a semi-infinite slab of magnetic material for all negative y in Fig. 3.16, $\bar{B}_i$ is oriented at an angle $\phi = \phi_0$ from the x-axis. By assumption, the angle ϕ_0 is a constant over the full range of x, z and for negative values of y. In other words

$$\bar{B}_i = B_x \hat{a}_x + B_y \hat{a}_y,$$

where

$$B_x = B_i \cos \phi \quad \text{and} \quad B_y = B_i \sin \phi. \tag{3.40}$$

The volume pole density, by (3.26), is a delta function

$$\rho = -\left[\frac{dB_x}{dx} + \frac{dB_y}{dy}\right] = B_i \sin \phi_0 \, \delta(y), \tag{3.41}$$

thus the incremental pole is a surface pole

$$\rho dv = \rho dx \, dy \, dz = B_i \sin \phi_0 \, dx \, dz, \tag{3.42}$$

and the total pole on the surface $x_0 z_0$ is

$$Q_m = B_i \sin \phi_0 x_0 z_0 \quad \text{Wb}. \tag{3.43}$$

The foregoing is similar to the cylindrical magnet, having a delta func-

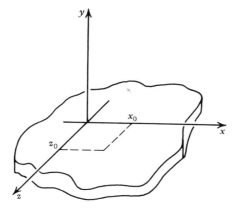

(a) Consider a finite typical region x_0z_0 on the top surface of a magnetic material.

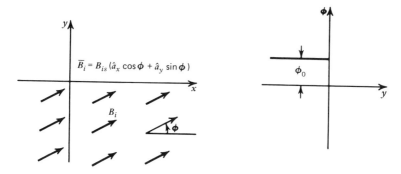

$$\bar{B}_i = B_{is} (\hat{a}_x \cos\phi + \hat{a}_y \sin\phi)$$

(b) The intrinsic induction is oriented at a constant angle $\phi = \phi_0$ for negative y, all x, z.

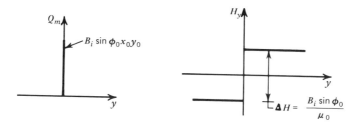

$-B_i \sin\phi_0 x_0 y_0$

$$\Delta H = \frac{B_i \sin\phi_0}{\mu_0}$$

(c) The magnetic pole distribution is a delta function of surface charge that causes a step-function change of H_y.

Figure 3.16 An example to illustrate the calculation of surface pole density.

tion of surface poles with pole density given by the normal component of B_i. So we expect an H-field to emanate from the sheet pole, the negative direction for $y < 0$ and positive for $y > 0$, with a total discontinuity given by the pole density

$$\Delta H_y = \frac{B_i \sin \phi_0}{\mu_0} \qquad \text{A/m.} \tag{3.44}$$

The field just calculated has a demagnetizing effect for negative y that tends to reorient the intrinsic induction near the $x - z$ surface, thereby creating a volume distribution of poles. To illustrate the concept, suppose the angle ϕ decreases from ϕ_0 in the uppermost layer as in Fig. 3.17 according to the linear equation

$$\phi = -\left(\frac{\phi_0}{a}\right) y \qquad -a < y \leq 0. \tag{3.45}$$

Instead of (3.41) the pole density now becomes

$$\rho = -B_i \cos \phi \, \frac{d\phi}{dy} = \frac{\phi_0}{a} B_i \cos \phi \qquad \text{Wb/m}^3. \tag{3.46}$$

It is easy to show the total magnetic charge in the region is equal to (3.43) and does not require the linear function (3.45).

$$Q_m = \int \rho \, dv = \int_{y=-a}^{0} \int_{x=0}^{x_0} \int_{z=0}^{z_0} \left[\frac{-d}{dy} (B \sin \phi) \right] dx \, dy \, dz. \tag{3.47}$$

After x, z integration, the remaining differential quantity yields the final result

$$Q_m = x_0 z_0 \int_{y=-a}^{0} -d(B_i \sin \phi) = x_0 z_0 B_i \sin \phi_0, \tag{3.48}$$

after substituting the limit $\phi = \phi_0$ at $y = -a$.

Let us turn now from the boundary between media and space to the boundary between two magnetic domains within the same material. Figure 3.18a shows a plausible configuration of four domains in a demagnetized I-bar. The small triangular domains on each end, closure domains, provide flux closure for the two longitudinal domains in a way that causes no net poles. A closed-flux domain structure without poles cannot generate an H-field. The fundamental principle of "pole avoidance" refers to the tendency of domain walls to so orient themselves. Consider a boundary between two domains (Fig. 3.18b), with coordinates defined so the $y - z$ plane coincides with the domain wall of negligible thickness, thus $\hat{a}_x$ is normal to the wall. The requirements of

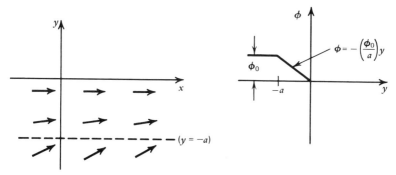

(a) The angle ϕ of Fig. 3.16 is now presumed to decrease to zero in the top layer $-a \le y \le 0$.

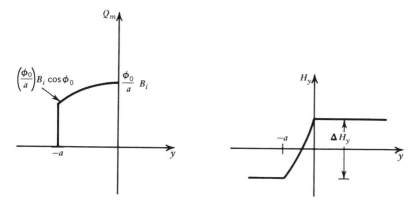

(b) The poles are distributed in the top layer, with the same total quantity as in Fig. 3.16.

Figure 3.17 A change of angle can cause the creation of a volume distribution of poles. Compare Fig. 3.16.

zero divergence applied to definitions

$$\bar{B}_{i1} = B_1(\hat{a}_x \cos \phi + \hat{a}_y \sin \phi) \tag{3.49}$$

$$\bar{B}_{i2} = B_2(\hat{a}_x \cos \theta - \hat{a}_y \sin \theta)$$

yield the results of continuous normal component

$$B_1 \cos \phi = B_2 \cos \theta. \tag{3.50}$$

If the two domains are in the same material, then $B_1 = B_2$ and $\phi = \theta$. The pole avoidance principle therefore leads to the conclusion that domain walls orient to bisect the angle between the two domains.

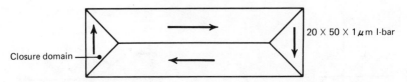

(*a*) A plausible configuration of four domains in a demagnetized I-bar of permalloy. This arrangement causes no poles.

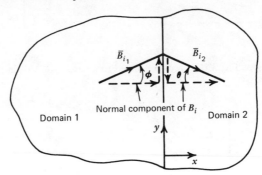

(*b*) Boundary wall between two domains, turned so that the *y*-axis is defined as the wall. See text for discussion of boundary conditions.

Figure 3.18 Geometry for illustration of magnetostatic boundary conditions at domain walls. It is typical that walls align for continuity of the normal component of B_i, yielding no net poles at the wall.

There is no requirement for continuity of tangential components of B_i at the domain wall boundary because the derivative dB_y/dx is not part of the divergence operation.

In summary, the existence of volume poles can be attributed to two mechanisms. Within a single domain, a distribution of poles can be induced by a change of angle of intrinsic induction. Although not discussed here, a distribution of net poles may be induced along a wall between two domains if the wall has a curvature. In either case the pole density is given by the divergence equation (3.26), is related to H through the magnetic Coulomb's law equation (3.27), and is related to magnetic potential by the magnetic Poisson's equation.

3.2.2 A Comparison of Models for Magnetic Materials

Two models for magnetic materials are implied by the two equations for flux density, repeated here for convenience.

$$B = \mu_0 H + B_i \tag{1.2}$$

$$B = \mu_0(H + M). \tag{1.1}$$

This text is oriented to the use of the pole model, beginning with (1.2). In (1.2) the material parameter B_i has the units of T, Wb/m², and Wb·m/m³ thus the basic magnetic moment is a magnetic dipole moment of units Wb·m. Maxwell's divergence equation $\bar{\nabla} \cdot \bar{B} = 0$ requires that B possess the solenoidal property, since no free monopoles exist. Yet each component of the right-hand side of (1.2) can diverge, and in fact the divergence of B_i gives the volume pole density by (3.26), repeated here for convenience

$$\rho = -\bar{\nabla} \cdot \bar{B}_i \qquad \text{Wb/m}^3. \tag{3.26}$$

The essence of the pole model lies in the calculation of H from the pole distribution, using magnetic versions of standard electrostatic techniques. The H-field that results is then added to the core model component B_i to yield the total flux density, as by (1.2).

The Amperian current model uses (1.1) to represent B, where the material parameter M has the units of A/m and A·m²/m³. It follows that the basic magnetic moment is an area moment of units A·m². If (1.1) is substituted into the static case of Maxwell's curl equation

$$\bar{\nabla} \times \bar{H} = \bar{\nabla} \times \left(\frac{\bar{B}}{\mu_0} - \bar{M}\right) = \bar{J} \qquad \text{A/m}^2, \tag{3.51}$$

thus

$$\bar{\nabla} \times \bar{B} = \mu_0(\bar{J} + \bar{\nabla} \times \bar{M}) \qquad \text{Wb/m}^3. \tag{3.52}$$

Amperian current is the equivalent current density defined as $J_m = \bar{\nabla} \times \bar{M}$ A/m². The essence of the Amperian current model lies in the calculation of B from the distribution of J_m. The methods for calculating B are the same as the methods described in Chapter 2 for an analogous problem, that of calculating the field strength H from a distribution of current density J. The flux density B that results is divided by μ_0, from which quantity the known M is subtracted to yield H, as by (1.1).

Each of the procedures above requires that for the appropriate spatial derivative to be taken, the material parameter M or B_i be known or assumed. The derivative quantity is the source for the calculation of one unknown field parameter, and from this result the second unknown is obtained by vector arithmetic. Thus from the basis of comparison of computation procedures, neither model has an evident advantage over the other. However a specific geometry may lend itself more simply to one of the vector operations—div or curl—in preference to the other. The pole model seems to be more widely used for static applications, possibly because of the existence of the principle of pole avoidance. The Amperian current model is often preferred for time varying calculations that involve dynamic losses.

Amperian Model of Cylindrical Magnet. Several steps are already accomplished toward the Amperian modeling of a cylindrical magnet. The *H*-field on the axis of a cylindrical coil was derived from the starting point of $\bar{\nabla} \times \bar{H} = \bar{J}$ to yield the result

$$H_z = \frac{K}{2}(\cos \theta_1 - \cos \theta_2) \qquad \text{from (3.9),}$$

where *K* is the sheet current of the solenoid (A/m).

The *B*-field on the axis of a cylindrical magnet was calculated from the pole model as

$$B_z = \frac{B_{is}}{2}(\cos \theta_1 - \cos \theta_2) \tag{3.37}$$

by adding the assumed B_i to the calculated H_z. Equation 3.52 asserts that $\bar{\nabla} \times \bar{B} = \mu_0 \bar{J}_m$ under the condition $\bar{J} = 0$, where $\bar{J}_m = \bar{\nabla} \times \bar{M}$ is Amperian current density (A/m²). Furthermore, the symbol manipulations are consistent, since $B_i = \mu_0 M$ from (1.1) and (1.2). The only remaining step in the derivation is to assure that $\bar{\nabla} \times \bar{M}$ has the physical geometry of a delta function of circumferential current. If so, it will follow that

$$B_z = \frac{\mu_0 M_s}{2}(\cos \theta_1 - \cos \theta_2). \tag{3.53}$$

In cylindrical coordinates, the general equation for curl $\bar{M}$ is

$$\bar{\nabla} \times \bar{M} = \hat{a}_r \left[(1/r)\frac{\partial M_z}{\partial \phi} - \frac{\partial M_\phi}{\partial z} \right) \right] + \hat{a}_\phi \left(\frac{\partial M_r}{\partial z} - \frac{\partial M_z}{\partial r} \right)$$
$$+ \hat{a}_z \frac{1}{r} \left[\frac{\partial(rM_\phi)}{\partial r} - \frac{\partial M_r}{\partial \phi} \right]. \tag{3.54}$$

But the derivation is for an ideal cylindrical magnet of uniform $\bar{M}$ inside. Using a step-function for the geometry (Fig. 3.13) of height $2h$ and radius a,

$$M_r = 0, \qquad M_\phi = 0, \tag{3.55a}$$

$$M_z = M_s[u(z+h) - u(z-h)]u(a-r). \tag{3.55b}$$

The results of substituting (3.55a) into (3.54), and $\partial M_z/\partial \phi = 0$ and $\partial M_r/\partial \phi = 0$, are

$$\bar{\nabla} \times \bar{M} = -\hat{a}_\phi \frac{\partial M_z}{\partial r}$$

$$\bar{J}_m = \hat{a}_\phi M_s[u(z+h) - u(z-h)]\delta(r-a). \tag{3.56}$$

Through the area $d\bar{s} = \hat{a}_\phi \, dz \, dr$ the increment of current is a surface current by the action of the delta function

$$\bar{J}_m \cdot d\bar{s} = M_s dz \qquad \text{for} \quad -h \le z \le h. \qquad (3.57)$$

Thus $\bar{\nabla} \times \bar{M}$ has been shown to be equivalent to a ϕ-direction Amperian sheet current density. This permits substitution of M_s for K in (3.9) and thereby validates (3.53).

3.2.3 Static Design with Permanent Magnets

The basic function of a magnet is to supply useful energy in an airgap, the energy being in the form of a magnetic field. For the time being we consider only static airgaps with dimensions that do not change, for instance, in meter movements or in loudspeaker magnets.

Generally a permanent magnet (PM) circuit includes three components (Fig. 3.19): the magnet, the iron pole pieces, and the airgap. A usual design criterion has the airgap dimensions matched to the magnet dimensions and properties in a way that results in a magnet of minimum volume. There are two key ideas in the design procedure: for any given type of PM material there exists an optimum operating point; the magnet is specified so the airgap will load the magnet to operate at its optimum point.

(BH) Product. The optimum operating point for a magnet is where it supplies the greatest energy. For B–H data in graphical form, as in Fig. 3.20, the preferable operating point is in the second quadrant where the product $B \times H$ is a maximum. For any type of PM material the point of

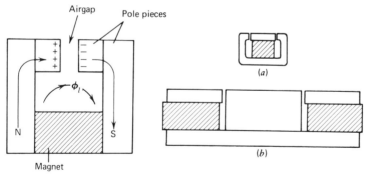

(*a*) Normal type, gap flux density about 9 kG with 0.625-in. diameter center pole, 0.033-in. gap length, 0.15-in. gap depth, using Alcomax II/Alnico 5 magnet, (*b*) Hi-fi type, gap flux density 11.5 kG with 2.00-in. diameter center pole, 0.063-in. gap length, 0.315-in. gap depth, using ferrite ring magnet.

Figure 3.19 (*Continued on following page*).

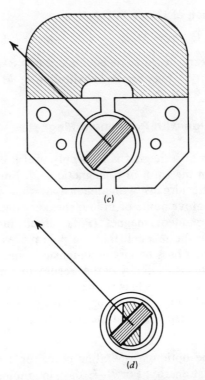

(*c*)

(*d*)

(*c*) External Alcomax magnet with iron poles and core, flux density 3 kG in two
1.5-mm gaps. (*d*) Center-core Hycomax III magnet with iron pole segments and iron
outer ring for return path, giving 2 kG in two 1.5-mm gaps.

Figure 3.19 Some examples of static magnetic circuit components and construction. (*a*)
and (*b*) speaker magnet (magnet material shaded). (*c*) and (*d*) Moving-coil instrument
magnet systems. (Modified from Gould [16]. Copyright © 1969 by the Institute of
Electrical and Electronics Engineers, Inc. Reprinted, with permission, from IEEE
Transactions on Magnetics, Dec. 1969, Vol. MAG-5, pp. 812–821.)

maximum *B–H* product is specified by the slope of a line to that point
from the origin, (B_m/H_m), where

$$(BH)_{max} \text{ defines } B_m \times H_m. \qquad (3.58)$$

Most of the PM literature now uses CGS units, but the same slope is
given in MKS units as

$$\frac{B_m}{\mu_0 H_m} \qquad \text{for maximum energy.} \qquad (3.59)$$

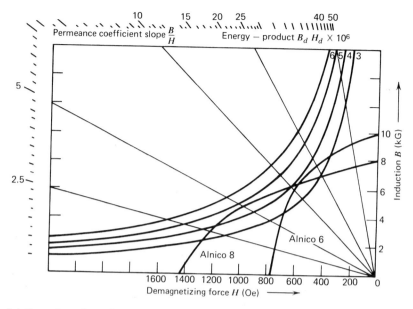

(a) Second-quadrant B–H data (CGS) for two commercial PM alloys, also called the demagnetizing curve. The hyperbolas are lines of constant (BH) to aid the determination of $(BH)_{max}$ for the material. The point of tangency also defines the desired slope of load line for maximum energy.

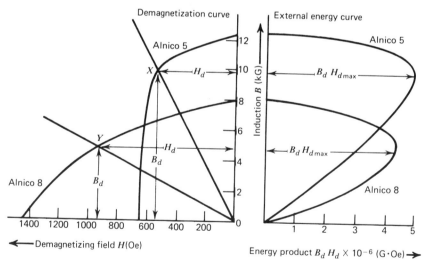

(b) Demagnetization and (BH) data (CGS) for two commercial grades of Alnico. Each load line OX and OY is drawn through the points of $(BH)_{max}$; $(BH)_{max}$ is the area of the largest rectangle that can be drawn inside the demagnetizing curve.

Figure 3.20 Two representations of $(BH)_{max}$ for a permanent magnet. (After Tebble and Craik [14], with permission of the publisher and of General Electric Co., Schenectady, New York.)

EXAMPLE O

(a) The CGS data in the table below were adapted from a paper by Gould. Convert the data for Alnico 5 to MKS units and check (3.59) against the CGS (B_m/H_m) ratio.

	Alnico 5 Alcomax III	Alnico 8 Hycomax III	High H_c Ferrite
B_r (G)	12,600	8800	3700
H_c (Oe)	650	1500	2960
$(BH)_{max}$ (MG·Oe)	5.4	5.0	3.06
B_m (G)	10,200	5000	1800
H_m (Oe)	530	1000	1700

(b) For each of the three listed materials, find the value (B_r/H_c) and compare it with (B_m/H_m) for the same material. This is a test of the hypothesis that a line drawn from the origin to the point $(H, B) = (-H_c, B_r)$ will intersect the demagnetization curve near $(BH)_{max}$.

ANSWER

(a) $10,200 \, G \times 530 \, Oe = 5.4 \times 10^6 \, G \cdot Oe$ for $(BH)_{max}$, which may also be expressed as $1.02 \, T \times 42176 \, A/m \approx 43 \times 10^3 \, J/m^3$. $B_r = 1.26 \, T$, $H_c = 517 \, A/cm$; CGS slope = $(10,200/530) = 19.24$. Equation 3.59 yields $1.02/(4\pi 10^{-7} \times 42176) = 1.02/0.053 = 19.24$.

(b) (B_r/H_c), (B_m/H_m) = 19.38, 19.24; 5.87, 5.0; 1.25, 1.06.

In addition to its use in defining the best static operating point for a PM, $(BH)_{max}$ also can serve as a figure of merit for comparing PM materials with one another. Data for various PM materials are tabulated in Section 3.2.4.

Airgap Reluctance. The reluctance of a magnetic element is given by the ratio of potential drop to flux, which is the reciprocal of permeance. For a short airgap of length l_g and area S_g the reluctance is given approximately by the formula

$$R_g = \frac{F_g}{\phi_g} \approx \frac{l_g}{\mu_0 S_g}, \tag{3.60}$$

which is derived subsequently.

Magnetic Analog Circuit. A lumped-parameter electric circuit analog of the magnetic circuit of Fig. 3.19 is given in Fig. 3.21a, including

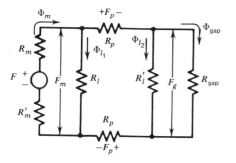

(a) Circuit analog of the magnetic circuit of Fig. 3.19.

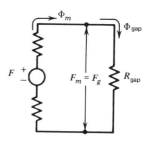

(b) Simplified circuit omitting leakage flux and pole-piece reluctance.

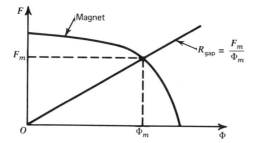

(c) Graphical solution for magnet source and air gap load. The curve shows the second quadrant of a permanent magnet, but rotated by 90° clockwise to suggest the analogous volt·ampere curve for a voltage supply. Maximum power transfer into an electrical load resistor is the analog of maximum energy transfer from a magnet into the airgap.

Figure 3.21   Permanent magnet circuit analogs.

models for the pole pieces and for leakage flux. Analogous quantities $V \sim F$, $I \sim \Phi$, and $R \sim R$ yield topologically similar circuits. The simplified circuit of Fig. 3.21b illustrates the principle of matching the airgap reluctance to the required operating point for the magnet. Figure 3.21c graphically interprets an $F - \Phi$ plane, which is a sideways plot of the second quadrant of a $B-H$ graph. The graph has also been scaled by the magnet dimensions as in Chapter 1. The two conditions that lead immediately to the required solution are magnet potential equal to load potential*

---

*A convention of opposite magnet field $H'_m = -H_m$ could be chosen, since F of Fig. 3.21c corresponds to the negative axis. By that convention Ampere's law yields $ni = \oint \bar{H} \cdot \bar{dl} = 0 = H'_m l_m + H_g l_g$ for (3.61).

$$H_m l_m = F_m = F_g = H_g l_g = \Phi_g R_g \qquad (3.61)$$

and magnet flux equal to airgap flux

$$B_m S_m = \Phi_m = \Phi_g = B_g S_g. \qquad (3.62)$$

Since μ_0 is the permeability in an airgap,

$$B_g = \mu_0 H_g, \qquad (3.63)$$

which permits (3.62) to be substituted into (3.61) as

$$H_m l_m = \frac{l_g B_g}{\mu_0} = \frac{l_g B_m S_m}{\mu_0 S_g},$$

yielding the desired relationship

$$\frac{S_g}{S_m} \frac{l_m}{l_g} = \frac{B_m}{\mu_0 H_m}. \qquad (3.64)$$

Since the right-hand side of (3.64) is a known quantity after the magnet material has been chosen, it is simple and straightforward to relate airgap dimensions to magnet requirements.

EXERCISE C

Equation 3.64 can be manipulated into other forms to give additional insight.

(a) Derive (3.64) using $R_g = F_m/\Phi_m$ of Fig. 3.21c.
(b) Solve for the magnet volume $V = S_m l_m$ and show that it is minimum if $B_m H_m$ is $(BH)_{max}$.
(c) Find the energy in the airgap, $E = (\mu_0 H_g^2 l_g S_g)$, as it relates to the magnet energy.
(d) Scale the axes of Fig. 3.21c by the magnet dimensions to replot the graph on axes of B versus H; find the equation for normalized airgap reluctance that passes through the magnet operating point B_m, H_m.

Several excellent review papers and books dealing with PM materials and applications have recently become available. The references at the end of this chapter list several sources that are general, readable, and authoritative [12–20].

Perspective on PM Circuit Design.   Let us now itemize the concepts and models for PMs that have been established at this point. Sections 3.2.1 and 3.2.2 dealt with the field theory of highly ideal magnets. For that ideal analysis it was assumed that the magnet was completely and uniformly magnetized, immune to the demagnetizing effects of its own internal field. Examples M and N suggest a plausible criterion for estimating whether the ideal field model would be expected to yield results that are qualitatively accurate, or whether in fact the field model of uniform surface poles is applicable at all. In principle the field can be calculated if the distribution of magnet poles is known, but at this point we have not examined any self-consistency criteria to help define the pole distribution. Chapter 8 will address that topic. The geometry for the field calculations was that of cylindrical magnets in free space; the field was calculated along the axis of the magnet. We conclude that elementary field calculations are not sufficient to be the only tool for detailed PM circuit design, although the qualitative insight is valuable.

A graphical design procedure introduced earlier in this section uses a load line drawn onto the magnetization curve for PM material. The static load line, representing the reluctance of a fixed airgap, is to be constructed through a specific point of $(BH)_{max}$ on the second quadrant of the BH curve. The basic principle of maximum energy from the magnet is analogous to the concept of maximum power transfer for a resistive electric circuit. The two concepts, airgap reluctance and analogous electric circuit models, are examined in Section 3.3. The reader may wish to refer ahead to Section 3.3 for clarification of reluctance and of analog circuits before studying Section 3.2.4 in detail. The tools of graphical constructions and of analog circuits provide a communication medium for concepts of PM design.

Finally, a valid tool for design of PM applications is a compilation of careful observations and their systematic detailed description. Many carefully observed aspects of PM applications do not readily lend themselves to simple analytical models. Consider the following observation that concerns the charging of magnets.

In the manufacture of devices that use PMs, it is common for the magnets to arrive at the factory production line in a demagnetized state. After the device is assembled the magnet must be charged to saturation, raising the question of how large a field is required. Although the second quadrant of the $B–H$ curve is used for applications design, the first quadrant defines the field required to magnetize. Parker and Studders [20] suggest the criterion $H_s \approx 5H_{ci}$, where H_s is the field required to magnetize to saturation and intrinsic coercivity H_{ci} is the H-axis intercept of the intrinsic induction curve B_i versus H. Figure 3.22 gives a family of curves of second quadrant $B–H$ data for Alnico 5, showing the effect of different values of peak magnetizing field. We note that an applied field of 600 Oe charged the magnet to less than half its rated induction, and that $H_s \approx 3000$ Oe was required to achieve the fully magnetized state.

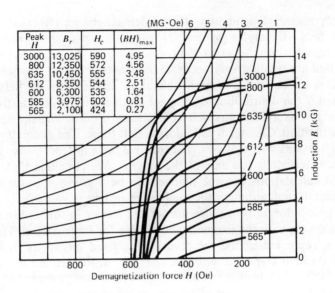

Figure 3.22 Demagnetization curves for Alnico 5 for various peak magnetizing fields. (Modified from Parker and Studders [20], with permission.)

A qualitative interpretation of Fig. 3.22 must identify *B* as some sort of average over the specimen. Considerations of magnetic theory suggest that partially magnetized specimens are comprised of distinct magnetic domains, each of which is magnetized to saturation along some orientation. The domain configuration is characteristic of the material in the following sense. In Fig. 3.22 the slope at $H = 0$ is the same for each of the minor hysteresis loops, furthermore the slope is approximately the same for the major loop. The slope, called recoil permeability μ_R, is a useful parameter for dynamic applications of PMs. The values of relative recoil permeability tabulated in Section 3.2.5 vary from 1.05 to 15 depending on the material. Since μ_R is a material property, it is likely that for each material the domains are in a configuration that is somehow typical of that material.

3.2.4 Dynamic Design with Permanent Magnets

The PM literature 15 years ago identified dynamic applications as the most rapidly growing component of the PM market. Since the early 1960s there has emerged a new class of PM materials, cobalt–rare earth magnets, that appear to be remarkably suited for dynamic applications. That technological breakthrough provides even greater motivation for examining some introductory concepts of magnet dynamics. Two types of dynamic application are *active recoil* and *passive* or *mechanical recoil.*

Mechanical Recoil.   Consider a PM that has been fully magnetized, then is operated at a point 1 in Fig. 3.23 by a small airgap of reluctance R_1. If the airgap subsequently is increased to reluctance R_2, the new state of the magnet would be expected to be at 2, the intercept of R_2 with the major demagnetization curve. If point 2 is past the knee of the B–H curve, a subsequent decrease of reluctance from R_2 to R_1 however does not return the magnet to state 1. Instead, the new state 3 lies along a recoil line from point 2 at its intercept with R_1. After a few more cycles of change the magnet reaches a stable trajectory between points 4 and 5.

Recoil lines are generally more stable than major demagnetizing curves. Even for static applications near $(BH)_{max}$ the magnet is sometimes intentionally perturbed to an interior point such as s in Fig. 3.23, to achieve greater immunity to changes of temperature or of magnet field environment.

Useful Recoil Product.   The hash-lined area of Fig. 3.23 is a measure of the dynamic energy supplied to the load reluctance. The "useful recoil product" appears in Fig. 3.24. For a given point A, the useful recoil product will be largest when P is at the midpoint of the recoil line A–A',

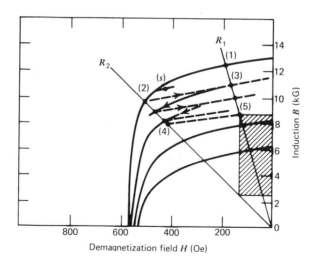

Figure 3.23   Change of induction for a PM due to the cyclic variation of load reluctances between values of R_1 and R_2. After a few cycles the magnet reaches a stable trajectory between points 4 and 5. The cross-hatched area is a measure of the useful dynamic energy.

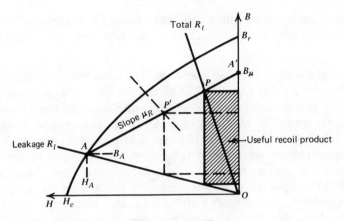

$$B_\mu = B_A + \mu_R \mu_0 H_A$$

For a given point *A*, the maximum useful recoil product = $H_A B_\mu /4$ for *P* at center point *P'*.

Figure 3.24 Graphical construction of useful recoil product. The initial working point *A* of the open-circuit magnet defines the magnet leakage reluctance R_l. The recoil line *AA'* with slope μ_R will intersect at point *P* the line of total reluctance R_t. The useful recoil product is an area constructed from point *P* as shown. For a given point *A*, the useful recoil product is maximum for *P* in the center of *A–A'*, as point *P'*.

as point *P'*. In addition if point *A* is chosen optimally for a given magnet material, the useful recoil product will reach its maximum value $(BH)_u$.

The maximum useful recoil product $(BH)_u$ is a figure of merit for PM materials, somewhat akin to $(BH)_{max}$ but defined for dynamic applications. For any material $(BH)_u$ is always smaller than $(BH)_{max}$ but approaches that value as a limit in the case of PM materials with very high coercivity.

To illustrate the concept of matching a magnet to its load for maximum energy transfer, consider the analogous electrical problem of matching a resistor load for maximum power transfer (Fig. 3.25). The volt·ampere graph (Fig. 3.25*a*) corresponds to the Thévenin models (Fig. 3.25*b*), the circuit is at state *A* (or *P*) when the Thévenin switch is open (or closed). The Thévenin source V_s is fictitious, defined by the extrapolation of the recoil line *A–A'* to *I* = 0. The short-circuit current I_μ is the limiting value for the condition *R* = 0.

Two concepts are central to the interpretation of Fig. 3.25. First, the hash-lined area represents the power dissipated in *R*, which is the product V_p and the current in *R*. The current at point *P* represents the sum of currents through *R* and R_l in parallel. From I_p we must subtract

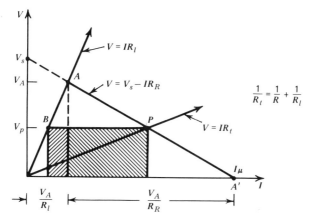

(a) A volt-ampere graph analogous to the graph of H versus B (Fig. 3.24). The cross-hatched region is the power in R, $V_A^2/4R$, under the matched condition that $R = R_R R_l/(R_B + R_l)$. Hence $V_A^2/4R = (V_A^2/4)(1/R_R + 1/R_l)$ and also equals $V_A I_\mu/4$.

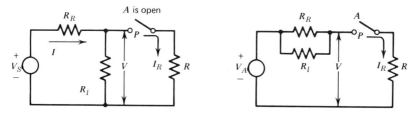

(b) Thévenin models that correspond to the graph of (a): $V_A = V_S R_l/(R_l + R_R)$, so $I_\mu = V_S/R_R = V_A(1/R_l + 1/R_R)$.

Figure 3.25   Electric circuit analog for the magnet recoil problem.

the current due to R_l alone, I at point B, to give the desired result. Thus distance B–P is the current I_R.

The second point regarding Fig. 3.25 is that the cross-hatched area is maximum when P is at the midpoint of A–A'; furthermore the condition of maximum power corresponds to R equal to the parallel combination of R_R and R_l. The geometrical condition, evident by construction, corresponds to the Thévenin circuit condition $V_P = \frac{1}{2}V_A$.

As noted in the legend of Fig. 3.25, the maximum power output $V_A^2/4R$ may also be written as $V_A I_\mu/4$. The latter formula follows from the construction in Fig. 3.25a, where $I_\mu = V_A/R_l + V_A/R_R$, hence equals V_A/R. The corresponding magnetic interpretation is the well-known formula for maximum recoil product

$$\frac{H_A B_\mu}{4} = \text{maximum recoil product} \qquad (3.65)$$

for a given initial working point *A*.

EXERCISE D

(a) Figure 3.25a is for the circuit model on the left-hand side of Fig. 3.25b. Draw a graph of $V - I_R$ for the right-hand side of Fig. 3.25b, where I_R is current through *R*.
(b) The Thévenin open-circuit voltage V_S and the Norton short-circuit current I_μ are shown as specific points in Fig. 3.25a. Find the analogous points in Fig. 3.24.
(c) Derive the equations for the cross-hatched area of Fig. 3.25a.
(d) Make a Norton circuit model and repeat the derivation.

Active Recoil. Active recoil, the second type of dynamic PM application, involves the interaction of a magnet with an externally applied field. For instance, in PM motors the environment of the magnet includes not only an airgap reluctance that varies with the angle of rotation of the motor shaft, but also a fluctuating field due to the applied ampere·*turns* of mmf. Active recoil is represented graphically on the second quadrant of the PM magnetization curve as a sideways translation of the reluctance line (Fig. 3.26). Permanent magnet materials for active recoil applications should possess an extraordinarily high coercivity, thus new interest can be attributed to the emergence of cobalt–rare earth magnets, RCo_5. For magnets of high coercivity there is a significant difference in the curve for intrinsic induction B_i versus *H* as compared with *B–H* (Fig. 3.26). Gould [16] suggests working with both forms of the magnet data, and advises against allowing the load line to pass the knee of the curve, point *c* of Fig. 3.26.

A review of applications literature reveals no additional figures of merit that are generally accepted for active recoil applications. In fact McCaig [18] cites surprising differences of opinion about what constitute desirable magnetic properties for active recoil applications.

3.2.5 PM Materials

The most basic parameter that characterizes permanent magnet materials is high coercivity, H_c. Four mechanisms have been identified in the

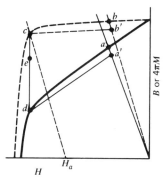

aa' normal unit permeance, slope $B/H = (1/D - 1)$, giving intercept at a when fully magnetized, at a' on recoil line after application and removal of H_a

bb' slope $B/H + 1 = 1/D$, giving equivalent intercepts on $4\pi M$ curve and recoil line

cH_a slope as bb' but displaced by H_a, giving intercept c on $4\pi M$ curve and equivalent B vertically below at d

e in a motor, if a',b' represent stabilized no-load conditions and H_a represents armature reaction at stall, then torque-producing flux density at stall is e (ratio $e/c = a'/b' = a/b$)

Figure 3.26 Working points with self-demagnetizing field and externally applied field, full curve $B = f(H)$, dashed curve $4\pi M = f(H)$. (From Gould [16]. Copyright © 1969 by The Institute of Electrical and Electronics Engineers, Inc. Reprinted, with permissions from IEEE TRANSACTIONS on Magnetics, Dec. 1969, Vol. MAG-5, pp. 812–821.)

development of PM materials of ever-wider B–H loops. These are:

1. Inclusions or defects in the hardened magnetic material which have the effect of retarding domain wall motion. The higher the value of field required to move a domain wall, the higher will be the value of coercivity for the material.

2. Single-domain magnetic inclusions. Chapter 8 demonstrates that a domain wall possesses a small but finite thickness. A magnetic particle smaller than the critical size to sustain a domain wall must exist as a single domain. The absence of domain walls rules out domain wall motion altogether as a mechanism for change of induction.

3. Shape anisotropy.* The dependence of internal demagnetizing fields on the geometry of the magnetized sample was alluded to earlier as a geometrical factor, f in (3.39), which is similar to a demagnetizing factor. It is well known that long, thin samples tend to retain their magnetization

---

*Anisotropic means not isotropic, thus not the same in every direction.

to a greater degree along the major axis, a property that is attributed to the lower demagnetizing factor. Permanent magnet materials have been developed that exploit the shape anisotropy concept in the metallurgical structure, either by means of a long columnar crystal growth, or by use of elongated single domain (E.S.D.) magnetic inclusions. Since coercivity H_c depends on a difference of geometrical demagnetizing factors less than unity, the ratio

$$\frac{\mu_0 H_c}{B_r} < 1 \qquad (3.66)$$

is always true for PMs that depend on shape anisotropy. In CGS units, this means H_c in oersteds will always be less than B_r in gauss.

4. Crystalline anisotropy represents a breakthrough from the previously supposed limitation expressed by (3.66). For most single-crystal magnetic materials there exist one or more crystallographic directions of preferred orientation of B_{is}. Macroscopic models of anisotropy (Chapter 4) include an orientation term, multiplied by an anisotropy constant K, which is a measure of the strength of alignment. Coercivity is usually about the same magnitude as the field H_k required to turn B_{is} from its minimum energy orientation,

$$H_c \sim H_k = \frac{\alpha K}{B_{is}}. \qquad (3.67)$$

Constant α is in the range 0.5–2, depending on the crystal type. The crystalline mechanism of magnetic anisotropy is thought to be spin-orbital coupling, which can be described qualitatively as follows. The crystal structure imposes a three-dimensional pattern of orbital electrons; in other words, the outer orbital electrons of an atom are influenced by the locations of neighboring atoms. The net magnetic moment of the orbital electrons can interact with the magnetic moment of the spin, thereby imposing an anisotropy of spin orientation.

Material Data. In many cases the material mechanisms for high coercivity may be a combination of several of the four factors just enumerated. Metallurgical considerations are discussed in the paper by Becker et al. [15], from which Tables 3.2 to 3.4 are taken.

Cobalt–Rare Earth Magnets. The search for strongly anisotropic magnetic materials led in the late 1960s to the discovery of cobalt–rare earth compounds such as YCo_5 and $SmCo_5$. The coercivity is so large for these materials that the knee of the $B–H$ curve is in the third quadrant. Figure 3.27 shows this property for a material of intrinsic coercivity $_M H_c$

Table 3.2 Properties of cast alnico alloys

Material	B_r (G)	H_c (Oe)	$(BH)_{max}$ ($\times 10^6$ G·Oe)	Recoil Permeability, μ_R	$(BH)_u$ ($\times 10^6$ G·Oe)	Reversible Temperature Coefficient of B_r (%/°C)	Specific Gravity	Maximum Operating Temperature (°C)
Alnico 2	7250	550	1.6	6.4	0.7	−0.02	7.1	450
Alnico 5	12500	620	5.3	4.1	1.5	−0.02	7.3	550
Alnico 5-DG	12900	650	6.1	4.0	—	—	7.3	550
Alnico 5-7	13200	730	7.5	3.0	2.1	—	7.3	550
Alnico 6	10500	750	3.7	4.8	1.3	−0.03	7.3	550
Alnico 8	8300	1600	5.0	2.3	2.1	−0.01	7.3	550
Alnico 8B	7800	1900	5.7	2.0	2.3	—	7.3	550
Alnico 9	10450	1550	10.5	1.3	3.6	—	7.3	550

From Becker et al. [15]. Copyright © 1968 by The Institute of Electrical and Electronics Engineers, Inc. Reprinted, with permission, from IEEE TRANSACTIONS on Magnetics, June 1968, Vol. MAG-4, p. 93.

Table 3.3 Properties of ferrite permanent magnet materials

Material	B_r (G)	H_c (Oe)	$(BH)_{max}$ ($\times 10^6$ G·Oe)	Recoil Permeability, μ_R	$(BH)_u$ ($\times 10^6$ G·Oe)	Reversible Temperature Coefficient of B_r (%/°C)	Specific Gravity	Maximum Operating Temperature (°C)
Barium ferrite								
Isotropic	2200	1850	1.0	1.15	1.0	−0.19	4.7	400
Oriented-high B_r	3840	2000	3.5	1.05	1.7	−0.19	5.0	400
Oriented-high H_c	3200	2550	2.6	1.05	1.7	−0.19	4.6	400
Rubber bonded	2200	1480	1.1	1.1	1.0	−0.19	3.7	100
Strontium ferrite								
Oriented-high B_r	4000	2200	3.7	1.05	1.8	−0.18	4.8	400
Oriented-high H_c	3550	3150	3.0	1.05	2.6	−0.15	4.5	400

From Becker et al. [15]. Copyright © 1968 by the Institute of Electrical and Electronics Engineers, Inc. Reprinted, with permission, from IEEE TRANSACTIONS on Magnetics, June 1968, Vol. MAG-4, p. 93.

Table 3.4 Properties of steels and miscellaneous permanent magnet materials

Material	B_r (G)	H_c (Oe)	$(BH)_{max}$ ($\times 10^6$ G·Oe)	Recoil Permeability, μ_R	$(BH)_u$ ($\times 10^6$ G·Oe)	Reversible Temperature Coefficient of B_r (%/°C)	Specific Gravity	Maximum Operating Temperature (°C)
1 Carbon steel	9000	50	0.2	—	—	—	7.8	100
5 Tungsten steel	10500	70	0.33	—	—	—	8.1	100
3 Cobalt steel	9700	80	0.38	—	—	—	7.9	100
17 Cobalt steel	9500	160	0.65	15	0.2	−0.01	8.35	150
36 Cobalt steel	10400	230	0.94	12	0.3	−0.01	8.2	150
Cunife	5400	550	1.5	3.7	0.5	—	8.6	350
Cunico	3400	680	0.8	3.2	0.4	—	8.3	500
Vicalloy 1	8400	240	0.9	—	—	−0.01	8.2	450
Vicalloy 2	9050	415	2.3	—	—	−0.01	8.2	450
Remalloy 2	8550	340	1.2	—	—	—	8.4	500
Cobalt platinum	6450	4450	9.2	1.1	4.9	−0.015	15.5	350

From Becker et al. [15]. Copyright © 1968 by The Institute of Electrical and Electronics Engineers, Inc. Reprinted, with permission, from IEEE TRANSACTIONS on Magnetics, June 1968, Vol. MAG-4, p. 93.

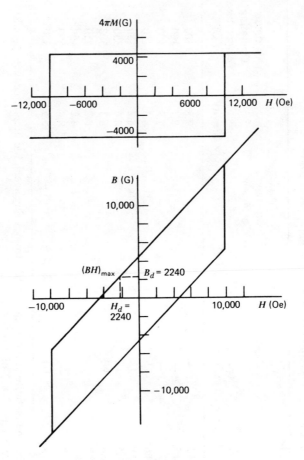

Figure 3.27 Hysteresis loops for *M* and *B* of a material with $_MH_c = 10,000$ Oe and $4\pi M_s = 4480$ G. (From Becker [17]. Copyright © 1968 by the Institute of Electrical and Electronics Engineers, Inc. Reprinted, with permission, from IEEE TRANSACTIONS on Magnetics, Sept. 1968, Vol. MAG-4, p. 247.)

or $H_{ci} = 10^4$ Oe and $B_r = 4480$ G, hence of the ratio $\mu_0 H_c / B_r = 2.23$ by (3.66). The graph of B_i versus H is a rectangular hysteresis loop, whereas the *B–H* characteristic has a significant slope due to μ_0, the magnetic constant of free space. For such materials flux density *B* is 0 at a value of *H*, called H_c or $_BH_c$, that differs significantly from the intrinsic coercivity at which the magnetization changes. It is also true that the useful recoil product $(BH)_u$ is almost equal to $(BH)_{max}$ with the approximate value $(B_r/2)^2$ in CGS units.

3.3 MAGNETIC CORES WITH SHORT AIRGAPS

Chapters 1 and 2 considered only ideal, mathematically tractable core shapes with no airgaps, to give attention to elementary magnetic processes in cores. An airgap is a material nonuniformity in the flux path, therefore would have complicted the initial mathematical description of the path. A modest combination of ideas from Sections 3.1 and 3.2 now serves to add the effect of an airgap to the core characteristic.

Airgaps are very commonly used in magnetic devices—see, for example, Fig. 3.28. In some applications an airgap is an undesirable feature, to be avoided or minimized. Indeed the primary concept of one-piece molded toroidal ferrite core geometry, or of tape-wound core geometry, is to avoid the necessity of an airgap. In other devices, such as recording heads or filter chokes, the airgap is an important component of the design.

In any event our important task is the modeling of the airgap, the potential drop across it, its value of reluctance, and finally its effect on core properties. The electric circuit analog is a useful tool.

3.3.1 Potential of an Airgap

Before getting into the details of the field calculations, it is well to establish the context of the discussion by a brief review. Section 3.1.2

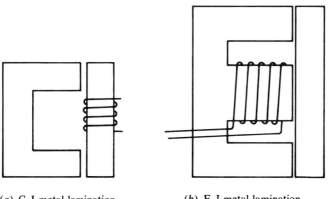

(*a*) C–I metal lamination.   (*b*) E–I metal lamination.

Ferromagnetic cores for inductors and transformers are built up by stacking several dozen thin laminations. Size depends on power level—typically a few centimeters for electronic applications.

Figure 3.28   (*Continued on following page*).

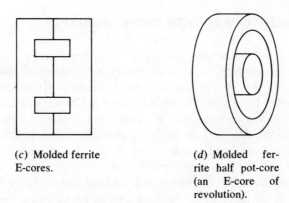

(*c*) Molded ferrite E-cores.

(*d*) Molded ferrite half pot-core (an E-core of revolution).

These widely used shapes for ferrite cores are simpler to wind than toroidal cores. The mating surfaces are polished to reduce the effective airgap. Size: 1–5 cm.

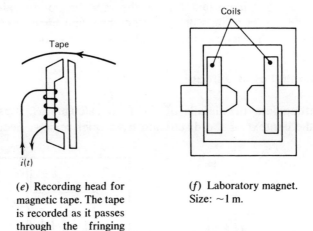

(*e*) Recording head for magnetic tape. The tape is recorded as it passes through the fringing field of the head.

(*f*) Laboratory magnet. Size: ~1 m.

Figure 3.28 Examples of airgaps in magnetic devices. In electronic cores (*a*) through (*d*) the airgap sometimes has an undesirable effect. In a recording head (*e*) the gap is vital to the design and must be accurately controlled. In a laboratory magnet (*f*), the region of interest is the gap between pole faces.

introduced the concept of the total potential around a magnetic circuit

$$nI = F = \oint \bar{H} \cdot d\bar{l}, \qquad (3.68)$$

which is equal to the current enclosed by the circuit, $F = nI$ A·t, according to Ampere's circuital law. The present discussion is addressed to configurations as in Fig. 3.28, in which the magnetic properties around the flux path possess at least one nonuniformity, namely, an airgap. It is convenient to separate the closed-line integral of (3.68) into two components

$$F = \int_{\text{material}} \bar{H} \cdot d\bar{l} + \int_{\text{airgap}} \bar{H} \cdot d\bar{l}, \tag{3.69}$$

to permit the airgap potential to be considered separately. As Section 3.2, brought out, magnetic poles arise at material interfacial surfaces crossed by normal components of flux, with the result that the H-field strength is large in the airgap. In many cases, the airgap is short enough that the value of H is essentially constant over the length of the gap; thus

$$F_{\text{gap}} = \int \bar{H} \cdot d\bar{l} \approx Hg, \tag{3.70}$$

where g is the length of the gap.

EXAMPLE P

A particular core has an airgap of 0.5 mm (about 0.02 in.). Find the potential in ampere·*turns* required to establish a magnetic flux density of 1000 G in the gap.

ANSWER. If $B = 1000$ G, then $H = 1000$ Oe in CGS units, so $F = Hg = 50$ Oe·cm (50 Gb) or about 40 A·t. Check in SI units: $Hg = (10^6/4\pi)$ A·t/m (5×10^{-4}) m $= 39.79$ A·t.

It can be inferred from (3.69) and from Example P that a significant fraction of the total ampere·turns applied to a core can be dropped across the airgap, leaving less to excite the magnetic material. An airgap was used in Section 3.2.3 as a load line in permanent magnet circuits. The reluctance equation (3.60) is now derived to support the further use of analog electric circuits.

3.3.2 Calculation of Gap Reluctance

The reluctance of an airgap is the ratio of the potential drop across the gap divided by flux,

$$R = \frac{F}{\Phi} \tag{3.71}$$

where F is given by (3.70). The accuracy of (3.71) is usually related to

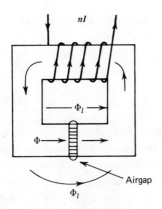

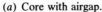

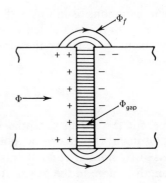

(*a*) Core with airgap.   (*b*) Airgap showing fringing flux.

Figure 3.29   The definition of gap reluctance by $R_g = F_g/\Phi$ may be more accurate than the formula $R_g = g/\mu_0 S$, where g is the length of the gap and S is area of one pole face. Flux Φ is the sum of flux in the gap Φ_g and fringing flux Φ_f.

the accuracy of determination of Φ inasmuch as F is a drop between equipotential surfaces. Three components of flux illustrated in Fig. 3.29 are leakage flux, fringing flux, and gap flux. Leakage flux also has been referred to previously (Fig. 3.21).

The reluctance defined for average flux in the gap of area S

$$\Phi = \int \bar{B} \cdot d\bar{s} \approx BS \tag{3.72}$$

is therefore

$$R_g = \frac{Hg}{BS} = \frac{g}{\mu_0 S}, \tag{3.73}$$

validating (3.60). Equation 3.73 assumes that the airgap length g is short compared with the dimensions of the pole face. Various semiempirical corrections* can be made to approximate the effect of fringing flux—for example, by increasing the cross-sectional area in (3.73) from the pole-piece area of $S = ab$ to an effective area

$$S = (a + g)(b + g). \tag{3.74}$$

*See references at end of chapter; in particular, Ref. 12, Chaps. 3 and 4, and Ref. 19. With some experience, the techniques in these references make attainable an accuracy of 10 to 20% for reluctance and for the ratio of leakage flux to useful flux. Field mapping techniques such as the graphical method of curvilinear squares also can be helpful for some configurations. Computer simulation by calculation of Laplace's equation is another method that has come into use more recently, with considerable success.

An important guideline to the reduction of leakage flux is to keep the source of magnetomotive force as close as possible to the gap. This principle accounts for the location of the coils in Fig. 3.28*f* and for the high flux efficiency of core magnet structures in Fig. 3.19. For each design the major support structure is a flux return path of low reluctance. This minimizes the amount of surface area at high magnetic potential.

Airgap in an Ideal Cylindrical Core. The airgap field and potential can be calculated using the magnetic Coulomb's law if the pole distribution is known. To illustrate that concept, consider the equations developed in Section 3.2.1 for an ideal permanent magnet of cylindrical shape. The original equations were derived for the special case of uniform pole density, hence for two circular disks of magnetic charge. The present adaptation assumes that the disks of charge are on either end of a cylindrical airgap (Fig. 3.30), thus interchanging the relative positions of free-space and magnetic material. Assuming that the direction of B_i is in the positive z-direction, a modified (3.35) yields

$$H_z = \frac{B_i}{2\mu_0}(\cos\theta_1 - \cos\theta_2) \qquad |z| > h \qquad (3.75a)$$

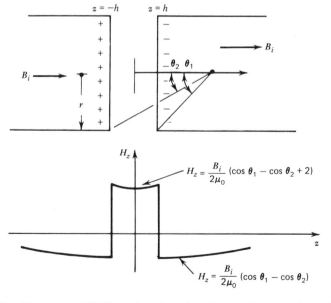

Figure 3.30 Adaptation of (3.36) to the calculation of the reluctance of an airgap in a cylindrical magnetic circuit.

$$H_z = \frac{B_i}{2\mu_0}(\cos\theta_1 - \cos\theta_2 + 2) \qquad |z| < h \qquad (3.75b)$$

for the field along the z-axis centerline. The angle θ_2 is associated with the positive polarity pole as in the earlier derivation.

EXAMPLE Q

Use (3.75b) to find the field at the center of the gap and at either pole fact for the case $g = 2h = 0.1$ diameter.

ANSWER. At the center of the gap $\theta_2 = \tan^{-1}(r/h) = \tan^{-1} 10 = 84.3°$ and $\theta_1 = 95.7°$, thus $H_z = (B_i/\mu_0)(1 - 0.0995) \approx 0.900\, B_i/\mu_0$. At the negative pole $\theta_1 = 90°$ and $\theta_2 = \tan^{-1}(r/2h) = \tan^{-1} 5$, so inside the airgap $H_z = (B_i/2\mu_0)(2 - 0.196) \approx 0.902\, B_i/\mu_0$. Just inside the material at the same pole $H_z = -0.098\, B_i/\mu_0$.

EXAMPLE R

Using the expressions in Example Q, find the values of H_z in MKS (CGS) units if $B_i = 1$ T ($4\pi M = 10{,}000$ G).

ANSWER. At the center of the gap $H_z = 7.16 \times 10^5$ A/m (9005 Oe), at either end of the gap $H_z = 7.18 \times 10^5$ A/m (9019 Oe). The material demagnetizing field at the pole is $H_z = -7.8 \times 10^4$ A/m (-981 Oe).

The results from Example R suggest that H is relatively constant in a short airgap, therefore support the approximation of (3.70). To further demonstrate the notion of magnetic potential difference, let us carry out the integral $\int \vec{H} \cdot d\vec{l}$ across the gap. Using (3.75b), the required integral is

$$F_g = \frac{B_i}{\mu_0} \int_{z=0}^{h} (2 + \cos\theta_1 - \cos\theta_2)\, dz, \qquad (3.76)$$

using $dl = dz$ and using symmetry to double the integral over half the gap.

The term $\cos\theta_1$ can be rewritten as a perfect differential, as

$$\int_0^h \frac{(z-h)\, dz}{[r^2 + (z-h)^2]^{1/2}} = [r^2 + (z-h)^2]^{1/2}\Big|_0^h. \qquad (3.77)$$

Carrying the same procedure for $\cos\theta_2$, after including the integration limits, (3.76) becomes

$$F_g = \frac{B_i}{\mu_0}\left[2h + r - \sqrt{r^2 + 4h^2} \right], \qquad (3.78)$$

which can be manipulated into an approximate result

$$F_g \approx \frac{B_i}{\mu_0} 2h \left(1 - \frac{h}{r}\right). \tag{3.79}$$

The flux through the airgap can be calculated from $\Phi = BS$ with $B = \mu_0 H$, where H is found from (3.75b) at the pole, where $\cos \theta_1 = 0$. The flux crossing the gap is

$$\Phi = \mu_0 H \pi r^2 = B_i \pi r^2 \left[1 - \frac{h}{\sqrt{4h^2 + r^2}}\right] \tag{3.80}$$

and the reluctance is F/Φ, which after some manipulation yields the equation

$$R = \frac{2h}{\mu_0 \pi r^2} \left[1 - \left(\frac{h}{r}\right)^2 - \cdots\right]. \tag{3.81}$$

This result confirms (3.73) to second order in h/r for the mathematically tractable, if physically simplistic, cylindrical airgap. The principal importance of the derivation lies in the exposure of the underlying assumptions and as a point of departure for other models.

3.3.3 Electric Circuit Analog

Kirchhoff's voltage law for electric networks is a lumped-parameter form of Maxwell's curl equation $\bar{\nabla} \times \bar{E} = -\partial \bar{B}/\partial t$, written in integral form as

$$\oint \bar{E} \cdot d\bar{l} + v = 0, \tag{3.82}$$

where $v = nd\phi/dt$. Kirchhoff's current law is similarly related to the current continuity relation $\bar{\nabla} \cdot \bar{J} = 0$. It is well known that these two basic rules for a circuit loop and a circuit node lend themselves by extension to the analysis of elaborate networks of many loops and nodes.

The similarity of (3.82) to Ampere's circuital law

$$F = nI = \oint \bar{H} \cdot d\bar{l} \tag{3.68}$$

is the main concept behind the use of electric circuit analogs for magnetic circuits, also supported by the flux continuity relation $\bar{\nabla} \cdot \bar{B} = 0$. The analog system takes voltage analogous to magnetic potential and current analogous to flux, and retains the same circuit topology. It follows that electrical resistance is analogous to magnetic reluctance such that a two-loop analog would appear as in Fig. 3.31. The analog is

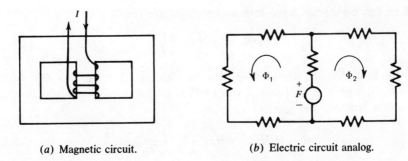

(*a*) Magnetic circuit.   (*b*) Electric circuit analog.

Figure 3.31 Lumped-parameter electric circuit analog for a two-loop magnetic circuit. Magnetic potential $F = nI$ is treated as a voltage in the electric circuit analog.

conceptually valuable and the accuracy of the reluctance model is better than qualitative.

If the closed-line integral (3.68) is used to describe a simple magnetic circuit with an airgap, the airgap potential can be separately identified as in (3.69)

$$F = \int_{\text{material}} \bar{H} \cdot d\bar{l} + \int_{\text{gap}} \bar{H} \cdot d\bar{l} \qquad (3.69)$$

from the magnetic potential drop across the core material. Figure 3.32 is a circuit representation of (3.69), where gap potential is given by $F_g = \Phi R_g$. In contrast with the representation of a core material as a

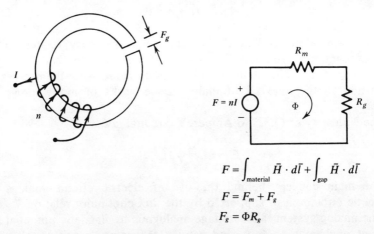

$$F = \int_{\text{material}} \bar{H} \cdot d\bar{l} + \int_{\text{gap}} \bar{H} \cdot d\bar{l}$$
$$F = F_m + F_g$$
$$F_g = \Phi R_g$$

Figure 3.32 Electric circuit analog for a simple magnetic circuit with an airgap. The magnetic material is represented here as a reluctance R_m. See Fig. 3.33 for an alternative graphical representation of material potential.

reluctance, gap reluctance is single valued and is not saturating. With certain limitations to be defined subsequently, (3.69) can be rearranged into a load line format as

$$nI - \Phi R_g = F_m(\Phi), \tag{3.83}$$

where nI is a source potential from which a load line $-\Phi R_g$ is drawn (Fig. 3.33). The operating point Q, where the load line intersects with the core characteristic $F_m(\Phi)$, represents the simultaneous solution of two required conditions, the left and right sides of (3.83).

Effect of Airgap on Linear Core. It is important to recognize that the effective permeance of a core can be varied by controlling the length of airgap. Figure 3.34 shows a class of commercial ferrite pot core designs based on this principle, useful for the design of adjustable inductors.

Consider a core made of material described by the linear relation $B = \mu H$, resulting in a core description $\Phi = P F_m$ where permeance $P = \mu S/l$, the reciprocal of reluctance R_m of Fig. 3.32. The effect of adding an airgap of reluctance R_g is to reduce the flux due to a given applied potential, as

$$\Phi = \frac{nI}{R_m + R_g}, \tag{3.84}$$

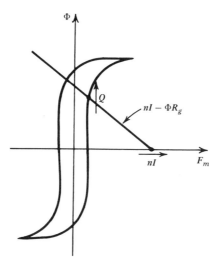

Figure 3.33 A graphical interpretation of (3.83) in which $nI - \Phi R_g$ is regarded as a source potential and load line.

where the core permeance is now reduced to

$$P = \frac{1}{R_m + R_g} = \frac{\mu S}{l + \mu_r g}. \tag{3.85}$$

The length of airgap g has a relatively larger effect, as though its length were multiplied by the relative permeability of the core. To retain the

(*a*) Pot cores for precision linear magnetic devices.

(*b*) Cutaway view of square core assembly.

Figure 3.34   Ferrite cores with adjustable airgaps. (Material furnished courtesy of Ferroxcube Division of Amperex Electronic Corporation, Sangerties, New York.)

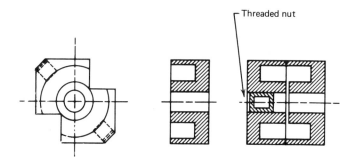

(c) Mechanical characteristics.

Figure 3.34 (*Cont'd*).

potentially large permeance of a high-permeability core with an airgap, it is necessary for the mating surfaces to be highly polished and for the core halves to be held tightly together.

EXAMPLE S

A particular type of ferrite pot core (see Fig. 3.28) has a measured permeance of $P = 10 \, \mu H/t^2$. Calculate the actual gap g and effective gap $g\mu_r$ using (3.85), given the core area $S \approx 1 \, cm^2$, $l \approx 3 \, cm$, and $\mu_r = 5000$. ANSWER. The denominator $l + g\mu_r = \mu S/P = 5000 \times 4\pi 10^{-7} \times 10^{-4}/10^{-5} = 6.28 \times 10^{-2} \, m \approx 6 \, cm$. Thus $g\mu_r \approx 3 \, cm$ and $g \approx 6 \, \mu m$.

Effect of Airgap on Square-Loop Core. In a final interpretation, (3.69) can be retained as a sum of two potential drops, rewritten as the sum of a material function and a gap potential

$$F = F_m(\Phi) + F_g, \qquad (3.86)$$

with a graphical interpretation as in Fig. 3.35. The important consequence is that an airgap can cause a "shearing" effect, yielding a linearized hysteresis characteristic for the core. For a material with small H_0 and large B_{sat}, an airgap tends to dominate the total characteristic. Alternatively stated, a large H_0 is required if the core is to remain saturated at $nI = 0$, despite the demagnetizing effect of the airgap.

EXAMPLE T

It is proposed to introduce an airgap into an Orthonol® tape-wound core, but with the condition that the airgap must not dominate the properties. That is, the amount of shearing must be so slight that $B_r = B_s$ is

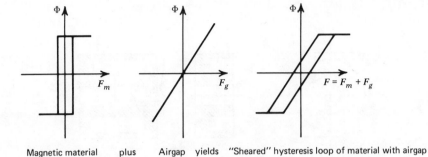

Magnetic material   plus   Airgap   yields   "Sheared" hysteresis loop of material with airgap

Figure 3.35 Illustration of (3.86) by the graphical addition of potential. The potentials are added for equal values of flux through the series elements. The right-most Φ-F loop is the final result for material with an airgap.

required, rather than the core being demagnetized as in Fig. 3.35. How much airgap can be tolerated in a core of mean path length l_m?

ANSWER.   The requirement that the square corner of the B–H loop not be tilted past the $H = 0$ axis implies $(H_g g) \leq (H_0 l_m)$, so $(g/l_m) \leq (H_0/H_g)$. Using data for Orthonol® as $B_{i_{sat}} = 1.4$ T defines the maximum field in the gap as $H_g = 1.4/\mu_0 = 1.11 \times 10^6$ A·t/m. Since $H_0 \approx 11$ A·t/m, the maximum gap must be less than $(g/l_m) \approx 10^{-5}$. For a 3-cm diameter core the maximum gap is less than $1 \, \mu$m, far less than the thickness of any known saw blade.

Nonuniform Demagnetizing Field.   The magnetic potential model of the foregoing circuit analog method omitted a detailed consideration of the H-fields near the gap. A full solution to this equation is beyond the scope of this text, but a few observations are in order. Consider a toroidal core of mean total flux-path length $2\pi r = l + g$, including material length l and airgap g. Figure 3.36 shows as a function of distance around the core, the presumed variation of intrinsic induction, of the field produced by the intrinsic induction, and of the total field. Equation 3.69 thus takes the form

$$nI = \int_l \bar{H}_m \cdot d\bar{l} + \int_g \bar{H}_g \cdot d\bar{l}, \qquad (3.87)$$

where the field acting on the material H_m is the sum of applied field H_a plus a nonuniform demagnetizing field H_d inside the material but caused by the poles near the airgap. Similarly the total field in the gap H_g is the sum of the applied field plus the field H_p due to the poles of B_i. A model for H_d and H_p for a different core geometry has been previously given as (3.75a) and (3.75b), respectively.

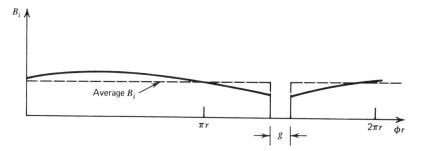

(a) The intrinsic induction has a zero value in the airgap.

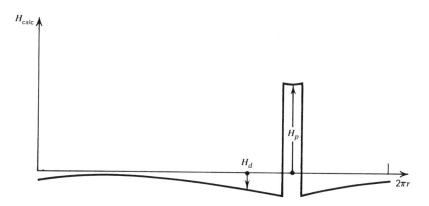

(b) Approximate form of field due to average B_i.

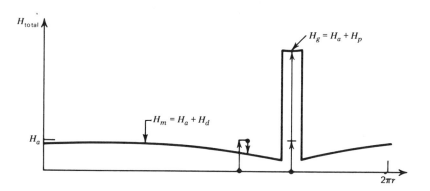

(c) The total field is the sum of applied field H_a plus the calculated field.

Figure 3.36 Qualitative representation of field parameters for a core with airgap, plotted as a function of the distance along the flux path around the core.

139

Thus (3.87) can be rewritten as

$$nI = \int_l (H_a + H_d)\, r\, d\phi + \int_g (H_a + H_p) r\, d\phi. \tag{3.88}$$

Under the assumption that superposition holds, the integration can be rearranged in the form

$$nI = \int_{l+g} H_a r\, d\phi + \int_l H_d r\, d\phi + \int_g H_p r\, d\phi. \tag{3.89}$$

The first integral on the right has the value $H_a(l + g)$, which merely serves to define $H_a = nI/(l + g)$, since the sum of the other two integrals is zero. In other words in Fig. 3.36b the positive and negative areas under H_{calc} are equal; this can be demonstrated analytically using (3.75).

For illustrative purposes an idealized form of (3.88) is

$$nI = (H_a + H_d)l + (H_a + H_p)g, \tag{3.90}$$

which is also equal to

$$nI = \frac{Bl}{\mu} + \frac{Bg}{\mu_0}, \tag{3.91}$$

assuming that B is uniform in the material and in the gap. A final substitution of $B = \Phi/S$ leads to the equation for core permeance (3.85).

3.4 SOME DESIGN EXAMPLES

Three examples conclude the chapter on H-fields. Section 3.4.1 gives design data for a commercial laboratory electromagnet, designed for the convenient production of laboratory fields in the range of a few thousand oersteds. For stronger fields, beyond the capability of the electromagnet, more specialized materials and design techniques are required. The next section, on superconductivity, introduces that important topic inasmuch as superconducting coils with high-field capability are now available. Section 3.4.3 briefly describes how the spiraling motion of moving electrons in a magnetic field has been applied to design a vacuum pump.

3.4.1 Laboratory Electromagnet

Let us describe the design features of a commercial electromagnet (Fig. 3.37). The magnet is designed to produce a field in the airgap, between two pole pieces in the center of the structure. Two large current-carrying

Figure 3.37 A commercial electromagnet with field regulation described in Section 3.4.1. The overall dimension from side to side is about 1 m. (Courtesy of Varian Associates, Inc., Palo Alto, California.)

coils, one located on either side of the airgap, provide the magnetic energy for the gap. The iron yoke structure provides the return path for the flux, thereby serving to concentrate the applied magnetic potential across the gap. Now if we neglect leakage and use a reluctance model to represent the yoke and working gap, we have

$$nI = \Phi(R_m + R_g) = H(l + g). \tag{3.92}$$

In the right-most expression l represents the yoke reluctance in the form of an equivalent airgap length, for convenience in defining the maximum field ratings.

It is typical of electromagnets that the maximum possible field depends on the airgap, as in (3.92) if nI is maximum. Furthermore the scale factor of field produced per ampere of current also varies when the gap is changed, which can be inconvenient. If a magnet does not possess the feature of field regulation, it is typical for the user to develop calibration data for *H* versus *I* for every value of gap. The more convenient field-regulated magnet includes a sensor for the field in the gap and electronically varies the coil current so that the measured field is equal to the desired field as set into the controls. Thus the controller can provide any desired field up to the maximum allowed for the particular gap setting.

Data for maximum field versus airgap setting for a commercial electromagnet appear in Fig. 3.38, where the allowed region of operation is above the diagonal line. The line is an adaptation of (3.92) as fitted to data points supplied by the manufacturer. The data are plotted in the form of $1/H$ versus $l + g$ to facilitate the determination of yoke reluctance parameter l at the extrapolated value of gap at which $1/H = 0$. For the subject magnet it was found that $l \approx 2$ in., to complete the determination of the right-hand side of (3.92) at 87×10^3 A·t; hence each coil probably contains about 260 turns. Because of the onset of core saturation, it is to be expected that the actual field points of Fig. 3.38 lie somewhere above the extrapolated line at high fields and small gap. Table 3.5 presents various parameters of this system.

Table 3.5 Parameters for the commercial magnet of Fig. 3.38

Parameter	Type or Value
Pole face diameter	6 in.
Field sensor type	Hall effect
Current regulation range	2–168 A
Coil resistance	$\frac{1}{8} \Omega$ each
Coil-cooling water	3.5 gallons/min
Electrical power input	11 kV·A
Maximum power to coils	7 kW

3.4.2 Superconductivity

In the late 1960s there began to emerge the new technology of superconducting materials for high-field coils. Superconductivity, discovered in 1911 by the Dutch scientist Kamerlingh Onnes, is a state of zero electrical resistivity that suddenly occurs at a temperature near absolute zero. A conductor with zero resistance is perfectly diamagnetic; that is, magnetic fields cannot penetrate the material. Thus a superconductor possesses the property of acting as an insulator or shield for magnetic

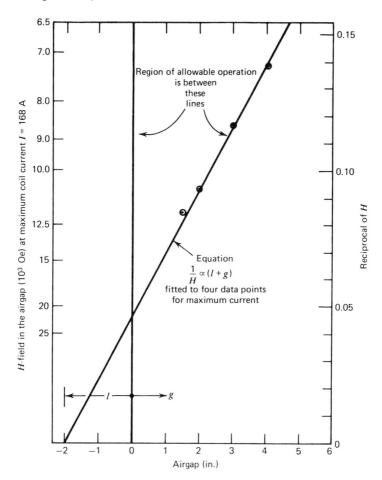

Figure 3.38 Experimental data from maximum field versus gap for the commercial electromagnet of Fig. 3.37. The reciprocal scale for H permits easy comparison with (3.92), yielding an estimate $l \approx 2$ in. for the yoke reluctance (expressed as an equivalent airgap length).

fields. Several applications have exploited a second property in which conduction by tunneling occurs through an insulating layer between two superconductors, as first proposed on theoretical grounds by Josephson while a graduate student. It turns out that the frequency of the tunneling signal is a precise measure of the voltage across the barrier. The U.S. National Bureau of Standards now uses Josephson junctions as the primary standard for voltage. The sensitivity of the frequency of oscillation to magnetic fields has led to still another class of devices called SQUIDs (superconducting quantum interference devices), the most sensitive field detectors now in existence.

The property of zero resistance has spurred the development of superconducting materials for coils to produce high magnetic fields. The saturation of iron at $B_s \approx 2.1$ T imposes a fundamental limit for the technology of iron-yoke electromagnets as described in Section 3.4.1. For example, if a field of 75 kOe (6×10^6 A·t/m) is required, an air-core coil is necessary. But to produce 75 kOe of field with a coil of normal conductivity may require half a megawatt of electrical power, depending on the required volume of high-field region. In many cases the inconvenience of operating a superconducting coil at low temperatures is less than the inconvenience of going to a laboratory that is equipped with appropriate power supplies and a high volume of cooling water that flows through special field solenoids.

The technology of high-field superconducting coils has come about as a consequence of two key developments: the helium cryostat and practical type II superconducting materials. A helium cryostat is a special low-temperature refrigerator that is capable of liquefying helium gas. The development of the helium cryostat in the mid-1950s made available liquid helium in commercial quantities. Since liquid helium boils at 4.2°K, a coil immersed in a Dewar flask of liquid helium will be held at the constant temperature of 4.2°K as the helium boils away. A type II superconductor is a type of superconductor that is relatively insensitive to magnetic fields.

For a superconductor there exists a critical temperature of transition between normal conductivity and superconductivity (Fig. 3.39). The

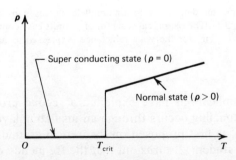

Figure 3.39 The resistivity of a superconductor drops abruptly to zero at a critical temperature. The T_{crit} decreases toward zero if the conductor carries current or is subjected to a magnetic field.

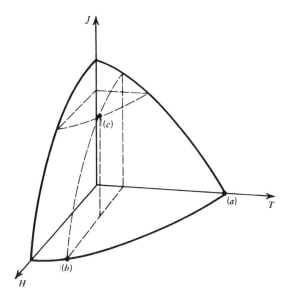

(a) $T_{crit} = 18.1°K$ at $H = 0$, $J = 0$.

(b) $H_{crit} = 221 \times 10^3$ Oe at $J = 0$, $T = 4.2°K$.

(c) $J_{crit} \geq 2 \times 10^5$ A/cm^2 at $H = 10^5$ Oe, $T = 4.2°K$.

Figure 3.40 The superconducting region is near the origin, inside the surface on the graph of J-H-T. Data values a, b, c are for the niobium-tin compound Nb$_3$Sn.

critical temperature decreases if the conductor carries current or if it is subjected to a magnetic field. An alternative representation shows the superconducting state as a region near the origin in J-H-T space (Fig. 3.40).

A variety of thin conductor geometries and fabrication techniques are used in coil design. The brittle superconductor niobium-tin is widely used, often in strands interspersed with copper strands for the purpose of maintaining good thermal contact. Conductor stress relief is said to be important to maintaining superconductivity, yet coil rigidity is vital if the coil is to withstand the enormous forces due to high currents in large fields.

It is noted that the electric power supply for such coils must supply current to a short circuit. Another interesting feature is the possibility of operating such coils in a persistent-current mode in which no externally supplied current is required to maintain the field for a substantial period of time.

EXAMPLE U

Find the force per centimeter of length acting on a strand of conductor of area 1 mm^2 that carries a current density of $J = 10^5$ A/cm^2 in a field $H = 10^5$ Oe.

ANSWER.   The incremental volume of 1 cm $\times$ 1 mm^2 = 0.01 cc. The force per volume is $\bar{F} = \bar{J} \times \bar{B}$, where $J = 10^9$ A/m^2, $B = 10$ T, hence $F = 10^{10}$ N/m^3 or 10^4 N/cc. Thus 100 N/cm = 22.4 lb/cm is the force acting on each strand of conductor.

3.4.3 Sputter-Ion Vacuum Pump

This section describes the principles of operation of a device that is useful in the low-pressure (high-vacuum) range: an electromagnetic vacuum pump with no moving mechanical parts. A sputter-ion pump is brought into operation after a so-called roughing pump has removed most of the gas from a closed volume. After a vacuum system has been opened to air, the pump-down procedure involves the sequential use of at least two types of pumps. The roughing pump reduces the pressure inside the system from 1 atm to the order of 10^{-5} atm* at which point there is brought into use a high-vacuum pump such as a sputter-ion pump. A sputter-ion pump may reduce the internal pressure by another factor of 10^{-5} to 10^{-12}, depending on a multiplicity of design details of the vacuum system. A vacuum pump must accomplish removal of gas molecules from the system. In the case of a sputter-ion pump the gas molecule is ionized, then attracted to a plate where it is retained in a stable form inside the system.

An ion pump (Fig. 3.41) consists of an array of electrodes located in a strong magnetic field. The anode structure is an array of hollow stainless steel cylinders with axes parallel to the magnetic field. A titanium cathode plate, maintained at ground potential, is located near each end of the anode array of cylinders. A gas molecule is ionized inside an anode cell by collision with a high-velocity electron (Fig. 3.42) in a process called a Penning discharge. Now positively charged because it has lost an electron, the ion is repelled by the positive anode voltage and impinges onto one of the cathode plates at high velocity. A variety of processes are available to retain the various types of gas molecules that

---

*One atmosphere (1 atm) of pressure is sufficient to support a column of mercury 760 mm high at 0°C; hence the designation of vacuum pressure in units of height. A pressure of 1 mm Hg is also called 1 torr.

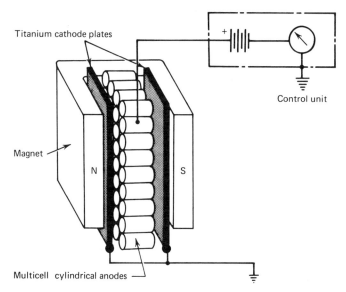

Titanium cathode plates

Control unit

Magnet

N   S

Multicell cylindrical anodes

Figure 3.41 Structure of a sputter-ion pump. In practice the magnet is located outside the vacuum system, separate from the electrode structure by a thin wall of stainless steel. (VacIon® Pump is a trademark of Varian Associates, Inc.; permission to reprint has been granted.)

exist in air. Hydrogen and helium are retained because they impinge to such a great depth. Oxygen and nitrogen can react chemically with titanium to form stable compounds. Heavy noble gas molecules are said to be buried by sputtered titanium.

The purpose of the magnetic field is to induce high-velocity electrons into a spiral or circular path. The complicated motion gives the electron

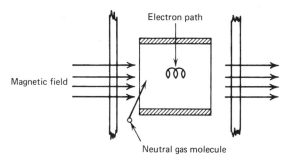

Electron path

Magnetic field

Neutral gas molecule

Figure 3.42 A typical cell of the sputter-ion pump. Electrons travel in a spiral path at high velocity, capable of ionizing neutral gas atoms by collision.

a long path length, hence a long lifetime at high velocity, thereby resulting in a higher probability of collision with a gas molecule to cause its ionization. The ionization process yields an electron as well as the positive ion. The ion is too heavy and slow to achieve a spiral path due to the magnetic field.

EXAMPLE V

Given an anode voltage of 5000 V, $B = 1000\,G$, and assuming that an electron possesses a circular path, find the particle's velocity, the radius of the circular path, and the frequency of path revolutions.

ANSWER. Assuming that the potential energy of the electron defines its kinetic energy, it follows that

$$E = qV = \Delta mc^2 \approx \frac{mv^2}{2}, \tag{3.93}$$

where the relativistic energy form Δmc^2 is required if v approaches the speed of light c. Using $q = 1.6 \times 10^{-19}\,C$, $m = 9.1 \times 10^{-31}$ kg, and $V = 5 \times 10^3$ yields $v = 2.96 \times 10^7$ m/s, thus the relativistic correction is unnecessary. The Lorentz force causes a circular orbit with Lorentz force equal to centripetal force as

$$|\bar{F}| = |q\bar{v} \times \bar{B}| = \frac{mv^2}{r}. \tag{3.94}$$

Solving for r yields the result for this case that

$$r = \frac{mv}{qB} = 1.69 \times 10^{-3}\,m. \tag{3.95}$$

A cell radius in the range of 1 cm is thus a practical size. The angular frequency $\omega = v/r$ yields $f = 2.8 \times 10^9$ Hz.

It can be conjectured that the high-vacuum pumping limitation of the sputter-ion pump is limited by the lifetime of the electron in its spiral path. If so, a strategy for extending the time duration of the electron orbit would result in an extension of the pumping range to lower pressures (i.e., less frequent gas molecules). I suppose that B is only nominally uniform and that a gradient dB/dx will cause a migration of the spiral path of the electron to move along the gradient until the electron collides with the anode cell wall. If these hypotheses are valid, the creation of a locally minimum field in each cell could confine the spiral path and thereby extend the lifetime of the electron.

PROBLEMS

1 **(Section 3.1.1).** Calculate the H-field in A/m, and plot a graph of the value of field versus distance along the axes of each of the two coils specified below. Each coil consists of one turn, which carries a current of 5 A. One coil is circular, of diameter 0.1 m; the other coil is a 0.1×0.1 m square. Plot the value for both coils on the same graph for comparison, over a distance range from zero to 0.1 m from each coil. Each axis passes through the center of the coil, perpendicular to the plane of the coil.

2 **(Section 3.1.1).** Calculate the value of a–c field between the conductors of a soldering gun, assuming the current path is a one-turn rectangle of 2×8 cm, with current $I_{rms} = 100$ A. Find the field at the center of the rectangle.

3 **(Section 3.1.1).** Derive expressions for each component of $\bar{H} = \hat{a}_x H_x + \hat{a}_y H_y + \hat{a}_z H_z$ in enough detail to permit each component to be calculated and plotted for the point $(x, 0, 0)$, where x varies over the range $0 \leq x \leq 0.3d$. The field is due to a $d \times d$ square coil that lies in the plane $z = 0$, centered on the z-axis with sides parallel to the x- and y-axes. Current I flows around the square in the general direction of the positive azimuthal angle ϕ.

Hint. The field contribution of each of the four sides can be found by using a variation of (3.2).

4 **(Section 3.1.1).** Work through the details of the derivation of (3.5), Example C. Make sketches to illustrate the geometry.

5 **(Section 3.1.1).** Calculate the field on the axis of a single-layer solenoidal coil, 20 cm long $\times$ 5 cm diameter. The coil is wound with 10 turns/cm and carries a current of 1 A.

a. Find the value of the field at $z = 0$, which is the center of the solenoid.

b. Find H_z in A/m at a general point z on the coil axis, and plot the value of H versus z over the range $z = 0$ to 15 cm.

6 **(Section 3.1.2).** Find the value of field H_ϕ in Example I at four points: $\phi = 0°$, 90°, 180°, and 270°, if radius $r = 5$ cm, parameter $s = 1$ cm, and $I = 1$ A. Use your results to put values on an approximate field profile of H_ϕ versus ϕ similar to Fig. 3.12b. What would you expect for the field profile due to 4 equally spaced turns?

7 **(Section 3.1.3).** Design a pair of Helmholtz coils, separated by 0.5 m, to generate a field of 100 Oe midway between the two coils.

a. Calculate the ampere·turns required for each coil.

b. Find the total weight of the two coils, assuming a current density of $155\,A/cm^2$ in copper conductors. The density of copper is 8.89 g/cc.

c. Choose a wire size such that the two coils in series can be supplied from about 30 V to give the desired field. Find the resistance and the dissipated power. It may be noted that volts per ampere·*turn* is ohms per *turn*, from which the wire size can be deduced.

8 **(Section 3.1.3).** Use (3.7) to find the field profile $H(z)$ along the axes of a pair of Helmholtz coils. What would the profile be if one coil were connected backward?

9 **(Section 3.2.1).** Suppose we have an ideal permanent magnet of $B_{is} = 1$ T, which is constant in value and directed parallel to the axis of a cylindrical magnet, diameter, 1 cm; length, 10 cm.

a. Use (3.36) and (3.37) to find model values for about 5 values of B and H along the axis, inside and outside the material. Make graphs using these 9 or 10 points.

b. If a solenoidal coil were wound to produce an H-field similar to the B above, how many ampere·turns would be required?

10 **(Section 3.2.3).** The cup-shaped magnetic circuit below is for a loud-speaker design, similar to Fig. 3.19. Assuming that Alnico 5 (for data see Example O or Table 3.2) is used for the magnet, and pole-piece reluctance and stray flux are neglected, work through the procedure for matching the magnet size to the airgap for optimum energy transfer into the gap. The dimensions in centimeters are $g = 0.1$, $D = 1.8$, $h = 0.5$, and $M = 1.5$.

a. Find the magnet length L so that the magnet will be operated at $(BH)_{max}$.

b. For the matched condition (a), find F, Φ, B, and H in the magnet and in the airgap. Either MKS or CGS units are acceptable.

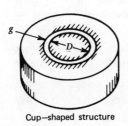

Cup–shaped structure

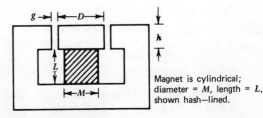

Cross section

Magnet is cylindrical; diameter = M, length = L, shown hash–lined.

11 (Section 3.2.3)

a. Do Problem 10 assuming that the permanent magnet is Alnico 8 instead of Alnico 5. Which type of magnet is better for this application?

b. Do problem 10 assuming that the dimensions for g, D, h, and M are all scaled 3 times larger.

c. What considerations will limit the power rating for such a loud-speaker? What will limit the low-frequency response?

12 (Section 3.2.4). Estimate the area of the cross-hatched region in Fig. 3.23, and compare the value with $(BH)_u$ for Alnico 5 in Table 3.2. How would you choose R_1 and R_2 for better agreement?

13 (Section 3.2.4). Figure 3.25 shows the principle of a permanent magnet circuit analog, which you are asked to make more specific. Define the parameters of a circuit model for an Alnico 5 magnet that will be reasonably valid for small values of airgap reluctance. Use the graphical data of Fig. 3.22 for a fully charged magnet. Devise both a Thévenin and a Norton model and explain the meaning of the circuit parameters.

14 (Section 3.2.5)

a. Find the value of $_BH_C$ for the material of Fig. 3.27.

b. Solve for B if $4\pi M = +4480\,\text{G}$ and $H = -7000\,\text{Oe}$. Give an example of how this combination can happen.

15 (Section 3.3.2). The paragraph at the top of page 131 briefly states a guideline to the reduction of leakage flux in magnetic circuits. Explain why the guideline minimizes the surface area that is held at a high magnetic potential.

16 (Section 3.3.3). Specify in centimeters the length of a precision airgap to be ground into a linear ferrite pot core, of a type as in Fig. 3.34. With no gap, the permeance of the core is $7.6\,\mu\text{H}/t^2$, corresponding to a magnetic path length of 4.5 cm, an effective core area of 1.38 cm², and an effective permeability of 2000. Find the gap that will result in a permeance of $1\,\mu\text{H}/t^2$.

17 (Section 3.3.3). A particular toroidal core has a cross-sectional area of 1 cm², extremely high permeability, and negligible H_0, rendering the path length irrelevent, and is made of magnetic material that saturates sharply at $B_s = \pm1\,\text{T}$. Assuming that the core is wound with 500 turns, we wish to make the core inductive by introducing an airgap. What length airgap corresponds to saturation at $I = 1.0\,\text{A}$? Find the inductance that results.

18 (Section 3.3.3). Suppose the square-loop core of Chapter 1,

Example C, is cut by a single small airgap of 0.2 mm (about 0.008 in.). Make an approximate graph of $\int v \, dt$ versus i for the modified core. What value of current is needed to saturate the core? Find the apparent value of inductance, in the piecewise-linear model, which is a consequence of the airgap. (The measured incremental inductance will be less than this amount and will vary with the amplitude of the a–c signal.)

19 (Section 3.3.3)

   a. Show that an effective permeability of a linear core with an airgap is $\mu_e = \mu_r l / (l + \mu_r g)$.

   b. Show that the saturation magnetic potential for an ideal linear core, given by $nI_s = n\Lambda_s/L$, is $B_s(l + \mu_r g)/\mu$.

   c. From the considerations above, show that the product $\mu_e \times nI_s$ is a figure of merit that is independent of the length of the airgap. Figure 6.26 gives an application of this concept.

20 (Section 3.4.3). The cyclotron frequency of an electron in a magnetic field, Example V, appears to have the same value as the Larmor frequency of precession of an electron spin. Review Section 2.1.5 and explain whether this is a coincidence or the values are fundamentally related.

REFERENCES

1. J. D. Jackson, *Classical Electrodynamics*, Wiley, New York, 1963. Section 5.5 gives the off-axis field of a circular loop of current, derived using the magnetic vector potential, and expressed in terms of elliptic integrals. This solution satisfies the criterion $\bar{\nabla} \cdot \bar{B} = 0$.

2. H. H. Kolm, "The Large-Scale Manipulation of Small Particles," *IEEE Trans. Magn.*, MAG-11, 1567 (1975). An introductory paper on the new field of high-gradient magnetic separation (HGMS). Other papers in the same issue address HGMS technical topics.

3. S. M. Rubens, *Rev. Sci. Instrum.*, 33, 243 (1945). Designed a cube coil for uniform fields, with 5 windings in the ratio 19:4:10:4:19.

4. Heinz Knoepfel, *Pulsed High Magnetic Fields*, North-Holland and American Elsevier, New York, 1970. A comprehensive treatment of the problems of the generation and application of transient magnetic fields, from the 10^3 to 10^7 Oe level, with a pulse duration typically less than 0.1 s. Includes extensive bibliography.

5. *Reference Data for Radio Engineers*, 6th ed., Howard W. Sams & Co., Indianapolis, Ind., 1975.

6. Report of the Coulomb's Law Committee, "The Teaching of Electricity and Magnetism at the College Level," *Amer. J. Phys.*, 18, (January 1950); 69–88 (February 1950). Equation 3.27 is adapted from (2-16b) of this paper.

7. A. Aharoni and E. Gunders, "Empirical Expression for the Axial Field of Cylindrical Bar Magnets," *IEEE Trans. Magn.* MAG-3, 587–589 (December 1967). Measurements are reported for five Alnico V magnets as a function of distance.

8. F. S. Lai and J. K. Watson, "A Sectioned Spheroid Model for Cylindrical Permanent Magnets", *IEEE Trans. Magn.* **MAG-16,** (March 1980). Sheds light on questions raised by Examples M and N, Section 3.2.1, page 101.

9. M. W. Garrett, "Axially Symmetric Systems for Generating and Measuring Magnetic Fields," *J. Appl. Phys.*, **22,** 1091 (1951).

10. W. Franzen, "Generation of Uniform Magnetic Fields by Means of Air-Core Coils," *Rev. Sci. Instrum.*, **33,** 933 (1962).

11. A. H. Firester, "Design of Square Helmholtz Coil Systems," *Rev. Sci. Instrum.*, **37,** 1264 (September 1966). Reports the Helmholtz spacing as $d = 0.5445$ for square coils and $d = 0.577$ for a pair of parallel wires. Computed contours of field deviation are given.

12. MIT Staff, *Magnetic Circuits and Transformers*, Wiley, New York, 1943. Chapter 3 includes example calculations of airgaps and fringing fields, Chap. 4 calculates permanent magnet circuits, including stabilization.

13. R. Bozorth, *Ferromagnetism*, Van Nostrand, New York, 1951, Chap. 9, "Materials for Permanent Magnets."

14. R. S. Tebble and D. J. Craik, *Magnetic Materials*, Wiley, New York, 1969, Chap. 12, "Permanent Magnet Materials."

15. J. J. Becker, F. E. Luborsky, and D. L. Martin, "Permanent Magnet Materials," *IEEE Trans. Magn.*, **MAG-4,** 84–99 (June 1968).

16. J. E. Gould, "Permanent Magnet Applications," *IEEE Trans. Magn.*, **MAG-5,** 812–821 (December 1969).

17. J. J. Becker, "Permanent Magnets Based on Materials with High Crystal Anisotropy," *IEEE Trans. Magn.*, **MAG-4,** 239–249 (September 1968).

18. M. McCaig, "Present and Future Technological Applications of Permanent Magnets," *IEEE Trans. Magn.*, **MAG-4,** 221–228 (September 1968).

19. H. C. Roters, *Electromagnetic Devices*, Wiley, New York, 1942. The classical reference for the design of a great variety of magnetic actuators. Includes procedures for permeance calculations.

20. R. J. Parker and R. J. Studders, *Permanent Magnets and Their Application*, Wiley, New York, 1962. The most comprehensive reference known to me on the general topic of applications of permanent magnets.

21. Superconductivity: general references include:

    (a) T. Van Duzer and C. W. Turner, "Superconductivity: New Roles for an Old Discovery," *IEEE Spectrum*, **9,** 53 (December 1972). A readable survey article.

    (b) Special Issue on Applications of Superconductivity: *Proc. IEEE*, January 1973.

    (c) *Physics Today*, July 1973, contains three papers on the Bardeen–Cooper–Schrieffer theory of superconductivity, the Nobel Prize acceptance speeches.

22. Z. J. J. Stekly and R. J. Thome, "Large Scale Applications of Superconducting Coils," *Proc. IEEE*, **61,** 85 (January 1973).

4.
Ferromagnetism and so forth

4.1   OVERVIEW

The design and use of magnetic devices often can be achieved with greater success if the designer possesses greater knowledge of the physics of magnetic materials. For instance, a designer must take the explicit design step of choosing the magnetic material for a given application. This chapter deals exclusively with the subject of material properties, seeking to summarize for the nonmagnetician some of the necessary background information.

First of all, the designer needs a background overview of the different kinds of magnetism, with emphases on ferromagnetic substances and on ferrites. Section 4.2 addresses that question, building on the notion advanced in Section 2.1 that the intrinsic induction of a material is the summation of its elemental, atomic magnetic moments.

The second topic of Chapter 4 is magnetic anisotropy, set forth in Section 4.3. Considerations of anisotropy determine, to a great extent, the general character of a $B-H$ curve—for instance, whether it is linear or square loop or something between. Furthermore, the coercivity of a square loop can be large or small depending on anisotropy and other factors. For a linear ferrite core, the anisotropy stiffness determines not only the material permeability but also the bandwidth over which the permeability is applicable.

4.2   KINDS OF MAGNETISM

Coupling between neighboring magnetic moments is an issue in three classes of magnetic material: paramagnets, ferromagnets, and antiferromagnets. No coupling exists for paramagnets; coupling causes opposite effects in the latter two. Our interest in paramagnetic materials lies in the theoretical basis they provide for the theory of the more important ferromagnetic substances. The coupling within antiferromagnets causes neighboring moments to be antiparallel. Ferrites possess a type of antiferromagnetic coupling in which the neighboring moments are opposite in their direction but are unequal in magnitude, so that a net moment exists. Therefore ferromagnets and ferrites are the materials of interest for applications.

4.2.1 Paramagnetism

Consider a system of particles of volume density N, uniformly distributed in space, each particle possessing a magnetic dipole moment j Wb·m. The moments act independently with negligible magnetic coupling from one to another. If a field H is applied, each moment will experience a vector torque $\bar{j} \times \bar{H}$, or in energy notation, each magnetized particle will be at a magnetostatic energy level of

$$E = -\bar{j} \cdot \bar{H} \qquad J \qquad (4.1)$$

that tends to align $\bar{j}$ parallel to $\bar{H}$. The preferred orientation of $\bar{j}$ parallel to $\bar{H}$ yields the minimum value of magnetostatic energy for the dipole.

Thus an applied H-field imposes a preferred orientation on each dipole of the system, however opposed by thermal fluctuations that cause a random orientation. If the magnetostatic energy jH greatly exceeds the thermal energy kT, the alignment will prevail to saturate the system at $J_s = Nj$. However if $jH/kT \ll 1$, the random orientation of dipoles will yield $J \approx 0$. Let us examine some energy and field values in order to understand the problem.

EXAMPLE A

Find the value of H required to establish $jH = kT$ at room temperature if $j = j_B$ (one Bohr magneton).

ANSWER. $H = 3.55 \times 10^8$ A/m, a value that is comparable to the largest field ever produced by man, $E \approx 4 \times 10^{-21}$ J/particle. This means that a paramagnet cannot be saturated at room temperature.

EXAMPLE B

Find the magnetostatic energy of two side-by-side dipoles $j = j_B$, separated by a distance of 2 Å units (1 Å = 10^{-10} m).

ANSWER.   The field of a point dipole is

$$\bar{H} = \frac{j}{4\pi\mu_0 R^3}(\hat{a}_r \cos \theta + \hat{a}_\theta \sin \theta), \qquad (4.2)$$

hence $E = \pm j^2/4\pi\mu_0 R^3 = \pm 1.07 \times 10^{-24}$ J, which equals kT at $T = 0.078°$K. These small values justify the neglect of magnetic dipole–dipole interactions in the paramagnetic system.

A single dipole of moment j oriented at angle θ to the applied field will have a projection onto H of $j \cos \theta$. The system of many randomly oriented dipoles will have an intrinsic flux density of effective value

$$J_{\text{eff}} = Nj\langle\cos \theta\rangle = Nj\mathcal{L}(a), \qquad (4.3)$$

where $\langle\cos \theta\rangle$ denotes the average of $\cos \theta$ over the ensemble of dipoles. The average cosine function, known as the Langevin function $\mathcal{L}(a)$ of variable

$$a = \frac{jH}{kT}, \qquad (4.4)$$

is named for the French scientist who devised it in the early 1900s. The derivation of the function follows a glance at its properties and an application.

Properties of the Langevin Function.   The Langevin function (Fig. 4.1) is defined as

$$\mathcal{L}(a) = \left[\coth a - \frac{1}{a}\right] = \left[\frac{e^a + e^{-a}}{e^a - e^{-a}} - \frac{1}{a}\right], \qquad (4.5)$$

which is approximately $\mathcal{L}(a) \approx [1 - 1/a]$ for large a.

The function increases from zero to unity as a increases and has an initial slope $d\mathcal{L}/da \approx \frac{1}{3}$ for small a, as we now show.

If e^a is written in the form of a series expansion, (4.5) becomes

$$\mathcal{L}(a) = \left[\frac{1 + a^2/2! + a^4/4! + \cdots}{a + a^3/3! + a^5/5! + \cdots} - \frac{1}{a}\right]. \qquad (4.6)$$

Now $1/a$ can be factored out, as

$$\mathcal{L}(a) = \frac{1}{a}\left[\frac{1 + a^2/2! + a^4/4! + \cdots}{1 + a^2/3! + a^4/5! + \cdots} - 1\right]. \qquad (4.7)$$

For $a \ll 1$, dropping the fourth-order terms and inverting the denominator, we have

$$\mathcal{L}(a) \approx \frac{1}{a}\left[1 + \frac{a^2}{2!} - \frac{a^2}{3!} + \cdots - 1\right] = \frac{a}{3}. \qquad (4.8)$$

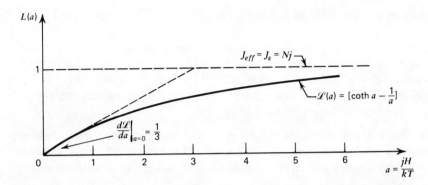

Figure 4.1 The Langevin function $\mathscr{L}(a)$ is a description of the classical statistics of a paramagnetic system of magnetic dipole moments j, whose alignment with applied field H is opposed by thermal fluctuation. The parameter $a = jH/kT$ is the ratio of magnetostatic energy to thermal energy per particle. The effective intrinsic flux density is proportional to $\mathscr{L}(a)$ as $J_{\text{eff}} = Nj\mathscr{L}(a)$.

The initial slope $d\mathscr{L}/da = \tfrac{1}{3}$ is now used in the derivation of the Curie law.

Paramagnetic Susceptibility: The Curie Law.   The parameter of interest is incremental magnetic susceptibility χ, which defines the dependence on H of intrinsic flux density J, as

$$\frac{dJ}{dH} = \mu_0\chi, \tag{4.9}$$

where $J = B - \mu_0 H$. Paramagnetic materials are modeled by (4.3) as $J = J_s\mathscr{L}(a)$, where $J_s = Nj$. Use of the chain rule $dJ/dH = (dJ/da)\cdot(da/dH)$, together with (4.8), leads to the final result

$$\chi = \frac{1}{\mu_0}\frac{J_s}{3}\frac{j}{kT} = \frac{J_s j}{3\mu_0 kT}. \tag{4.10}$$

An alternate form of this important result emphasizes the inverse dependence on temperature as in Fig. 4.2

$$\chi = \frac{C}{T}, \tag{4.11}$$

where Curie constant C is defined by the constants of the specific material using dipole moment j or area moment m

$$C = \frac{Nj^2}{3\mu_0 k} = \frac{\mu_0 Nm^2}{3k}. \tag{4.12}$$

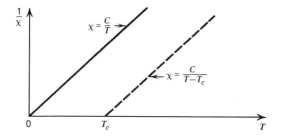

Figure 4.2 The Curie law for paramagnetic substances shows reciprocal susceptibility proportional to temperature. The dashed line is the Curie–Weiss equation for susceptibility of a ferromagnet above the Curie temperature, (4.18).

EXAMPLE C

To review the meaning of the physical constants in the equations above, substitute J_s and j from Section 2.1.3 to find the values for C and χ that would exist for iron at room temperature, if iron were paramagnetic. Since iron is ferromagnetic, of course we do not expect a paramagnetic model to be valid.

ANSWER. From (4.12) $C = 1.06$, hence at $T = 300°K$, $\chi = 0.0035$, which is lower by several orders of magnitude than measured values of χ for iron.

Derivation of the Langevin Function. Consider a system of magnetic dipoles of moment j, subjected to an external field H and thermal agitation. According to Boltzmann statistics, the probability is proportional to $e^{-E/kT}$ that j will be oriented within the incremental angle between θ and $(\theta + d\theta)$, where E is given by (4.1). Furthermore, the ensemble average of $\cos\theta$ is obtained from carrying out the integral

$$\langle \cos\theta \rangle = \frac{\int e^{-E/kT} \cos\theta \, d\Omega}{\int e^{-E/kT} \, d\Omega}, \qquad (4.13)$$

where solid angle $d\Omega = 2\pi \sin\theta \, d\theta$ as in Fig. 4.3. After substitution, we have

$$\langle \cos\theta \rangle = \frac{\int_0^\pi e^{jH(\cos\theta)/kT} \cos\theta \, 2\pi \sin\theta \, d\theta}{\int_0^\pi e^{jH(\cos\theta)/kT} 2\pi \sin\theta \, d\theta} \qquad (4.14)$$

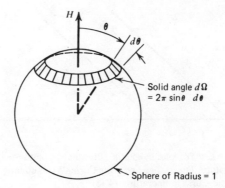

Figure 4.3 In a sphere of unit radius, the solid angle $d\Omega$ is the same as the incremental surface area $2\pi \sin \theta\, d\theta$. Integration of θ from zero to π includes the entire spherical surface.

It is convenient to change variables to let $a = jH/kT$, $x = \cos \theta$, which yields a simpler form that can be integrated by parts

$$\langle \cos \theta \rangle = \frac{\displaystyle\int_{-1}^{1} x e^{xa}\, dx}{\displaystyle\int_{-1}^{1} e^{xa}\, dx} = \frac{(1/a)[e^{xa}(x - 1/a)]_{-1}^{1}}{(1/a)[e^{xa}]_{-1}^{1}} = \left[\frac{e^a + e^{-a}}{e^a - e^{-a}} - \frac{1}{a}\right]. \qquad (4.15)$$

The Brillouin Function. A quantum mechanical derivation of $\langle \cos \theta \rangle$ yields the Brillouin function $B_J(\alpha)$, which has a shape somewhat similar to the Langevin function but provides a better fit to experimental data (Fig. 4.4). Since the quantum mechanical treatment is beyond the scope of this book, the reader may refer to a modern book on the physics of the solid state.

4.2.2 Ferromagnetism

How substances could be magnetic at room temperature was one of the early mysteries of magnetism. According to paramagnetic theory, an enormous field should be required to magnetize, yet certain metals could retain a magnetized state even with no field applied. Nowadays ferromagnetism is attributed to a coupling between neighboring magnetic spins, explained by Heisenberg's exchange model. But the explanation given by Pierre Weiss in 1907 has a certain intuitive appeal.

The Weiss Molecular Field Model. Weiss suggested that the total field acting on each elementary dipole included not only the applied field, but also a second component of field proportional to the average mag-

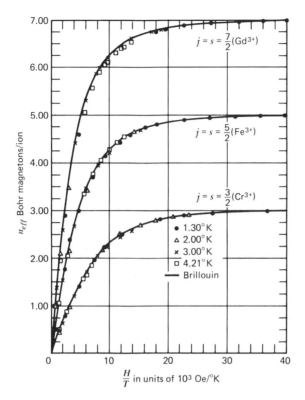

Figure 4.4 Measured data for paramagnetic salts agree very well with Brillouin function $B_J(\alpha)$. [From W. E. Henry, *Phys. Rev.*, **88**, 559 (1952), reprinted with permission.]

netization of the substance, as

$$H_{\text{total}} = H_{\text{applied}} + WM, \qquad (4.16)$$

where W is the Weiss constant of proportionality and M is magnetization. If (4.16) is now combined with the basic paramagnetic relation $M = \chi H$, the result is

$$M = \chi(H_a + WM)). \qquad (4.17)$$

After collecting M, the response to the applied field is the Curie–Weiss equation for a ferromagnet

$$\frac{M}{H_a} = \frac{\chi}{1 - \chi W} = \frac{C}{T - T_c}. \qquad (4.18)$$

The right-most expression uses (4.11) to define Curie temperature $T_c =$

WC, a measure of the strength of the ferromagnetic interaction between dipoles. Strictly interpreted, (4.18) gives the paramagnetic susceptibility of a ferromagnet in the temperature range $T > T_c$, where the material is no longer ferromagnetic (see Fig. 4.2).

We now model the more important region $T < T_c$, where the material is ferromagnetic. As shown by the signal-flow graph of Fig. 4.5, the Weiss model represents a type of positive feedback within the magnetic material. If the analogy is valid of an electronic circuit with d–c positive feedback, such as an analog operational amplifier or a digital flip-flop, we would expect a nonlinear relationship of M/H_a generally characterized by $M = \pm M_s$. Indeed the analogy appears to have qualitative merit.

A second form of the Weiss model of ferromagnetism uses a graphical representation as in Fig. 4.6. Similar to (4.3) we use the Langevin model as one equation for $M = M_s \mathscr{L}(a)$, where parameter a is defined by the Weiss model of (4.16) as

$$a = \frac{j(H_a + WM)}{kT}. \tag{4.19}$$

The straight lines represent the condition of spontaneous magnetization such that M is proportional to a if $H_a = 0$, namely,

$$M = \frac{kT}{Wj} a. \tag{4.20}$$

The simultaneous solution of the two equations for M can occur for $T < T_c$, as at points 1 and 2 to yield the value of M_s at T_1 and at T_2. This means that the value of saturation magnetization M_s is actually a

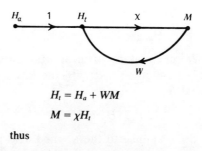

$$H_t = H_a + WM$$

$$M = \chi H_t$$

thus

$$\frac{M}{H_a} = \frac{\chi}{1 - \chi W} = \frac{C}{T - T_c}$$

Figure 4.5   A signal-flow graph of the Curie–Weiss equations illustrates the positive feedback aspect of ferromagnetism.

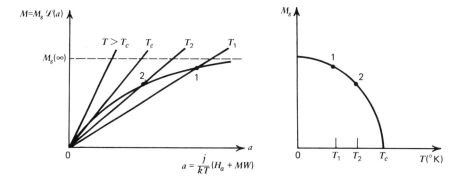

Figure 4.6   Graphical construction to deduce the temperature dependence of the saturation magnetization M_s of a ferromagnetic material in the ferromagnetic temperature range $T < T_c$. The construction in the left-hand graph finds the simultaneous solution of two equations, with results for M_s presented in the right-hand graph.

function of temperature, decreasing monotonically from a maximum at $T = 0$ to $M_s = 0$ at $T = T_c$. It follows that the apparent value of magnetic moment per atom varies in the same manner. The upper temperature limits for ferromagnetic materials were first studied by Pierre Curie in the 1880s. Values of T_c for the pure elements iron, cobalt, and nickel have been found experimentally to be 1043°K, 1388°K, and 631°K, respectively. The Curie temperatures for many alloys of these elements are listed in the literature.

4.2.3   Ferromagnetism and Antiferromagnetism

The theory of antiferromagnetism is the starting point for the study of modern magnetic materials of the ferrite families. These materials have been evolving tremendously since around 1950 to make possible an enormous variety of new applications such as high-frequency transformers, memory cores, magnetic tapes, microwave magnetics, and magnetic bubble memories.

A qualitative first description of antiferromagnetism involves, like ferromagnetism, strong coupling between neighboring magnetic moments. However the direction of interaction is such that the neighboring moments are antiparallel. As a consequence of changing the sign of W in Fig. 4.5, the effective susceptibility is

$$\chi_{\text{eff}} = \frac{\chi}{1 + \chi W} = \frac{C}{T - T_A}, \tag{4.21}$$

where T_A is an asymptotic temperature limit less than zero Kelvin. This equation is applicable only in the high-temperature region.

The Heisenberg Model. For the entire class of solid elements, antiferromagnetism is much more prevalent than ferromagnetism. In 1928 Werner Heisenberg published a theory to explain both phenomena, based on exchange coupling between neighboring spins. The following classical interpretation treats quantum spin operators as classical vectors. The reader will recall that spin is fundamentally related to magnetic moment.

Consider spins $\bar{S}_1$ and $\bar{S}_2$ associated with electrons on two adjacent atoms, where the exchange energy is given by the dot product

$$E_{ex} = -2X\bar{S}_1 \cdot \bar{S}_2 = -2XS^2 \cos\theta, \tag{4.22}$$

where X is a material parameter called the exchange integral.* If X has a positive value, the minimum energy configuration is the ferromagnetic configuration of S_1 parallel to S_2. However if X is negative, the minimum energy configuration is antiferromagnetic with S_1 antiparallel to S_2.

It should be mentioned that the net spin of an atom is attributed to an unfilled inner shell of electrons, the unfilled 3-d shell in the case of iron, cobalt, and nickel. Qualitatively, the polarity of the exchange integral X depends critically on the overlap of orbitals of neighboring atoms. This concept is illustrated by the Bethe curve (Fig. 4.7). Only a few elements meet the special requirements that give rise to ferromagnetism.

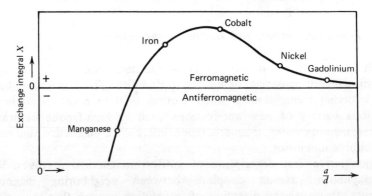

Figure 4.7 Bethe-Slater curve illustrating the change of polarity of exchange integral X with a/d. Diameter d is the unfilled orbital and a is the lattice parameter for the material.

*Although the usual symbol for exchange integral is J, X is used here to avoid confusion with intrinsic induction.

It may be tempting to ascribe the coupling between magnetic moments to classical dipole–dipole interaction, (4.2), since the orbitals of neighboring atoms are in close proximity to one another. However the coupling of the spins is not due to magnetic dipole forces but is a consequence of the Pauli exclusion principle. Orbital electrons are exchanged between host atoms only if they satisfy a set of requirements that includes spin orientation. This effect is called the exchange interaction.

Magnetic Metal Oxides. Certain metal oxide single crystals consist of alternate layers of metal atoms and oxygen atoms in which both polarities of magnetic coupling are important. For instance, in manganese oxide (MnO) all the manganese ions in one layer possess the same orientation of magnetic moment, just opposite to the orientation of the moments in each of the adjacent planes of manganese ions. Within each plane the coupling is ferromagnetic, whereas from one plane to the next the coupling is antiferromagnetic through the intervening layer of oxygen ions.*

These interactions can be shown by a signal-flow graph similar to Fig. 4.5, presented in Fig. 4.8 for the case of two magnetic lattices with coupling between. Figure 4.9 represents an antiferromagnet because of

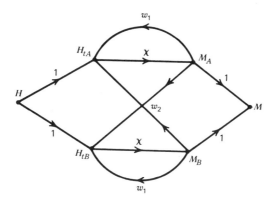

Figure 4.8 A signal-flow graph model for an antiferromagnetic material of two sublattices. Within each lattice the intralattice Weiss constant is ferromagnetic with value w_1. Between the lattices the interlattice field constant is antiferromagnetic with value $-w_2$. See Fig. 4.9 for further clarification.

*Since the antiferromagnetic coupling between manganese ions is developed through an interposed ion, the coupling is said to occur by a "superexchange" process, a detail that need not concern us here.

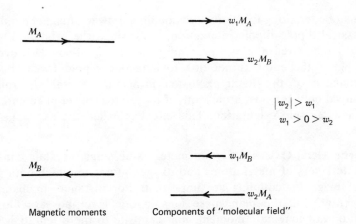

Figure 4.9 Magnetic moments M_A and M_B are equal and opposite because of the strong antiferromagnetic component of molecular field.

the symmetry. That is, the total magnetization is zero because M_A and M_B are equal and opposite at low temperatures. A flow diagram for a ferrite is similar except the total magnetization is nonzero because the symmetry conditions are removed.

For Fig. 4.8 the equations for M_A and M_B are

$$M_A = \chi H_{tA} = \chi[H + w_1 M_A + w_2 M_B], \tag{4.23a}$$

$$M_B = \chi H_{tB} = \chi[H + w_1 M_B + w_2 M_A], \tag{4.23b}$$

where each $\chi = C/2T$ and $C = \mu_0 N m^2/3k$ for the magnetic ions. Equations 4.23 can be decoupled, to yield, for example,

$$M_B = H\left\{\frac{2T/C - w_1 + w_2}{(2T/C - w_1)^2 - w_2^2}\right\}. \tag{4.24}$$

For M_B to exist spontaneously, the denominator must be zero, thereby identifying two critical temperatures

$$T_A = \left(\frac{w_1 + w_2}{2}\right)C \quad \text{and} \quad T_N = \left(\frac{w_1 - w_2}{2}\right)C. \tag{4.25}$$

The asymptotic temperature T_A has a negative value, since

$$|w_2| > |w_1| \quad \text{and} \quad w_1 > 0 > w_2, \tag{4.26}$$

whereas Néel temperature T_N is positive for the same reason. The Néel temperature is the temperature above which the material is paramagnetic.

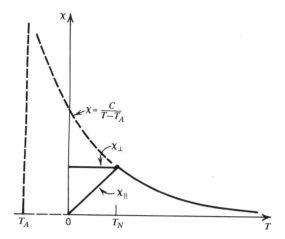

Figure 4.10   Susceptibility of an antiferromagnet versus temperature, obeying a paramagnetic equation above the Néel temperature T_N. At T_N $\chi = -1/w_2$, which is a maximum value. See Fig. 4.11 for discussion of susceptibility below T_N.

At temperatures above the Néel temperature the susceptibility of an antiferromagnet obeys a paramagnetic equation, with negative asymptotic temperature T_A (Fig. 4.10). In this temperature range the orientation of the component moments is in thermal disorder. At the Néel temperature T_N, the susceptibility

$$\chi_{\text{eff}}(T_N) = -\frac{1}{w_2} \qquad (4.27)$$

is predicted by substitution of (4.25) into (4.21). For single-crystal antiferromagnets, below the Néel temperature the susceptibility is no longer isotropic (Figs. 4.10 and 4.11). The susceptibility of polycrystalline materials lies between $\chi_{\|}$ and $\chi_{\perp}$.

(*b*) Parallel susceptibility, $\chi_{\|}$.

Figure 4.11   Below the Néel temperature the crystalline order defines a directional dependence of χ. The vector cross-product $\vec{J} \times \vec{H}$ is large for H perpendicular to the two components of magnetization. For H parallel, χ tends toward zero as thermal agitation decreases for the component magnetic moments.

4.2.4 Ferrites

Ferrimagnetism is a more complicated type of antiferromagnetism in which the two magnetic sublattices are opposite but unequal. As a result of the inequality, the magnetization $M = |M_A - M_B|$ has a net value (Fig. 4.12).

In the temperature range below their Curie temperatures, ferrites are similar to ferromagnets in possessing a spontaneous magnetization. Figure 4.12 also shows that the two components M_A and M_B possess the same Curie temperature, a property that is attributed to antiferromagnetic coupling between the two magnetic subsystems. If M_A and M_B are nearly equal in value, and furthermore if the two lattices vary quite differently with temperature, the net magnetization may possess one of the peculiarities shown in Fig. 4.12b. For instance, the net magnetization may go through zero at a compensation temperature where $|M_A| \equiv |-M_B|$. Alternatively, the net magnetization may possess a positive temperature coefficient over a substantial range of temperature. The two special cases, first predicted theoretically by Néel in 1948, have been validated experimentally. Ferrites of each type have been developed for specific applications.

The basic ferrite chemistry is a double metal oxide such as $MOFe_2O_3$, where M is a divalent metal such as manganese or zinc. The natural ferrite magnetite ($FeOFe_2O_3$) has been known since ancient times. By changing the composition of a basic antiferromagnet, it is possible to upset the equality $M_A = M_B$ by substituting different metal ions into either the A or B lattice sites. For instance, the substitution of metal ions that prefer the B site will cause M_B to be decreased if the added ions possess fewer Bohr magnetons per atom than the displaced ion. The

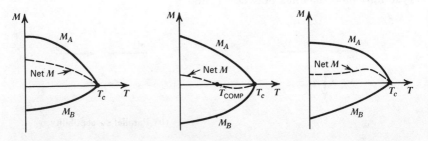

(a) Typical ferrimagnet.   (b) Ferrimagnets with special temperature properties.

Figure 4.12 Ferrimagnets possess a net magnetization below the Curie temperature, given by the difference of magnetization of two magnetic subsystems M_A, M_B.

expected result is an unbalanced moment as in Fig. 4.12. The reader will
recall that an electron possesses one Bohr magneton of magnetic
moment because of its spin. It follows that ions can possess magnetic
moments in integral multiples of one Bohr magneton, the value depending on the atom structure of the ions. For a more detailed treatment of
this fascinating topic, the interested reader can refer elsewhere to
Hund's rules and to the physical chemistry of ferrites.

The crystallographic definition of the A and B lattice sites (Fig. 4.13)
presumes a basic framework of oxygen ions, curiously enough, with
metal ions in the voids between. The oxygen ions of a ferrite structure
are not only more numerous than metal ions, but are also larger by about
a factor of 2 than the light metal ions near iron in the periodic table.
Oxygen has a radius of about 1.3 Å as compared with 0.6 to 0.8 Å for the
metal ions. A key discovery in the physical chemistry of ferrites is that
substitute metal ions have a preference for one site A or B, over the
other. One of several preferential factors is said to be the larger size of
octahedral sites as compared to tetrahedral.

A great deal of experimental evidence and supporting theory have
been accumulated in the development of microwave ferrites, as well as
the subsequent development of magnetic garnets for bubble memories.
One of the spectacular achievements of modern magnetism is the
technology that to a large extent permits materials to be tailored to
individual application requirements.

The research literature of ferrimagnetic materials draws on the language of crystallography. Spinels, inverse spinels, garnets, corundum-
type oxides, magnetoplumbite structures, perovskite-type structures,
and others have been studied with various magnetic elements. The
elementary model of antiparallel A and B lattice sites is generalized to
include additional crystallographic sites and moment orientations that
are canted from antiparallel [3]. These brief comments are intended to
support the observation that commercial ferrites are well established

A tetrahedral (A) site is the small
void surrounded by four oxygen
ions.

An octahedral (B) site is the void
surrounded by six oxygen atoms.

Figure 4.13 Two sites for metal ions in a ferrimagnet.

scientifically and technologically. We may realistically expect a continuing increase in the range and variety of commercial ferrite products in
the years ahead.

Susceptibility versus Temperature. Our major interest in ferrites lies in
the range of temperature below the Curie temperature. In this low-
temperature range the material possesses a net spontaneous moment
similar to ferromagnets, as shown in Fig. 4.12. The net saturation
magnetization is described as so many Bohr magnetons *per formula unit*,
or *per unit cell* rather than *per atom* as in the case of ferromagnetic
metals.

Above the Curie temperature, thermal energy of agitation exceeds the
coupling energy of alignment as described earlier for ferromagnets.
However in the high-temperature region the susceptibility has a temperature dependence different from that of any material we have considered before (Fig. 4.14*a*). Reciprocal susceptibility of a ferrimagnet
possesses a zero at the Curie temperature, like a ferromagnet, but
asymptotically resembles antiferromagnetic behavior at higher temperatures. As a curiosity we note that an extra kink can occur in the
susceptibility curve if the antiferromagnetic Néel temperature is higher
than the Curie temperature (Fig. 4.14*b*). Between the two temperatures
the material is antiferromagentic.

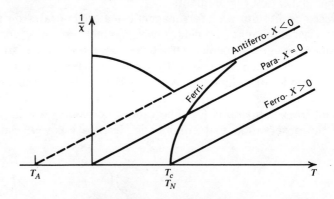

Curie constant C is equal in all cases.
X is the exchange integral; see (4.22).

(*a*) Comparison of susceptibility for four classes of magnetic materials under the
assumption of equal Curie constant. Ferrimagnetic susceptibility approaches antiferromagnetic behavior at high temperature.

Figure 4.14

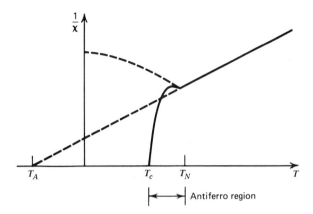

(b) If the Néel temperature of a ferrite exceeds the Curie temperature, the material will have a region of antiferromagnetism.

Figure 4.14 Reciprocal susceptibility of ferrites versus temperature. [After Smit and Wijn, [3], p. 44, with permission.]

4.3 MAGNETIC ANISOTROPY

If the physical properties of a material are independent of the direction of measurement, the material is said to be *isotropic*, which means the same regardless of orientation. The prefix "an-" indicates negation; hence an anisotropic material possesses properties that vary significantly with the orientation of the material sample. Magnetic anisotropy refers to a specific property, a tendency for alignment of the magnetization to be along a preferred direction under quiescent conditions. Two general classes of anisotropy are discussed subsequently: one type that is a property of single crystals and a second type that can be induced by heat or mechanical treatment.

Magnetic anisotropy is analogous to a mechanical spring in the sense that M can be turned from the preferred orientation by applying an external field but will return when the external field is removed. The strength of the magnetic anisotropy can be measured if the shape of the sample possesses rotational symmetry—for instance, as a thin circular disk. This geometry avoids confusion of magnetic anisotropy with shape anisotropy of the specimen. One technique for measuring the strength of magnetic anisotropy is by use of a torque magnetometer (Fig. 4.15). This type of magnetometer is intended to measure the strength of the torque that causes the quiescent alignment of magnetization M to be along a preferred direction, furthermore it is intended to measure the angular

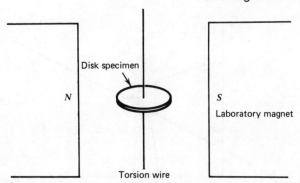

Figure 4.15 Elementary torque magnetometer. The strong field of the laboratory magnet holds the magnetization of the specimen in alignment. A torque is required to rotate the easy axis of the disk away from the alignment of *M*. See Fig. 4.16*a*.

dependence of the torque. The principle of operation is as follows. A large external field is applied to the specimen, strong enough to hold *M* in a fixed orientation. Then the specimen is rotated around its axis of symmetry, permitting the torque to be measured as a function of the angle of rotation of the specimen.

EXAMPLE D

Consider a sample with a single preferred direction or easy axis. It has been shown that uniaxial anisotropy energy per volume *W* is well modeled by the equation

$$W = K \sin^2 \theta \qquad J/m^3, \tag{4.28}$$

where *K* is the anisotropy constant and θ is the angle between *M* and the easy axis (Fig. 4.16*a*). The torque required to rotate *M* away from the easy axis is

$$L = \frac{dW}{d\theta} = 2K \sin \theta \cos \theta = K \sin 2\theta \qquad N \cdot m/m^3. \tag{4.29}$$

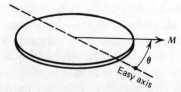

(*a*) The uniaxial disk is magnetized in the plane, at an angle θ from the easy axis.

Figure 4.16

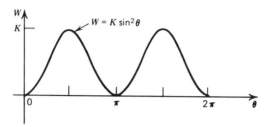

(*b*) Energy versus angle for a uniaxial specimen with $W = K \sin^2 \theta$. Minima at $\theta = 0, \pi$ indicate the easy axis. Units of W are Joules/m^3.

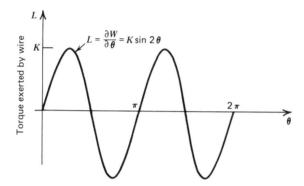

(*c*) Torque versus angle for a uniaxial specimen. A negative value indicates the torque from the specimen tends to increase θ. Units of L are N · m/m^3.

Figure 4.16 Illustration of energy density W and torque density L for a specimen with uniaxial anisotropy.

It is to be noted that the normalized equations (4.28) and (4.29) are to be multiplied by the volume of the specimen to give the actual anisotropy energy and measured torque. Figure 4.16 shows the variation of W and L with angle θ. The maximum anisotropy energy occurs at $\theta = 90°$, at which angle the restoring torque changes sign.

4.3.1 Magnetocrystalline Anisotropy

One of the important material parameters for describing a single magnetic crystal is its anisotropy. Magnetocrystalline anisotropy typically possesses a high magnitude of the anisotropy constant K and an angular dependence that is characteristic of the particular crystal structure. The physical cause of magnetocrystalline anisotropy is attributed to spin-orbital coupling. Qualitatively, it is reasonable that magnetic moments due to spin and those due to orbital motion might influence one another. It is also reasonable that the orientation of orbital modes should be fixed very strongly by the location of neighboring atoms. Thus it follows as no great surprise that principal crystallographic directions often turn out to be either easy axes or hard axes of the magnetic system. For instance, both iron and nickel have cubic structures, body-centered cubic for iron and face-centered cubic for nickel. The easy axes of single crystal iron lie along the cube edges ([100]-axis), whereas the easy axes of nickel are along the major diagonals of the basic cube [(111)-axis), as indicated in Fig. 4.17a. On the other hand, cobalt has a hexagonal close-packed crystal with a single easy axis normal to the basal plane (i.e., the c-axis).

The easy axis of cobalt along the hexagonal axis represents an anisotropy energy minimum. The additional energy required to rotate the magnetization to an angle θ from the easy axis is given by

$$W = K_1 \sin^2 \theta + K_2 \sin^4 \theta \qquad \text{J/m}^3 \qquad (4.30)$$

on the assumption of isotropy in the azimuthal direction. For some hexagonal materials the hexagonal axis is the hard direction, and (4.30) must be modified to include 6ϕ azimuthal dependence.

The basic mathematical model for anisotropy energy of cubic crystals is usually given in the form of a polynomial series expansion in direction cosines

$$W = K_1(\alpha_1^2\alpha_2^2 + \alpha_1^2\alpha_3^2 + \alpha_2^2\alpha_3^2) + K_2(\alpha_1^2\alpha_2^2\alpha_3^2) \qquad \text{J/m}^3. \qquad (4.31)$$

Anisotropy constants K_1, K_2 are characteristic constants of the material

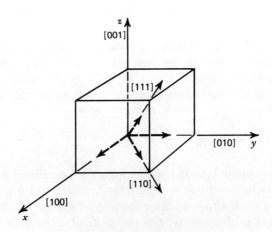

(a) Indices of cubic crystal directions.

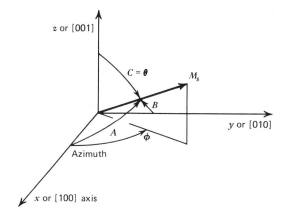

Comparison of direction cosines and polar coordinates:

$$\alpha_1 = \sin \theta \cos \phi$$
$$\alpha_2 = \sin \theta \sin \phi$$
$$\alpha_3 = \cos \theta$$

(b) α_1, α_2, α_3 are the cosines of angles A, B, C between M_s and the axes of the cube.

Figure 4.17 Indices of cubic crystal direction, and the direction cosine notation for the direction of magnetization relative to the crystal direction.

with units of energy density (i.e., J/m³). The values can be determined from a series of torque magnetometer measurements of disk specimens that have been carefully cut with different orientations from single crystals. The format of (4.31) and the even power of the α's are required by conditions of cubic symmetry. The direction cosines α define the angles between M_s and the cube edges (Fig. 4.17b). The relation between the direction cosines and the ϕ, θ notation of spherical coordinates, also given in Fig. 4.17b, leads to the relation

$$\alpha_1^2 + \alpha_2^2 + \alpha_3^2 = 1. \tag{4.32}$$

EXAMPLE E

Using (4.31), find the direction cosines and the anisotropy energy for the following cases of M_s alignment: along the [100] axis; along the [110] axis; along the [111] axis.

ANSWER. $\alpha_1 = 1$, $\alpha_2 = \alpha_3 = 0$, hence $W = 0$; $\alpha_1 = \alpha_2 = 1/\sqrt{2}$, $\alpha_3 = 0$, hence $W = K_1/4$; $\alpha_1 = \alpha_2 = \alpha_3 = 1/\sqrt{3}$, hence $W = K_1/3 + K_2/27$.

The adaptation of (4.31) to represent iron is straightforward because the [100] orientation for computed zero energy is the same as the easy axis of iron. The easy axis corresponds to an energy minimum. However the easy axis of nickel is along the [111] axis, which therefore requires that K_1 be negative for nickel (Table 4.1).

EXAMPLE F

Rewrite (4.31) in the notation of azimuthal angle ϕ for the case of a thin disk specimen from a single crystal with disk surfaces parallel to the x–y plane (Fig. 4.17).

ANSWER. Assuming that M will lie in the x–y plane, angle $C = \theta = 90°$, hence $\alpha_3 = 0$. Thus (4.31) becomes $W = K_1 \alpha_1^2 \alpha_2^2 = K_1 \sin^2 \phi \cos^2 \phi = (K_1/4) \sin^2 2\phi$, which is a biaxial anisotropy with minima at 90° intervals.

Table 4.1 Anisotropy constants at room temperature in units of 10^4 J/m^3 (10^5 erg/cc).

Material	K_1	K_2
Iron	4.8	± 0.5
Nickel	-0.45	0.23
Cobalt	47 ± 6	10
Manganese-bismuth	89	—
Barium ferrite	3.3	—

(Data adapted from Bozorth [2] and Tebble and Craik [4]).

4.3.2 Induced Anisotropy

It is probably fair to say that most magnetic materials in commercial applications are not single crystal, but rather are polycrystalline. At least one would be safe in assuming that a material is polycrystalline unless rather special circumstances indicate otherwise. Although the typical random orientation for the myriads of microscopic crystallites effectively cancels the crystalline anisotropy, an induced anisotropy can still be significant.

Anisotropy can be induced by mechanical treatment such as cold-rolling to give a grain orientation. Alternatively, annealing by heat treatment and cooling of a specimen in a field environment can induce a preferred axis of magnetization. The identification of the internal mechanisms that cause the anisotropy is usually a research activity. When the dependencies are understood and the inducing procedures are controlled, the resulting anisotropy can often be held constant within reasonable tolerance.

For instance, thin magnetic films of nickel-iron alloy have been widely investigated for the purpose of developing digital memory systems. Annealing procedures yield reproducible uniaxial anisotropy with values of K of the order 100–200 J/m³; this is a small value, of the order of 1% of magnetocrystalline values.

4.3.3 Effect of Anisotropy on Magnetization Curve

The following calculation of magnetization curves for a thin magnetic film will illustrate a striking result of uniaxial anisotropy. The magnetization curve is linear in the hard direction but has a square-loop property in the easy direction (Fig. 4.18). The method of calculation uses energy minimization, a widely used procedure that we shall need again in other applications.

Consider a uniaxial specimen in the shape of a very thin disk with the easy axis defined as the x-axis (Fig. 4.19). The sample is assumed to be a single domain, which requires that the thickness be 10^{-5} diameter or less to ensure that the demagnetizing field will not be excessive. This geometry is consistent with permalloy of saturation induction $J_{sat} \sim 1$ T and anisotropy $K = 100$ J/m³. The single-domain assumption permits the specimen to be modeled with only two energy terms, magnetostatic and anisotropy.

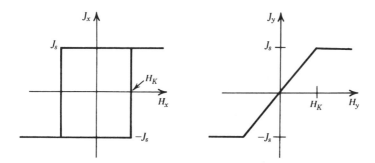

(a) Easy-axis characteristic.   (b) Hard-axis characteristic.

Figure 4.18 Magnetization curves for an ideal thin magnetic film.

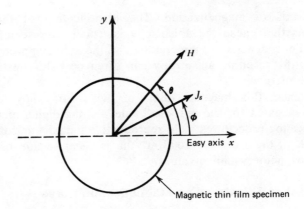

Figure 4.19   Geometry for calculation of magnetization curves.

Suppose a field H is applied at angle θ as in Fig. 4.19, which causes the magnetization to rotate from the easy axis to an intermediate angle ϕ. The magnetostatic energy density

$$W_m = -\bar{J}_s \cdot \bar{H} = -J_s H \cos(\theta - \phi) \qquad \text{J/m}^3 \qquad (4.33)$$

would be a minimum if J_s were aligned with the applied H. However the energy of uniaxial anisotropy

$$W_K = K \sin^2 \phi \qquad \text{J/m}^3 \qquad (4.34)$$

would be minimum if J_s remained along the x-axis. The sum of the two energies W_t will be minimum for some intermediate angle ϕ, to be determined for the conditions

$$\frac{\partial W_t}{\partial \phi} = 0 \qquad \text{and} \qquad \partial^2 W_t / \partial \phi^2 \geq 0. \qquad (4.35)$$

Noting that

$$\cos(\theta - \phi) = \cos \theta \cos \phi + \sin \theta \sin \phi \qquad (4.36)$$

and the projections of H along the axes are

$$\begin{aligned} H_x &= H \cos \theta \\ H_y &= H \sin \theta, \end{aligned} \qquad (4.37)$$

the total energy is the sum of (4.33) and (4.34) as

$$W_t = -J_s(H_x \cos \phi + H_y \sin \phi) + K \sin^2 \phi. \qquad (4.38)$$

The first and second derivatives are

$$\frac{\partial W_t}{\partial \phi} = -J_s(-H_x \sin \phi + H_y \cos \phi) + 2K \sin \phi \cos \phi \qquad (4.39)$$

$$\frac{\partial^2 W_t}{\partial \phi^2} = J_s(H_x \cos\phi + H_y \sin\phi) + 2K \cos 2\phi. \qquad (4.40)$$

For simplicity, the hard-axis and easy-axis responses are considered separately.

If the field is applied in the hard direction, $H = H_y$, $H_x = 0$, and $\theta = 90°$. Equation 4.39 then satisfies (4.35) at

$$J_s H_y \cos\phi = 2K \sin\phi \cos\phi. \qquad (4.41)$$

If $\cos\phi \neq 0$, the angle of the magnetization is defined by

$$\sin\phi = \frac{H_y}{H_K}, \qquad (4.42)$$

where anisotropy field H_K is defined by

$$H_K = \frac{2K}{J_s} \quad \text{A/m}. \qquad (4.43)$$

Equation 4.42 is the result of interest, since the hard-axis component of J is linearly dependent on H_y as shown in Fig. 4.18b

$$J_y = J_s \sin\phi = \frac{J_s H_y}{H_K}. \qquad (4.44)$$

It is to be noted that saturation of J occurs for $H_y \geq H_K$, for which $\sin\phi = 1$ as can be shown from applying condition (4.35) to (4.40).

Now if the field is applied along the easy axis, $H_x = \pm H$, $H_y = 0$, and $\theta = 0°$ or $180°$. If we again try to use (4.39) we find that

$$\frac{\partial W_t}{\partial \phi} = 0 = H_x \sin\phi + H_K \sin\phi \cos\phi, \qquad (4.45)$$

which is inconclusive because $\sin\phi = 0$ in each term. However use of (4.40), with condition (4.35) yields

$$H_x \cos\phi + H_K \cos 2\phi \geq 0, \qquad (4.46)$$

which leads to two conditions.

If $\phi = 0°$, the energy is minimum for

$$H_x \geq -H_K, \qquad (4.47a)$$

which is the condition for $J_x = +J_s$ in Fig. 4.18a.

If $\phi = 180°$, the energy is minimum for

$$H_x \leq H_K, \qquad (4.47b)$$

which is the condition for $J_x = -J_s$ in Fig. 4.18a. If an inequality (4.47) is not satisfied, the magnetization is presumed to switch polarity to satisfy the alternative inequality.

The foregoing hard-axis and easy-axis responses are special cases of a more general case of a field applied in an arbitrary direction. Chapter 8 gives the more general case, with the result described by a switching astroid.

4.3.4 Effect of Anisotropy on Bandwidth

The preceding section has shown the remarkable result that the curve of intrinsic induction J versus H for a uniaxial specimen can be either square loop or linear, depending on the orientation of the specimen. This section concerns only the linear response. Since the slope $dJ/dH = \mu_0\chi$ varies inversely as the anisotropy field H_K, it follows that rotational permeability can be defined from the anisotropy constants of the magnetic material. The bandwidth of ferrites also varies with anisotropy in such a way that the bandwidth·susceptibility product is a constant. The product relationship was first explained by Snoek in 1948.

Anisotropy Field, H_K. The derivation of the hard-axis magnetization curve for uniaxial thin magnetic film led to a definition of H_K that we now can extend. In the earlier definition H_K was represented as a critical value of applied field, just sufficient to cause saturation of the material in the hard direction. The anisotropy field was defined as

$$H_K = \frac{2K}{J_s},\qquad(4.43)$$

where K is the anisotropy constant and J_s is intrinsic induction.

When the hard-axis field is less than H_K, the hard-axis component of intrinsic induction is found to be linearly proportional to applied field

$$J_y = \frac{J_s}{H_k} H_y,\qquad(4.44)$$

thus defining relative permeability for such a material from

$$\frac{dJ}{dH} = \mu_0\chi = \mu_0(\mu_r - 1) = \frac{J_s}{H_K}.\qquad(4.48)$$

A material that possesses a large anisotropy constant requires a high applied field for its intrinsic induction to be rotated to saturation. Such a material is said to have a low value of permeability, specified by (4.48). The permeability is called "rotational" because of the mechanism of the change of $\bar{J}$.

An alternative definition of H_K is useful for crystals with more complicated forms of anisotropy. For perturbations $d\theta$ around an equilibrium orientation for J, H_K is defined as

$$H_K = (1/J_s)\frac{d^2 W_K}{d\theta^2}, \qquad (4.49)$$

which is to be evaluated for the minimum energy condition $dW_K/d\theta = 0$.

Although the derivations of the following relations are beyond our scope of interest, Smit and Wijn [3] have noted that for a cubic crystal the anisotropy stiffness is isotropic for perturbations about the [100] axis and the [111] axis of equilibrium, with values of H_K given by

$$H_K[100] = \frac{2K_1}{J_s} \quad \text{and} \quad H_K[111] = -\frac{\frac{4}{3}K_1 + \frac{4}{9}K_2}{J_s}. \qquad (4.50)$$

For other equilibrium orientations the stiffness may be anisotropic, with different value of H_K rotation in the ϕ- and θ-directions. Various other relationships have been worked out for hexagonal crystals, poly-crystalline materials, and materials that are subject to stresses.

Snoek's Limit. Experimental studies of the initial permeability of linear ferrites have shown that high permeability materials have a much lower range of frequency than low-permeability materials (Fig. 4.20). It can be seen that the bandwidth hardly exceeds 100 kHz if $\mu_r = 3500$, yet for a specimen of nickel ferrite with $\mu_r \approx 12$ the bandwidth is some 200 MHz. The bandwidth limit for the set of curves of Fig. 4.20 is matched reasonably well by the empirical formula

$$\mu_r f \approx 3 \times 10^9 \, \text{Hz}. \qquad (4.51)$$

The theoretical curve that runs diagonally in Fig. 4.20 does not fit as well as (4.51) but is derived below. Similar frequency dependence is shown by commercial ferrites in Fig. 4.21.

Derivation of the $\chi\omega$ Product. The bandwidth term of Snoek's limit is an extension of the Larmor precession described in Section 2.1.5. A system of magnetic spins in free space was found to precess about an applied field at an angular frequency $\omega = \gamma H$, where γ is the magnetomechanical ratio. In a ferrite material of anisotropy constant H_K the frequency is increased by an increment

$$\omega = \gamma H_K \quad \text{rad}/s, \qquad (4.52)$$

as though the applied field were increased by H_K.

Although the susceptibility of a linear ferrite is more complicated, a qualitative approximation is obtained from the rotational susceptibility

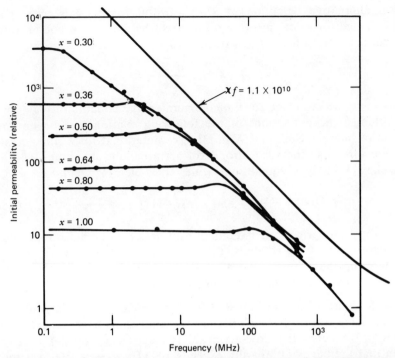

Figure 4.20 Frequency dependence of the real part of the initial permeability of poly-crystalline specimens of nickel-zinc ferrite. The chemical composition is denoted by the value of parameter x in the formula $Ni_x Zn_{1-x} Fe_2 O_4$. The theoretical curve is given by (4.54). (Adapted from Smit and Wijn, [3], p. 269, with permission.)

(4.48) as

$$\chi = \mu_r - 1 = \frac{J_s}{\mu_0 H_K} = \frac{M_s}{H_K}. \tag{4.53}$$

Multiplying (4.52) by (4.53) yields the desired approximation of Snoek's limit*

$$\chi\omega = \omega(\mu_r - 1) = \gamma M_s. \tag{4.54}$$

EXAMPLE G

As an exercise in units, use (4.54) to find the value of χf in hertz for Fig. 4.20. Assume $J_s = 0.4\,\text{T}$ is constant, independent of various H_K.

ANSWER.   From Chapter 2, $\gamma = 2.21 \times 10^5\,\text{(rads/s)/(A/m)}$ so $\gamma J_s/\mu_0 = 7 \times 10^{10}\,\text{rads/sec}$ or $\chi f = 1.12 \times 10^{10}\,\text{Hz}$. The latter value is plotted in Fig. 4.20.

*Snoek's original result was multiplied by the factor $\frac{2}{3}$, as $\chi\omega = \frac{2}{3}\gamma M_s$, to account for the statistics of anisotropy in polycrystalline hexagonal ferrites.

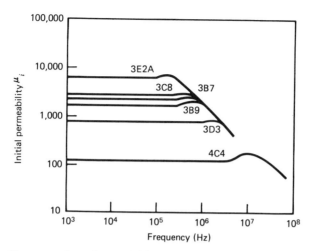

Figure 4.21 Frequency dependence of initial permeability for a family of commercial linear ferrites. The saturation magnetization is in the range of $J_s \simeq 0.37 \pm 0.05$ for this collection of materials. (Material furnished courtesy of Ferroxcube Division of Amperex Corporation, Saugerties, New York.)

4.4 SUMMARY

This chapter introduced two basic properties of magnetic materials, kinds of magnetism and anisotropy. It has been assumed that the applied fields are uniform over the specimen, and that the specimen is uniformly magnetized. In essence this means that we have begun to address one of the processes by which the magnetization of a specimen is changed, the process of rotation of M_s due to a field applied in a hard direction. Since we have so far omitted the important process of domain wall motion, we have not touched on its contribution to average permeability.

PROBLEMS

1 (Section 4.2.1). Let us pretend that the H-field of Example A is caused by current flow on a long wire of infinitesimal dimensions, located one atomic distance (~ 0.25 nm) away. What value of current is needed to cause the value of H of the example?

2 (Section 4.2.1). Find Curie constant C and classical paramagnetic susceptibility χ at room temperature for a fictitious paramagnetic material that is identical to nickel with regard to density, magnetic

moment per atom, and atoms per cubic meter. (The atomic weight of nickel is 58.7; see Table 2.2 for other information.)

3   **(Section 4.2.2).** The flow graph of Fig. 4.5 suggests that the Weiss model represents magnetic positive feedback, which qualitatively accounts for ferromagnetic behavior below the Curie temperature. As an exercise in positive feedback, make a graph of v_0 versus v_{in} for the following operational amplifier circuit. The maximum $|v_0| \approx |V_s| = 10$ V. How is this relevant to ferromagnetism?

$$a = 10^4 \text{ for } |v_0| < 10v$$

$$\frac{R_2}{R_1 + R_2} = 0.05$$

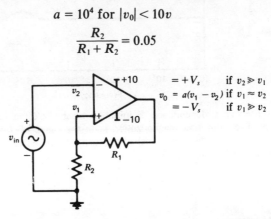

$$
\begin{aligned}
&= +V_s && \text{if } v_2 \gg v_1 \\
v_0 &= a(v_1 - v_2) && \text{if } v_1 \approx v_2 \\
&= -V_s && \text{if } v_1 \gg v_2
\end{aligned}
$$

4   **(Section 4.2.2).** Calculate the value of Weiss molecular field constant W for iron, and for nickel.

5   **(Section 4.2.3).** Find the relative values of exchange integral X in (4.22) for iron, cobalt, and nickel in comparison with Fig. 4.7. For this purpose we may assume that the magnitude of exchange energy between a typical pair of atoms is proportional to Curie temperature, as $|E_{ex}| \approx kT_c$.

6   **(Section 4.2.3)**

   a. Find the values of Weiss constants w_1 and w_2, then find the maximum susceptibility for a fictitious antiferromagnet with $C = 3$, asymptotic temperature $T_A = -400°K$ and Néel temperature $T_N = 100°K$.

   b. What is a plausible value for Curie constant C for an antiferromagnet? Work out a number for MnO, recognizing that the ion Mn^{2+} has a moment of 5 Bohr magnetons. Note that the molecular weight of MnO is 70.94 and the density is about 5.4 g/cc.

7   **(Section 4.2.3).** Derive (4.21) by adding together the two parts of (4.23) and solving for M/H.

8 (**Section 4.2.3**). Equations 4.18 and 4.21 describe the susceptibility of ferromagnets and antiferromagnets in the high-temperature range where both kinds of materials act as paramagnets. For this range, compare each susceptibility with that of a classical paramagnet as described by the Curie law, assuming equal Curie constants for each material. Show that $\chi_F > \chi_P > \chi_A$ in general. In particular, let $C = 1$, $T_c = 200°K$, $T_A = -100°K$ and $T = 300°K$.

9 (**Section 4.2.4**). Look up the following references. Read them and describe what each is about on one page or less.

    a. Snelling [5]. b. Cullity [6].

10 (**Section 4.3.1**). Suppose you have two single-crystal spheres, one of nickel and one of iron. How many easy axes will each sphere possess? What will be the angles between the easy axes?

11 (**Section 4.3.1**). A thin disk specimen (1 mm height × 1 cm diameter) of iron is cut from a single crystal with the disk surfaces parallel to the [100] axes (the $x - y$ plane). Predict the value of torque versus angle for this specimen in a torque magnetometer (Fig. 4.15).

12 (**Section 4.3.1**). Rewrite the cubic anisotropy equation (4.31) in the notation of polar angle θ for the case of a thin disk specimen cut from a single crystal with disk surfaces parallel to the plane that includes the [110] and [111] axes.

13 (**Section 4.3.3**). A small sinusoidal a–c magnetic field, much smaller than coercivity H_c or anisotropy field H_k, is applied to a magnetic thin film in a direction parallel to the plane of the film. It is known that the magnetic state of the film is a single domain, that the saturation induction of the material is $J_s = 1$ T, and that the film has uniaxial anisotropy along an unknown axis.

    a. Assuming the film can be rotated in its own plane while monitoring the response (in the same direction as the applied field), how can you determine the easy axis of the film?

    b. If H_k is found to be 400 A/m, find anisotropy constant K and the relative permeability (for the rotational model of reversal).

    c. If a d–c field of 2 Oe is applied to the film along the hard axis, find the quiescent angle ϕ of J_s relative to the easy axis.

14 (**Section 4.3.4**). Specify a commercial ferrite core material, and list its permeability and approximate bandwidth to meet the minimum requirements below. You may refer to Fig. 4.21 or to data from other ferrite manufacturers.

    a. The permeability in the audio range should be as high as possible.

    b. The bandwidth of the material should be as great as possible.

REFERENCES

1. S. Chikazumi, *Physics of Magnetism*, Wiley, New York, 1964.
2. R. M. Bozorth, *Ferromagnetism*, Van Nostrand, New York, 1951.
3. J. Smit and H. P. J. Wijn, *Ferrites*, Wiley, New York, 1959.
4. R. S. Tebble and D. J. Craik, *Magnetic Materials*, Wiley-Interscience, New York, 1969.
5. E. C. Snelling, "Ferrites for Linear Applications," *IEEE Spectrum*, **9**, No. 1, 42–51 (January 1972).
6. B. D. Cullity, *Introduction to Magnetic Materials*, Addison-Wesley, Reading, Mass., 1972. Chapter 6 is a brief (22 pages) but readable and authoritative introduction to the physics of ferrites and ferrimagnetism.

5.
Losses Due to Changing Induction

This chapter is a collection of topics, that are all related to reversal processes and to dynamic losses in magnetic cores. The designer of power transformers is interested in reducing losses because of a desire for a high-efficiency product. Furthermore, the wattage loss in the core and windings will cause a temperature rise that must not become excessive. The designer of inductors is interested in low losses when in need of a high-Q inductor. How losses are related to the basic physical processes of magnetic flux reversal is a fascinating topic of general interest.

The chapter begins by reviewing the piecewise-linear model for the terminal characteristic of a magnetic core device, Section 5.1. The present emphasis is on the dynamic width component of the model, not previously treated, and on the power loss in the core. Section 5.1 shows how magnetic core losses affect the terminal properties of the core model, and the rest of the chapter addresses material properties and reversal processes. A high-frequency limitation for conducting cores arises because of eddy current losses. Section 5.2 treats eddy currents in an elementary approach from basic principles. The notation of complex permeability, Section 5.3, is the format for core loss data as presented by ferrite manufacturers. Section 5.4 concludes the chapter with models for two general processes of magnetic reversal—rotation and wall motion.

5.1 TERMINAL PROPERTIES OF MAGNETIC DEVICES

5.1.1 Piecewise-Linear Model

Chapter 1 presented a piecewise-linear model for magnetic materials

$$H = H_0 \left(\text{sgn} \frac{dB}{dt} \right) + \frac{B}{\mu} + g_e \frac{dB}{dt} \qquad |B| < B_{\text{sat}} \qquad (1.10)$$

based on approximations to the $B-H$ loop as regards its static width H_0, slope parameter μ, and dynamic width that was tentatively defined as

$$H_{dy} = g_e \frac{dB}{dt}. \qquad (5.1)$$

It would be convenient if g_e were a well-defined constant for a given core material. Loss coefficient g_e, with MKS units of m/Ω, does vary with core material conductivity and lamination thickness but evidently also varies with the mode of flux reversal, and perhaps with core geometry. The use of a single loss parameter g_e leads to a more unified view of dynamic magnetic processes, but the imperfection of the parameter should be recognized at the outset. When core area S, path length l, and the number of turns n are taken into account, (1.10) is converted to a current equation of the form

$$i = I_0(\text{sgn } v) + \frac{1}{L} \int v \, dt + G_e v \qquad |\Phi| < \Phi_s, \qquad (1.13)$$

where conductance* $G_e = g_e l/n^2 S$. The corresponding electric circuit appears in Fig. 5.1.

If a sinusoidal voltage is applied to the circuit model of Fig. 5.1

$$v = V_m \cos \omega t \qquad (5.2)$$

---

*This equation is not a standard formula for conductance, first of all because loss coefficient g_e is not a standard conductivity (reciprocal of resistivity in $\Omega \cdot$m) but is instead reciprocal of resistivity per area. Furthermore the relationship between magnetic and electric quantities is not direct but is one of duality. That is, magnetic potential is proportional to electric current rather than to electric potential. See Section 6.4.1 for the use of duality in modeling magnetic circuits, and the paper by Cherry [1] for a further discussion of modeling of losses.

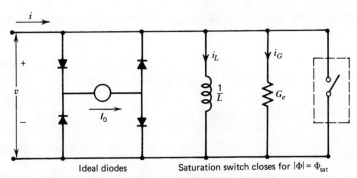

Figure 5.1 Electric circuit for (1.13), a piecewise-linear model for a magnetic core. In an application, other components will be in series and/or parallel with the core model.

the steady-state current equation (1.13) becomes

$$i = I_0(\text{sgn} \cos \omega t) + \frac{V_m}{\omega L} \sin \omega t + G_e V_m \cos \omega t \qquad (5.3)$$

with waveforms as in Fig. 5.2, to emphasize the phase relations among

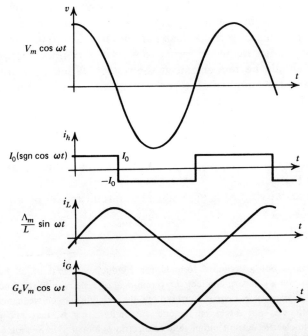

Figure 5.2 Three components of core current in phase relation to $v(t)$. The inductive component of current is out of phase with the voltage, thus represents reactive power.

the components of current. The instantaneous power vi is the product of (5.2) and (5.3),

$$vi = V_m I_0 |\cos \omega t| + \frac{V_m^2}{\omega L} \sin \omega t \cos \omega t + G_e V_m^2 \cos^2 \omega t, \qquad (5.4)$$

where only the first and third terms possess average values and thus represent dissipated power. In the analysis that follows two integral formats interest us particularly: the energy per cycle

$$E = \int_{\substack{\text{one} \\ \text{cycle}}} vi \, dt \qquad \text{J/cycle} \qquad (5.5)$$

and E divided by time per cycle $= Ef$, which is the average power dissipated in the core.

Hysteresis Loss in Square-Loop Cores. If we carry out (5.5) on the first term of (5.4), we have

$$E_h = 4 V_m I_0 \int_{\omega t = 0}^{\pi/2} \cos \omega t \, dt = \frac{4 V_m I_0}{\omega}, \qquad (5.6)$$

which is the energy required to drive the square-loop component of the core through one cycle of reversal. It is customary to express losses on a normalized basis to avoid treating every device as a completely special case. From the definition of flux linkage in (2.30) it follows that

$$\Lambda(t) = \frac{V_m}{\omega} \sin \omega t = \Lambda_m \sin \omega t. \qquad (5.7)$$

Hence (5.6) becomes

$$E_h = 4\Lambda_m I_0 \approx 4 B_m H_0 S l \qquad \text{J/cycle}, \qquad (5.8)$$

which is the hash-lined area of Fig. 5.3. We note that $\Lambda = nBS$ and that $I_0 = H_0 l/n$. Multiplication of (5.8) by frequency, and division by the volume of the core Sl, give the hysteresis component of power loss as

$$p_h = P_h / V = 4 B_m H_0 f \qquad \text{W/m}^3 \qquad (5.9)$$

for an ideal square-loop core, the result of interest.

Dynamic Core Losses. From (5.9), the equation for hysteresis loss, we can quickly see that if the hysteresis loop gets wider in proportion to frequency, there will result a component of loss proportional to frequency squared. Such is the essence of (5.1) in the sinusoidal steady

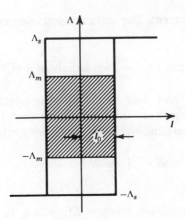

Figure 5.3 The hash-lined area $4\Lambda_m I_0$ is the energy required per cycle of reversal, a component of core loss.

state, where

$$\frac{d}{dt} B_m \sin \omega t = \omega B_m \cos \omega t. \tag{5.10}$$

Going back to carry out (5.5) on the third term of (5.4) yields a result that can be written as

$$E_e = V_m^2 G_e \frac{\pi}{\omega} = \frac{\frac{1}{2} V_m^2 G_e}{f} = \Lambda_m^2 G_e \pi \omega \qquad \text{J/cycle} \tag{5.11}$$

or as an eddy current power density

$$p_e = \frac{P_e}{V} = \frac{1}{2} B_m^2 g_e \omega^2 = 2\pi^2 B_m^2 g_e f^2 \qquad \text{W/m}^3, \tag{5.12}$$

after making substitutions into (5.11), multiplying by f, and dividing by Sl. Equation 5.12 is the result we were after, but we need an equation or a value for loss parameter g_e. Section 5.1.4 deduces an empirical value and Section 5.2.2 gives an equation. The equations above are intended for modeling metal core devices. Ferrite cores are better modeled by complex permeability (Section 5.3).

Quality Factor Q. A common figure- of- merit for inductors is the quality factor Q, which can be defined as the ratio of reactive power to dissipative power

$$Q = \frac{\frac{1}{2} V_m^2 / \omega L}{4\Lambda_m I_0 f + \frac{1}{2} V_m^2 G_e}. \tag{5.13}$$

For high-Q inductors the denominator must be small. Typically a core of zero coercivity is chosen so that $I_0 = 0$ in (5.13). For that case the Q increases to

$$Q = \frac{1}{G_e \omega L} = 1/g_e \omega \mu \qquad (5.14)$$

or the familiar formula $Q = R/\omega L$. For a core that possesses coercivity it is sometimes convenient to define a fictitious conductance $G' = 4I_0/\pi V_m$, which is power-equivalent to the coercive power loss $4\Lambda_m I_0 f = (2/\pi)V_m I_0$. Equation 5.13 can be put into the same form as (5.14) by replacing G_e as follows:

$$G_e + G' = \frac{l}{n^2 S}\left(ge + \frac{4H_0}{\pi B_m}\right). \qquad (5.15)$$

At the time of writing there exists no systematic listing of core loss parameters g_e to use in the equations above to predict Q for a coil to be wound on a conducting core. Conversely, the same equations may help provide a systematic interpretation of measured values of Q on existing inductors that are wound on conducting cores. For high-frequency applications ferrites are usually the preferred core material; see Section 5.3.1.

5.1.2 Empirical Fit to Core Loss Data

Tape-wound square-loop core. Let us now examine the plausible expression for the total core loss obtained by adding (5.9) and (5.12)

$$p_t = \frac{P_t}{V} = 2\pi^2 B_m^2 g_e f^2 + 4B_m H_0 f \qquad \text{W/m}^3. \qquad (5.16)$$

I used catalog values for H_0 in (5.16), in comparison with general core loss data for square-loop cores* to try to deduce values for g_e, but the accuracy was poor. After rewriting (5.16) as

$$p_t = 2B_m f(\pi^2 g_e B_m f + 2H_0) = 2Bf(aBf + b), \qquad (5.17)$$

a second strategy was tried. Equation 5.17 models power density as a function of the single variable $(B_{max}f)$, with two parameters a, b that can be adjusted for best fit to experimental power data. Figure 5.4 shows a typical result of comparing catalog data against (5.17). In deciding the

---

*Data for core loss in the United States usually is given in units of watts per pound: 1 W/lb is the same power density as 2.2 W/kg = 2.2 mW/g. For core material of density 8.2 g/cc, 1 W/lb may also be expressed as 18.04 mW/cc = 18.04 kW/m³.

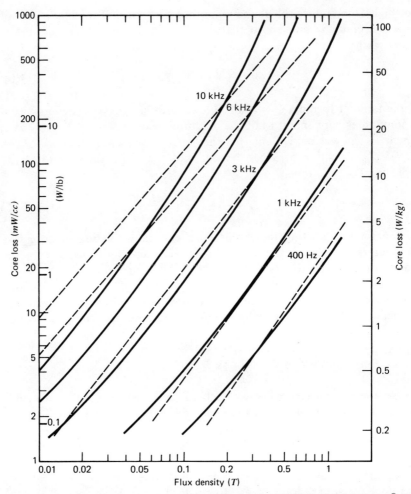

Figure 5.4 Comparison of core loss catalog data (dashed curves) for 2-mil Orthonol® with empirical calculation (5.17) using $\pi^2 g_e = 0.025$ and $2H_0 = 18$ A/m (solid curves). (Catalog data presented with permission of Magnetics, Butler, Pennsylvania.)

values $a = 0.025$, $b = 18$ the following procedure was convenient. First, tabulate separate values for f, B that give constant measured p_t; second, determine the best fit of the fB product for that p_t; third, divide $p_t/2fB$ to get one equation with unknowns a, b. The procedure should be repeated for several values of p_t to get several equations in a, b, which then are solved for best fit to a, b.

Depending on the ratio b/a, p_t can vary with (Bf) almost linearly, or with nearly a square-law dependence. In the example above, the hysteresis and eddy current losses were equal at $Bf \approx 700$, at $p_t \approx$ 50 mW/cc.

The empirical values $H_0 = 9$ A/m, $g_e = 2.5 \times 10^{-3}$ may be compared with catalog coercivity $H_c \approx 12$ A/m and a theoretical $g_e = \sigma d^2/8 = 0.7 \times 10^{-3}$ derived for a square-wave reversal mode in Section 5.2.2. I believe that the empirical values are plausible.

Silicon Iron Losses. Around 1900 during the development of commercial magnetic materials for transformers, the addition of a few percent of silicon was found to improve the performance of iron. The particular benefits were an increase in permeability, a decrease in core loss (Fig. 5.5), and the elimination of aging problems. The hysteresis properties of one important commercial material, Fe–Si 3.75% with trade name U.S.S. Transformer 72–29 gauge,* are plotted in Fig. 5.6. Clearly the hysteresis loop of this material is far from an ideal rectangle. The coercivity does not remain constant, but increases almost in proportion to B_m. Amazingly, the area of each hysteresis loop can be approximated within 10% accuracy by the equation

$$e_h \approx 4 H_c B_m \qquad \text{J/m}^3\text{·cycle} \qquad (5.18)$$

as tabulated in Fig. 5.6.

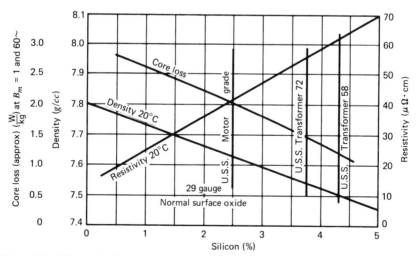

Figure 5.5 Effect of silicon on electrical steel sheets. (From Attwood [2], p. 345, with permission.)

*Number 72 means the core loss is guaranteed not to exceed 0.72 W/lb at $B_m = 1$ T, 60 Hz; 29 gauge is a lamination thickness of 14 mils (0.014 in.).

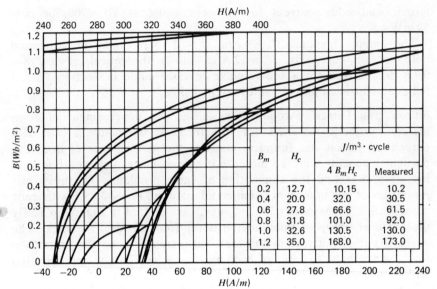

Figure 5.6 Hysteresis loop for U.S.S. Transformer 72–29 gauge. (From Attwood [2], p. 340, with permission.)

A standard procedure for calculating core losses for such materials uses the following empirical equation for core loss, the sum of hysteresis plus eddy current losses

$$p_t = \eta B_m^x f + \epsilon d^2 B_m^2 f^2 \qquad \text{W/m}^3 \tag{5.19}$$

or the corresponding energy density per cycle

$$e_t = \frac{p_t}{f} = \eta B_m^x + \epsilon d^2 B_m^2 f \qquad \text{J/m}^3 \cdot \text{cycle.} \tag{5.20}$$

Hysteresis parameter η and exponent x are determined from very low-frequency data as in Fig. 5.6. On a graph (not shown) of $\log B_m$ versus $\log e_t$, η is the intercept at $B_m = 1$ T ($\eta = 130$) and x is the slope ($x = 1.58$).

The second term of (5.20) represents eddy current losses as proportional to the square of the lamination thickness d. The unknown coefficient ϵ is determined from measurements of core loss* versus frequency.

---

*The standard test fixture for measuring core loss of laminated sheets is an Epstein frame, devised in 1900. Strips of the specimen to be tested are stacked in a closed-path array shaped like a rectangular picture frame. Each leg of the frame is enclosed by a coil by which excitation can be supplied to the core as input power is measured.

The present model is equivalent to (5.12) with the empirical parameters proportional to each other

$$2\pi^2 g_e = \epsilon d^2. \tag{5.21}$$

Attwood [2] gives the experimental value of $\epsilon = 0.747 \times 10^7$ for U.S.S. Transformer 72-29 gauge. His theoretical value is $\epsilon = 0.22 \times 10^7$ using the equation

$$\epsilon = \frac{\pi^2 \sigma}{8}, \tag{5.22}$$

which he derived using a continuum model of the type described in Section 5.2.1. The empirical value of ϵ is translated by (5.21) into loss coefficient $g_e = 0.04785$. The theoretical value of g_e is 0.02822, by (5.49) of Section 5.2.2, which is a domain type of model.

EXAMPLE A

Find eddy current coefficient ϵ for U.S.S. Transformer sheet 72–29 gauge, and find the core loss in W/kg at $B_m = 1$ T, $f = 60$ Hz given the following information: $\eta = 130$, $e_t = 187$ J/m^3·cycle at $f = 60$, $B_m = 1$ T.

ANSWER.   Substitution into (5.20) gives $187 = 130 + \epsilon(14 \times 25.4 \times 10^{-6})^2 \times 1 \times 60$, which yields $\epsilon = 0.75 \times 10^7$. $p_t = 187 \times 60$ W/m^3, using density = 7.54 g/cc from Fig. 5.5 gives $p_t = 1.49$ W/kg = 0.68 W/lb.

The main purposes of this treatment were to introduce (5.19), to demonstrate its use, and finally to relate ϵ to g_e. More detailed treatments are available from several other sources. Perhaps the most thorough combination of engineering magnetics and classical field theory known to me is given by Attwood [2]. Bozorth [13] gives a comprehensive historical review of the metallurgical developments.

5.2   EDDY CURRENT LOSSES

According to Maxwell's equations, a time variation of flux density is necessarily accompanied by a curl of electric field

$$\nabla \times \bar{E} = -\frac{\partial \bar{B}}{dt}. \tag{5.23}$$

The integral form of the same equation states that a voltage drop must exist around any path that surrounds a time variation in flux. If the path lies inside a magnetic core in which the flux is changing, the voltage will induce a current if the core happens to be a conductor. The current, called an eddy current, has several important consequences in magnetic design.

Eddy currents tend to flow around the surface of the core, in the manner of a sheet current solenoid, and in a direction to oppose the flux change. That is, the H-field of the eddy current is opposite to the applied field, thereby shielding the interior of the core from the applied field.

5.2.1 Magnetic Diffusion Equation

Derivation of Skin Depth. The two curl equations of Maxwell can be combined by taking the curl of (5.24) then inserting (5.23), as follows.

$$\nabla \times \bar{H} = \bar{J} + \frac{\partial \bar{D}}{\partial t}. \tag{5.24}$$

Taking the curl of each side, we write

$$\nabla \times (\nabla \times \bar{H}) = \nabla \times \bar{J} + \nabla \times \frac{\partial \bar{D}}{\partial t}. \tag{5.25}$$

But $\bar{J} = \sigma \bar{E}$ and $\bar{D} = \epsilon \bar{E}$, so if σ and ϵ are uniform as in a homogeneous material, the right-hand side of (5.25) becomes

$$\sigma(\nabla \times \bar{E}) + \epsilon \frac{\partial}{\partial t}(\bar{\nabla} \times \bar{E}) = -\sigma \frac{\partial \bar{B}}{\partial t} - \epsilon \frac{\partial^2 B}{\partial t^2}$$

$$= -\left[\mu\sigma \frac{\partial \bar{H}}{\partial t} + \mu\epsilon \frac{\partial^2 H}{\partial t^2}\right], \tag{5.26}$$

also using the continuum model approximation that $B = \mu H$.

The left-hand side of (5.25) by a vector identify is

$$\nabla \times (\nabla \times \bar{H}) = \nabla(\nabla \cdot \bar{H}) - \nabla^2 \bar{H}, \tag{5.27}$$

where the first term is the negative gradient of pole distributions as noted in Chapter 3. Neglect of $\nabla \cdot \bar{H}$ in combining (5.26) and (5.27) yields the following intermediate result

$$\nabla^2 \bar{H} = \mu\sigma \frac{\partial \bar{H}}{\partial t} + \mu\epsilon \frac{\partial^2 \bar{H}}{\partial t^2}, \tag{5.28}$$

which is a combination of the diffusion equation and the wave equation (Table 5.1). It often happens that one of the terms of (5.28) is negligible— for instance, in a conductor $\sigma \gg \epsilon\omega$, thus diffusion is the dominant process. Alternatively, as in free space or in ferrites, the conductivity term is

Table 5.1 Comparison of types of $\nabla^2 \bar{H}$ equation

Equation	Name	Use
$\nabla^2\bar{H} = 0$	Laplace's equation	In pole-free region
$\nabla^2\bar{H} = C$	Poisson's equation	Where poles occur
$\nabla^2\bar{H} = \sigma\mu(\partial\bar{H}/\partial t)$	Diffusion equation	In conducting media
$\nabla^2\bar{H} = \mu\epsilon(\partial^2\bar{H}/\partial t^2)$	Wave equation	In insulators or free space

negligible so that the wave equation is dominant. In the latter case both μ and ϵ may become complex quantities.

Sinusoidal Steady-State Solution (One Dimension). Consider an ideal geometry of an iron core with surface on the x–y plane where positive z points into the material. Let a field be applied in the y-direction on the surface

$$\bar{H} = \hat{a}_y H_a \cos \omega t \qquad \text{at} \quad z = 0, \tag{5.29}$$

and consider the penetration of the field into the conducting core. Since iron is a conductor with σ in excess of 10^6 $(\Omega\cdot\text{m})^{-1}$ and since ϵ is probably of the order of 10^{-11}, clearly $\sigma \gg \epsilon\omega$ for almost any likely frequency; thus the diffusion equation is applicable. Since the field is a function of both z and t, we use the standard method of separation of variables

$$\bar{H}(z, t) = \hat{a}_y H_a Z(z) T(t). \tag{5.30}$$

Substitution into the one-dimensional diffusion equation

$$\frac{\partial^2 \bar{H}}{\partial z^2} = \mu\sigma \frac{\partial \bar{H}}{\partial t} \tag{5.31}$$

results, with prime notation indicating derivative, in

$$\hat{a}_y H_a Z'' T = \hat{a}_y \mu\sigma H_a Z T'. \tag{5.32}$$

The final step is to divide by (5.30), which leads to separate equations in z and in t,

$$\frac{Z''}{Z} = \frac{\mu\sigma T'}{T} = \gamma^2, \tag{5.33}$$

where γ^2 is the separation constant, a function of neither z nor t,

$$Z'' - \gamma^2 Z = 0 \tag{5.34a}$$

$$\mu\sigma T' - \gamma^2 T = 0. \tag{5.34b}$$

The equation in Z is satisfied by

$$Z(z) = e^{-\gamma z}. \tag{5.35}$$

Using $T(t) = e^{j\omega t}$ in (5.34b) gives $\gamma^2 = \mu\sigma j\omega$, which leads to

$$\gamma = \frac{\sqrt{\mu\sigma\omega}\,(1+j)}{\sqrt{2}} = \sqrt{\mu\sigma\pi f}\,(1+j). \tag{5.36}$$

Using the more compact notation for skin depth δ, we have

$$\delta = \frac{1}{\sqrt{\mu\sigma\pi f}}. \tag{5.37}$$

Equation 5.35 becomes

$$Z(z) = e^{-z/\delta}e^{-jz/\delta} \tag{5.38}$$

to define the amplitude and phase variation with depth z. The final result (Fig. 5.7) is

$$\bar{H} = \hat{a}_y H_a e^{-z/\delta} \cos\left(\omega t - \frac{z}{\delta}\right) \qquad z \geq 0. \tag{5.39}$$

Further Inferences Regarding Skin Depth. Let us review the geometry of the diffusion equation above, noting in particular that the magnitude of H_y is found to diminish as a function of distance in the z-direction into the conductor. A physical explanation for the decrease in H is its partial cancellation by the induced current in the positive x-direction. The value of current density J can be obtained from curl $\bar{H}$ as

$$\bar{J} = -\hat{a}_x \frac{\partial H_y}{\partial z} = \hat{a}_x \gamma H_a e^{-\gamma z} \qquad \text{A/m}^2. \tag{5.40}$$

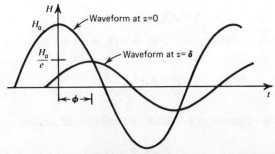

Figure 5.7 Waveform of H of (5.39) at the surface $z = 0$ compared with the waveform calculated for $z = \delta$. The amplitude of the latter is smaller by a factor $1/e$ and the phase lags by 1 radian.

Since eddy currents are attenuated by the same exponential factor as is
H, there is negligible penetration of J or H at a distance greater than 2
or 3 units of skin depth. Therefore practical sizes for current conductors
and for magnetic cores are determined by the skin depth.

For current-carrying conductors the depth that current penetrates into
the conductor is limited by the diffusion of the accompanying magnetic
field.

EXAMPLE B

Use (5.37) to calculate the skin depth for hard-drawn copper at $f =$
60 Hz.

ANSWER. $\delta = 8.65$ mm, using $\mu = 4\pi\ 10^{-7}$ and $\sigma = 5.63 \times 10^{7}\ (\Omega\cdot m)^{-1}$.
This interesting value limits the largest practical thickness of bus-bar
conductors for carrying large currents, as at power plants and sub-
stations.

For magnetic cores that possess electrical conductivity (e.g., iron alloys),
the shielding effect of eddy currents limits the penetration of H into the
core. Figure 5.8 illustrates the need for core laminations to be thin, the
order of skin depth or less, if the core is to be capable of responding to
an applied field.

EXAMPLE C

Use (5.37) to calculate the skin depth for transformer sheet at $f = 60$ Hz.
How does this compare with the common thickness U.S. gauge 29,
thickness = 0.014 in.?

ANSWER.   Bozorth [13] gives the following data for grain-oriented iron–
3% silicon: resistivity, $47\ \mu\Omega\cdot cm$; initial permeability, 1500; maximum
permeability, 40,000. It is not obvious what value of μ is appropriate,
but use of $\mu_r = 16,000$ and $\sigma = 2.12 \times 10^{6}\ (\Omega\cdot m)^{-1}$ gives the result $\delta =$
0.35 mm, or 0.014 in. It is interesting to compare this result with copper
and to note that silicon iron is nearly 25 times more effective than
copper as an eddy current shield.

This general approach can be applied to the calculation of eddy current
losses in laminated sheets of core material, yielding theoretical equations
that are similar to (5.50), below. The classical equations are not
reproduced here because experimental losses exceed the classical theory
substantially. See Brailsford [4] for more details on the eddy current
anomaly.

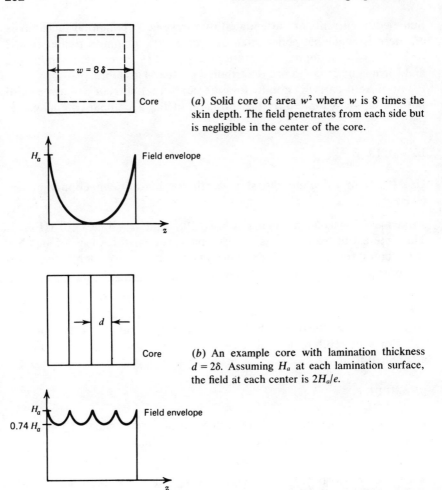

(a) Solid core of area w^2 where w is 8 times the skin depth. The field penetrates from each side but is negligible in the center of the core.

(b) An example core with lamination thickness $d = 2\delta$. Assuming H_a at each lamination surface, the field at each center is $2H_a/e$.

Figure 5.8 Envelope of peak amplitude of a–c field versus distance through a conducting magnetic core, a qualitative extension of (5.39). For the case of a single solid core, only about a quarter of the core receives a–c excitation because the field penetration is limited by the skin depth. The laminated core is more efficiently used because the field has time to diffuse through the laminations.

The classical calculations for skin depth using (5.37) require permeability as a material constant. It has been assumed that $B = \mu H$ uniformly such that a time-varying H will induce a proportional time-varying B at the same point of space. However in many materials the process of flux change is highly nonuniform because flux change is associated with the movement of one or more domain walls. For such

materials the average permeability consists of domains of low permeability separated by walls of very high permeability of motion.

5.2.2 Reversal by Domain Wall Motion

In contrast to the foregoing models that presume a linear homogeneous
flux density, we now consider the existence of magnetic domains. Our
particular interest is the excess field required to move a domain wall
across a conducting core to cause the reversal of its magnetization.
Changes of B are more localized than in the continuum models and the
eddy currents are more concentrated, resulting in greater dynamic core
losses.

A Model of the Dynamic Process.   Consider a conducting core on the
positive z-axis, with surface on the x–y plane. Let a domain wall of
negligible width be moving along the z-axis passing through $z = z_0$ at the
instant in question (Fig. 5.9). The intrinsic induction is saturated in the
y-direction at $+B_s$ for $z < z_0$ and $-B_s$ for $z > z_0$. The rate of change is an
impulse function at $(z - z_0)$.

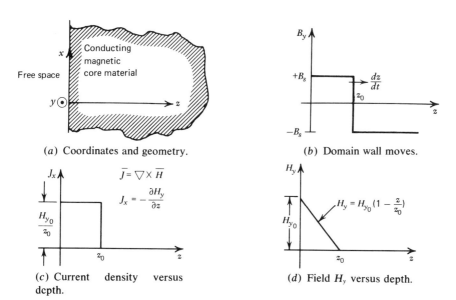

(a) Coordinates and geometry.

(b) Domain wall moves.

(c) Current density versus
depth.

(d) Field H_y versus depth.

Figure 5.9   Applied field $+H_a$ induces domain $+B_s$ with wall that moves inward (b). The
change of induction dB/dt induces a field E_x, hence a current J_x outside the wall (c). The
current has a shielding effect for field H_y, causing a decrease of H_y with distance (d). The
decrease of H_y is assumed to be linear as a simple example.

$$\frac{dB}{dt} = \frac{dB}{dz} \cdot \frac{dz}{dt} = -2B_s \, \delta(z - z_0) \frac{dz}{dt}. \tag{5.41}$$

The core is driven by a field in the y-direction. Presumably H_0 is required to overcome wall coercivity, and an excess field $H_y = H - H_0$ is required to overcome the surface eddy current induced by the flux change. According to Maxwell's curl equation the excess field will diminish with distance through the current-carrying region. The total change of field is given by the total sheet current density H_{y0} A/m.

Switching Coefficient Using the Sandwich Model. Consider a toroidal core of cross-sectional area $S_c = Nwd$, consisting of N laminations of thickness d and width w. One typical lamination appears in Fig. 5.10. The other laminations and the drive coil windings are omitted for simplicity. It is assumed that the coil is driven hard by a current, from one level of magnetic saturation to the other, with all laminations reversing polarity at the same time.

Other modes of reversal can be postulated. For instance, at a very slow reversal of a tape-wound core the flux change might be more localized, beginning at the inside wrap of the core and spiraling outward along each successive wrap of the tape core.

The flux reversal is assumed to take place by domain wall motion, from the outside surface of a wrap to the interior. We want to find the time required for a complete flux change if the wall velocity is limited by the damping effect of eddy currents.

Referring to Fig. 5.10, the lamination of area wd is assumed to have a domain wall at a depth z_0, with flux density $\hat{a}_y B_s$ around the periphery and $-\hat{a}_y B_s$ inside the domain wall. The total flux in the y-direction is therefore approximately

$$\Phi_y = B_s[wd - 2(d - 2z_0)(w - 2z_0)] \approx B_s[-wd + 4z_0(w + d)], \tag{5.42}$$

neglecting terms of z_0^2.

The voltage induced by the moving domain wall is approximately

$$e = \frac{d\Phi_y}{dt} \approx 4B_s(w + d)\frac{dz_0}{dt} \quad \text{V}, \tag{5.43}$$

which is consistent with an electric field

$$E \approx 2B_s \frac{dz_0}{dt} \quad \text{V/m} \tag{5.44}$$

averaged over the approximate current path length of $2(w + d)$. The

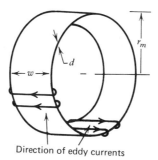

(a) One typical wrap of a toroidal tape-wound core.

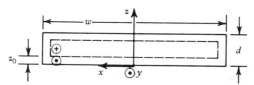

(b) Cross section of tape having width w, thickness d, and domain walls at z_0 and $d - z_0$.

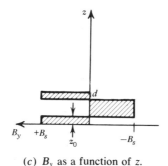

(c) B_y as a function of z.

Figure 5.10 Geometry for derivation of switching coefficient.

sheet current density K follows from $J = \sigma E$ as

$$K = Jz_0 = 2B_s\sigma z_0 \frac{dz_0}{dt} \quad A/m, \quad (5.45)$$

which in turn is equal to the excess applied field H_{dy}. The time can now be found for the domain walls to move from $z_0 = 0$ to the point where they meet at $z_0 = d/2$. Multiplying (5.45) by dt and integrating (the dynamic field should be considered as an average)

$$H_{dy} \int_0^\tau dt = 2B_s\sigma \int_0^{d/2} z_0 dz_0 \quad (5.46)$$

leads to the final result of interest

$$(H - H_0)\tau = B_s\sigma \frac{d^2}{4} = S_w. \tag{5.47}$$

The term on the right is called the switching coefficient S_w due to wall motion, assuming that the wall is slowed by eddy currents. Switching coefficients have been widely used to compare different magnetic materials, particularly for use as memory elements. Experimentally, switching time τ is measured as a function of applied pulse field H. When the data are plotted on a scale of reciprocal time versus H, H_0 is determined from the intercept onto the H axis and S_w is determined from the (reciprocal of) slope.

Square-Wave Response of Tape-Wound Cores. To evaluate the applicability of (5.47) to tape-wound cores, catalog data for two different cores are plotted on a scale of frequency versus H (Fig. 5.11). The test conditions are specified in the legend. The straight lines in the figure indicate qualitative agreement with (5.47). In a further evaluation, the slopes from the figure are listed in Table 5.2 and compared with calculated values. The values agree within about a factor of 2, which I regard as adequate (under the circumstances that the data are merely catalog data of unknown reliability).

Loss coefficient, g_e. We are now in a position to comment further on the loss parameter in the assumed equation for dynamic field

$$H_{dy} = g_e \frac{dB}{dt}, \tag{5.1}$$

which is very similar to the equation for switching coefficient

$$(H - H_0)\tau = B_s\sigma \frac{d^2}{4} = S_w. \tag{5.47}$$

Since the average rate of flux change for the square-wave current-driven experiment is

$$\left| \frac{dB}{dt} \right|_{avg} = \frac{2B_s}{\tau}, \tag{5.48}$$

it follows that for this mode of reversal, the loss coefficient can be defined as

$$g_e = \sigma \frac{d^2}{8}. \tag{5.49}$$

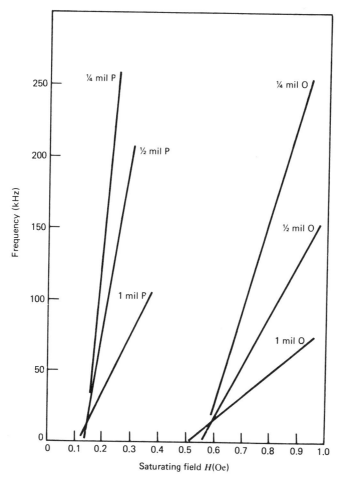

Figure 5.11 Frequency of square-wave current drive versus average H required to saturate for tape-wound toroidal cores of Permalloy (P) and Orthonol® (O). Data are for tape thicknesses of 1, $\frac{1}{2}$, and $\frac{1}{4}$ mil. (Data adapted from Catalog TWC-300R with permission of Magnetics, Inc., Butler, Pennsylvania.)

While keeping in mind that the derivation above was for a specific type of reversal process, it is instructive to plug (5.49) into (5.12):

$$p_e = \frac{B_m^2 \sigma d^2 \pi^2 f^2}{4} \qquad W/m^3. \tag{5.50}$$

It is interesting to compare (5.50) with the classical calculation of eddy current losses (assuming uniform permeability rather than domains). For

Table 5.2 Extrapolated coercivity H_0 and switching coefficient $S_w{}^a$

Thickness (mil)	Orthonol®			Permalloy 80		
	H_0 (A·t/m)	S_w (μs·A/m) From Fig. 5.11	Calculated from (5.47)	H_0 (A·t/m)	S_w (μs·A/m) From Fig. 5.11	Calculated from (5.47)
$\frac{1}{4}$	44.9	59	31.4	11.2	17.4	10.6
$\frac{1}{2}$	42.7	114	125.4	10.9	32.5	42
1	40.3	239	502	9.0	98	170

[a] τ of (5.47) $= \frac{1}{2f}$ of Fig. 5.11 by assumption. For this calculation B_s/ρ was taken as $1.4\,\text{T}/45 \times 10^{-8}\,\Omega\cdot\text{m}$ for Orthonol® and $0.6\,\text{T}/57 \times 10^{-8}\,\Omega\cdot\text{m}$ for Permalloy 80.

instance, an equation given by Brailsford [4] is identical except that his denominator is 6 instead of 4. Attwood's classical derivation [2] yields an 8 instead of the usual 6, which the author attributes to an end-effect correction. This comparison is consistent with the well-known fact that the continuum model predicts losses that are too low.

5.3 COMPLEX PERMEABILITY

Some engineers prefer to use the concept of complex permeability μ^* to represent the losses of all types of magnetic cores. For the case of conducting cores, the effects of eddy current losses in that perspective would be represented as the lossy component of complex μ rather than as a separate loss parameter g_e. Our use of μ^* is more specific as to material type; it is applied here to nonconducting magnetic materials such as ferrites. Because the electrical resistivity is very high—of the order of 10^7 times that of iron alloys—the macroscopic eddy current model of Section 5.2 is not applicable.

Even in nonconducting cores with zero coercivity some energy is dissipated as the elementary magnetic moments are reoriented back and forth. The loss processes are conveniently modeled as the imaginary component of a complex permeability

$$\mu^* = \mu_0\mu_r^* = \mu_0(\mu' - j\mu''). \tag{5.51}$$

Figure 5.12 is a vector representation of μ_r^* and the definition of loss tangent.

5.3.1 Circuit Models

Because inductance is proportional to permeability, a complex μ gives rise to a complex L

$$L^* = \frac{n^2\mu_0(\mu' - j\mu'')S}{l} \tag{5.52}$$

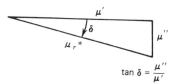

$$\tan \delta = \frac{\mu''}{\mu'}$$

Figure 5.12 Vector representation of complex relative permeability and definition of loss tangent.

The impedance $j\omega L^*$ will appear as

$$j\omega n^2 \mu_0 \mu' \frac{S}{l} + \omega n^2 \mu_0 \mu'' \frac{S}{l}, \tag{5.53}$$

which models the losses as a series resistor

$$r = \omega n^2 \mu_0 \mu'' \frac{S}{l} = \omega L \tan \delta. \tag{5.54}$$

For series RL circuits the formula for quality factor Q is $\omega L/r$, which becomes

$$Q = \frac{\mu'}{\mu''} = \frac{1}{\tan \delta} \tag{5.55}$$

The loss tangent, $\tan \delta$, is shown in Fig. 5.12. Equation 5.55 evidently represents a fundamental limitation of high-Q coils, imposed by loss tangent of the core material. For instance, if a coil is required with $Q = 100$, the loss tangent of the core material must be enough less than 0.01 to allow for some loss in the windings. A figure of merit for materials is μQ or $\mu_i/\tan \delta$, which is the reciprocal of the loss factor specified by manufacturers.

Parallel Q.   The intrinsic losses of core materials, evidenced as a lossy or complex inductance, can be represented by either a series or a parallel circuit model (Fig. 5.13). From the viewpoint that inductance and Q are the fundamental quantities, the values of the lossy components can be calculated as follows:

$$R = \omega L Q \qquad \text{for the parallel model} \tag{5.56}$$

$$r = \frac{\omega L_s}{Q} \qquad \text{for the series model.} \tag{5.57}$$

The components of complex admittance $Y = G - jS$ for Fig. 5.13a are readily calculated from

$$Y = \frac{1}{r + j\omega L_s}, \tag{5.58}$$

with the result

$$G = \frac{1}{R} = \frac{1}{r(1 + Q^2)} \quad \text{and} \quad -jS = \frac{1}{j\omega L_s \left(1 + \frac{1}{Q^2}\right)} \tag{5.59}$$

EXAMPLE D

An inductance $L_s = 1\,\text{mH}$ has $Q = 20$. Find the components of the circuit models at $\omega = 10^3$.

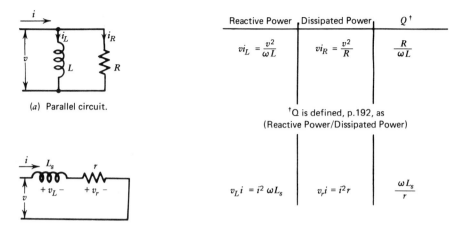

(a) Parallel circuit.

†Q is defined, p.192, as
(Reactive Power/Dissipated Power)

(b) Series circuit.

Figure 5.13 Two circuit models for a lossy inductor.

ANSWER. Impedance $\omega L_s = 1\ \Omega$, so $r = \frac{1}{20}\ \Omega$ for the series model. For the parallel model $L = 1.0025$ mH, $R = 20.05\ \Omega$. For this case the values of L are equal within the accuracy of nominal measurement and $R \approx Q^2 r$.

5.3.2 Core Loss Model

If a sinusoidal field is applied to a core of complex permeability,

$$H = H_a \cos \omega t. \tag{5.60}$$

Assuming

$$B = \mu^* H, \tag{5.61}$$

it follows from (5.51) that

$$B = \mu_0 H_a (\mu' \cos \omega t + \mu'' \sin \omega t), \tag{5.62}$$

which corresponds to an elliptical B–H characteristic (Fig. 5.14). At the instant of time $t = 0$ H is at its maximum value, and B takes the value $\mu_0 H_a \mu'$. Subsequently at $\omega t = \pi/2$, $H = 0$ and $B = \mu_0 H_a \mu''$. It is convenient to use the angle θ at which the ellipse is tilted

$$\tan \theta = \mu_0 \mu' \tag{5.63}$$

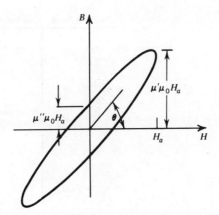

Define $\tan \theta = \mu'\mu_0$

Semimajor axis $a = \dfrac{H_a}{\cos \theta}$

Semiminor axis $b = \mu''\mu_0 H_a' \cos \theta$

Area $= \pi ab = \pi H_a^2 \mu'' \mu_0$

Figure 5.14 Geometry of elliptical hysteresis loop for a low-loss material of complex permeability.

to help determine the lengths of the semimajor and semiminor axes,

$$a = \frac{H_a}{\cos \theta}$$

$$b = \mu_0 \mu'' H_a \cos \theta. \tag{5.64}$$

It follows that the area of the ellipse πab is

$$\text{area} = \pi H_a^2 \mu_0 \mu'' \quad \text{J/m}^3\text{·cycle}, \tag{5.65}$$

which is the dissipated energy density per cycle.

A more useful format, after using (5.61), is

$$e_l \approx \frac{\pi B_m^2}{\mu_0}\left(\frac{\tan \delta}{\mu_r^*}\right) \quad \text{J/m}^3\text{·cycle}, \tag{5.66}$$

assuming $\mu_r^* \approx \mu'$.

The term in parentheses is the *loss factor*, a ferrite material property commonly specified by manufacturers, equivalent to $1/Q\mu_r$. Finally, the core loss (W/m^3) is given by (5.66) multiplied by frequency in hertz.

EXAMPLE E

Calculate the loss of a linear ferrite core driven at 100 kHz to a peak value of $B = 0.1$ T if the loss factor is 4×10^{-6}.

ANSWER.   Using $p_l = (\pi B_m^2/\mu_0)$ $[(\tan \delta)/\mu_r]f$, the result is 10^4 W/m^3, which is the same as 10 mW/cc.

The value of calculated power loss in Example E was found to be a little low when compared with core loss data given in ferrite catalogs. Depending on the type of ferrite, the specified loss is larger than the calculation by a factor of 2 to 50 times. The discrepancy is probably due to an increase of loss factor with amplitude B. Loss factor usually is specified for $B_m \leq 10^{-4}$ and was assumed constant in Example E. The B^2 exponent of 2.0 in (5.66) could be replaced by an empirical exponent of perhaps 2.3 for a better fit.

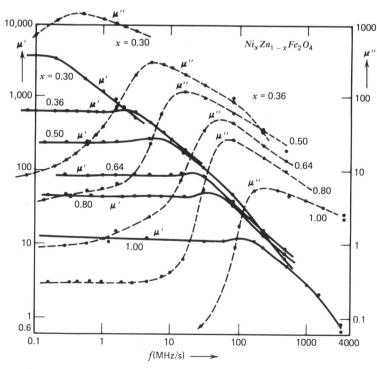

Figure 5.15 Frequency dependence of the real and the imaginary parts of the initial permeability, μ' and μ'', for polycrystalline ferrites of differing chemical compositions. (From Smit and Wijn [10], p. 269, with permission.)

5.3.3 Frequency Dependence of Losses

Chapter 4 established that ferrites are limited in frequency response by electron spin resonance, with the product of permeability and bandwidth approximately constant. Figure 5.15 shows that both components of μ^* vary with frequency. Not only does μ' decrease with frequency above resonance, but at the same time μ'' becomes larger by 1 or 2 orders of magnitude. It is evident that the ratio μ''/μ' will increase even more rapidly near resonance, and furthermore that the loss factor $(\tan \delta)/\mu_r$ will be even still more sensitive. Because of the enormous increase of losses so implied, magnetic power circuits using ferrite cores are usually operated at frequencies well below resonance.

5.4 DYNAMIC PROCESSES

We now move away from the special geometries of devices and circuits that use magnetic cores, to examine the general physics of flux reversal. Two processes that have been clearly identified are rotation and wall motion.

Rotation is occurring when the array of magnetic moments within a single domain turn together uniformly, more or less coherently throughout the entire domain. Section 2.2.2 gives a plausible domain configuration for a core, assuming that rotation is the dominant process. Several research studies have been done on special sample shapes that permit the entire specimen to consist of one single domain. For such cases, a rotation process would change the induction of the entire specimen simultaneously. The most widely used mathematical model of rotation is the Landau-Lifshitz equation, given in Section 5.4.1.

Domain wall motion is a very inhomogeneous process in which flux changes occur at moving boundaries of domains. If coherent rotation is nonexistent so that wall motion is the only reversal process, the induction changes only locally at the wall itself. This means, in effect, that relative permeability is unity (zero susceptibility) everywhere except at domain walls, where the wall mobility must be large enough to account for the average permeability of the whole specimen. That is, an applied ΔH induces wall motion that produces a ΔB. This process may be perceived as permeability. Wall motion is modeled as a very localized precession in Section 5.4.2.

5.4.1 The Landau–Lifshitz Equation

Chapter 2 described precession as the basic mechanism by which the orientation of intrinsic induction is changed. At that time we considered only lossless motion at the Larmor angular frequency $\omega = -\gamma H$, the natural frequency at which a system of magnetic moments precesses as a free vector about a field H. To the equation of motion given earlier

$$\frac{d\bar{J}}{dt} = \gamma \bar{J} \times \bar{H} = \gamma \bar{\tau} \qquad (2.14)$$

we now add a second term to represent losses. The result is

$$\frac{d\bar{J}}{dt} = \gamma \bar{\tau} + \alpha \gamma \left(\frac{\bar{J}}{J}\right) \times \bar{\tau}, \qquad (5.67)$$

a widely used equation first presented in 1935 by the two Russian physicists L. Landau and E. Lifshitz [11]. Figure 5.16 notes that torque density $\bar{\tau} = \bar{J} \times \bar{H}$, when multiplied by the negative constant* γ, causes the system of magnetic dipole moments $\bar{J}$ to precess about $\bar{H}$ in a right-handed direction. The second term will act in an orthogonal direction to the first term with a relative value defined by the dimensionless loss factor α. Typical values of α are in the range of 10^{-2} to 10^{-1} for many magnetic materials. In fact (5.67) is applicable only if $\alpha \ll 1$. The type of loss described in (5.67) is called *relaxation* or *intrinsic* damping,

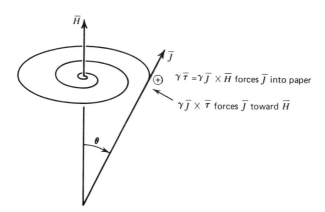

Figure 5.16 The two components of torque in (5.67) combine vectorially to cause $\bar{J}$ to spiral in toward $\bar{H}$.

*The reader will recall from Section 2.1.4 that γ is the gyromagnetic ratio (magnetic moment/angular momentum), with MKS value -2.21×10^5 (rads/s)/(A/m) for electron spins.

a phenomenological factor, since no specific process is implied.

The Landau-Lifshitz equation is widely used by researchers to characterize materials. For instance, the width of the peak of a magnetic resonance experiment may be used to deduce a value for α. The equation has also been used to interpret pulsed switching data for materials.

EXAMPLE F

Work out the components of the Landau–Lifshitz equation for the geometry of Fig. 5.16, $\bar{H} = H\hat{a}_z$, $\bar{J} = J(\cos \theta \, \hat{a}_z + \sin \theta \, \hat{a}_r)$ using cylindrical coordinates.

ANSWER.   The left-hand side of (5.67) is the time derivative of the given equation

$$\frac{d\bar{J}}{dt} = J(-\sin \theta \, \frac{d\theta}{dt} \, \hat{a}_z + \cos \theta \, \frac{d\theta}{dt} \, \hat{a}_r + \sin \theta \, \frac{d\phi}{dt} \, \hat{a}_\phi). \tag{5.68}$$

The first term on the right-hand side of (5.67) becomes

$$\gamma \bar{J} \times \bar{H} = -\gamma JH \sin \theta \, \hat{a}_\phi, \tag{5.69}$$

and the second term is

$$\alpha\gamma \left(\frac{\bar{J}}{J}\right) \times \bar{\tau} = -\alpha\gamma JH \sin \theta(\cos \theta \, \hat{a}_z + \sin \theta \, \hat{a}_r) \times \hat{a}_\phi$$
$$= -\alpha\gamma JH \sin \theta(\cos \theta[-\hat{a}_r] + \sin \theta \, \hat{a}_z). \tag{5.70}$$

Collecting $\hat{a}_\phi$ components from (5.68) to (5.70), after canceling common terms, gives the main mode of precession as

$$\frac{d\phi}{dt} = -\gamma H. \tag{5.71}$$

The collapse of θ is defined by collecting either of the other sets of components.

$$\frac{d\theta}{dt} = \alpha\gamma H \sin \theta. \tag{5.72}$$

Equation 5.71 has the general form $|\omega| = \gamma H$, independent of angle θ. The collapse of θ by (5.72) brings $\bar{J}$ into alignment with $\bar{H}$ at a rate proportional to damping factor α.

5.4.2 Domain Wall Motion

Precession Model. Our description of domain wall motion consists of four steps: (a) the direction of wall motion, (b) the structure of the wall,

(c) wall motion as a precession about the Becker field, and (d) the origin of the Becker field.

Consider the geometry of Fig. 5.17 with a domain wall in the y–z plane. The x–y plane is cut away for convenience in defining the coordinates. The domain for negative x is saturated at $\bar{J} = J_s \hat{a}_z$, whereas along the positive x-axis $\bar{J} = -J_s \hat{a}_z$. For an applied field $H_a \hat{a}_z$, the wall will tend to move in the positive x-direction, provided H_a is greater than some threshold value H_0. The wall moves in the direction that increases the size of the favored domain, the domain that is magnetized parallel to H_a. Incidentally, for the 180° wall shown, the equivalent pressure difference across the wall is $2 J_s H_a$ N/m², which tends to cause its motion.

It is important to recognize that a domain wall possesses a small but finite thickness δ rather than having zero thickness. Exchange coupling between neighboring magnetic moments is strong enough to keep nearest neighbors almost parallel to one another. As a result, the 180° change of angle takes place across a few hundreds of atomic distances. It is convenient to define θ as the local angle of $\bar{J}$ in the y–z plane, and to assume that the entire angle change $\Delta\theta = \pi$ rad is complete within the wall thickness δ. This definition corresponds to $\theta = 0$ for $x \ll 0$, $\theta = \pi$ for $x \gg 0$.

The wall moves in the x-direction past a given point x_0, and the local moment at x_0 undergoes an angle change as the wall moves by. The time derivative of angle change is a precession that is proportional to the wall

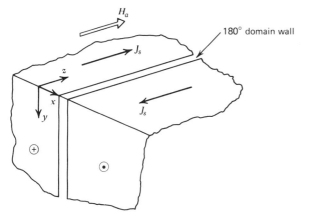

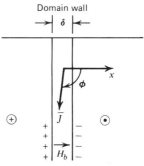

(a) Field is applied in z-direction parallel to 180° domain wall.

(b) Precession of $\bar{J}$ about H_a inside domain wall gives rise to Becker field across wall.

Figure 5.17 Details of Bloch wall motion.

velocity

$$\frac{d\theta}{dt} = \frac{d\theta}{dx}\frac{dx}{dt} = \frac{\pi}{\delta}\,v. \tag{5.73}$$

These considerations led R. Becker to postulate in 1951 [15] the existence of a field across the wall,

$$H_b = \frac{v}{\gamma}\frac{d\theta}{dx} \approx \frac{v}{\gamma}\left(\frac{\pm\,\pi}{\delta}\right) \tag{5.74}$$

about which the wall spins precess.

For the ideal geometry of Fig. 5.17 it is interesting to note that $\bar{J} \times \bar{H}_a$ is zero everywhere except within the wall itself, where $\bar{J}$ has a y-component. Furthermore from (5.71) the spins within the wall precess about H_a in a direction to increase the azimuthal angle ϕ, thereby creating poles on either side of the wall. Figure 5.17b illustrates that the Becker field across the wall is due to the poles from the initial precession.

In summary, the applied field causes an initial precession of the moments within the wall. The demagnetizing field from the initial precession is the Becker field that must exist in proportion to wall velocity.

Wall Mobility.   The equation most widely used to define the velocity of a single domain wall is of the form

$$v = m(H - H_0) \qquad \text{if} \quad H > H_0, \tag{5.75}$$

where m is wall mobility. MKS units for wall mobility are (m/s)/(A/m) or $m^2/s\cdot A$. Field H_0 is a threshold field for movement of an existing wall, which is generally smaller than the field required to nucleate a wall initially. The form of (5.75) with velocity proportional to drive field implies some sort of viscous damping. The damping mechanism is attributed to eddy currents for walls in conducting magnetic materials thicker than about 1 μm, and otherwise is attributed to intrinsic damping. This entire discussion assumes that the specimens are free of defects that can cause a wall to hang up spuriously.

Although there are exceptions, the general range of values for wall mobility that have been reported by researchers are within an order of magnitude of $4 \times 10^{-4}\,m^2/s\cdot A$ (3 cm/s·Oe) for conductors and $0.5\,m^2/s\cdot A$ (4000 cm/s·Oe) for ferrites. It is a matter of considerable practical interest, particularly for magnetic memory device applications where speed is important, to know whether (5.75) has an upper limit imposed by some sort of mobility saturation.

It has been shown theoretically by L. R. Walker [16] that an upper limit does exist. The derivation is not straightforward, but an existence argument can be given as follows. Since from (5.74) wall velocity is proportional to the Becker field, a limitation of the Becker field implies a maximum velocity. But the Becker field is a demagnetizing field that cannot exceed M_s, even for the case of large angle ϕ in Fig. 5.17, so a maximum velocity must exist if (5.74) is valid.

Equations for wall mobility have been derived in research literature, but the derivations are too complicated to include here. For the case of intrinsic damping, wall mobility has been given as inversely proportional to damping parameter α as

$$m \sim \frac{\gamma \Delta}{\alpha} \quad \text{m}^2/\text{s·A}, \tag{5.76}$$

where $\Delta = \sqrt{A/K}$ is a wall width parameter defined in Section 8.3.2. Numerically, $m \sim 2$ using $\gamma = 2.21 \times 10^5$, $\Delta = 10^{-6}$, $\alpha = 0.1$.

No one equation exists for wall mobility damped by an eddy current because each specimen geometry gives a different geometrical factor. A plausible format for an equation for a 180° wall can be seen by manipulating (5.1) into the form

$$H - H_0 = g_e \frac{dB}{dt} \approx g_e \frac{dJ}{dx}\frac{dx}{dt}, \tag{5.77}$$

which yields

$$m = \frac{v}{H - H_0} = \frac{\delta}{g_e 2 J_s} \quad \text{m}^2/\text{s·A}, \tag{5.78}$$

after defining $dJ/dx = 2J_s/\delta$.

Numerically $m \sim 2 \times 10^{-4}$ using $\delta = 10^{-6}$, $g_e \sim 10^{-3}$, $J_s = 2$. Equation 5.78 is given only for the sake of interest, since its validity has not been demonstrated.

PROBLEMS

1 (Section 5.1.2)

   a. Suppose a transformer that weighs 5 kg is made of the tape-wound core material of Fig. 5.4. Use the empirical results to predict how many watts of core loss would be expected if the transformer is used at 60 Hz with sinusoidal excitation $B_{\max} = 1.2$ T. In other words, extend the range of Fig. 5.4.

   b. Estimate the power loss to be expected if the core of the transformer is wound of material of 0.014 in. thick, rather than 0.002 in. as in Fig. 5.4.

   c. Use the empirical equations and data to predict the expected core loss of a 5-kg transformer of U.S.S. Transformer 72–29 gauge, excited as above.

2 **(Section 5.2).** Section 3.1.2 uses Ampere's circuital law to deduce the H-field in and near a cylindrical current distribution from Maxwell's curl H equation (3.11). Carry out an analogous procedure for the curl E equation (5.23), to deduce the electric field in and near a cylindrical distribution of dB/dt.

3 **(Section 5.2).** Read and summarize the key ideas of the paper by Watson and Leis [14], which models the diffusion of stray flux as an RC transmission line.

4 **(Section 5.2.2).** Work through the derivation of switching coefficient (5.47), adding a few more steps to replace (5.45) as follows:

   a. Find an expression for the voltage around the eddy current path.

   b. Divide by the resistance of the path to find the total eddy current I_e.

   c. Use Ampere's law $I_e = H_{dy}2\pi r_m$ to relate eddy current to the dynamic field. Briefly discuss the meaning of each step.

5 **(Section 5.2.2).** Equation 5.47 in the form $(H - H_0)\tau = S_w$ is sometimes called the Menyuk-Goodenough equation after its inventors. Think through the experiment for which results are given in Fig. 5.11, then use the equation to explain the findings. Find values for H_0 in oersteds and S_w in Oe·s for "1 mil O" and "1 mil P" from the figure.

6 **(Section 5.2.2).** A catalog of square-loop, tape-wound cores gives data as follows for the field required to saturate the core (50% Ni-Fe), using a square-wave current drive. The experiment consists of finding the particular value of H, which is required to drive the core from saturation of one polarity to the other saturation polarity in a period of time equal to half the period of the square-wave drive field. Three data points for $\frac{1}{2}$-mil tape show the amplitude of square-wave field versus frequency as follows:

f (kHz)	20	40	60
H (Oe)	0.604	0.66	0.72

   a. Assuming that reversal takes place by domain wall motion, and that $S_w = \tau(H - H_0)$, find a value of coercive field H_0 that makes a good fit to the data.

   b. Find the value of switching coefficient S_w consistent with (a).

c. As an exercise in units, and to check the theoretical derivation, compare your result (b) with the calculated value of switching coefficient that was derived as the MKS equation $S_w = B_s d^2/4\rho$. Note in English units that $d = 0.005$ in., CGS $\rho = 45 \times 10^{-6}$ $\Omega \cdot$cm, and MKS $B_s = 1.4$ T.

7 (**Section 5.3.1**). Suppose that the 1-mH inductor of Example D is wound on a ferrite core using magnet wire with a resistance of 0.03 Ω, so that $Q = 20$ includes the lossy effects of the wire as well as the core. With the assumption above, what is the loss tangent of the core?

8 (**Section 5.3.2**). Estimate the power loss of a 50-g ferrite core used at 50 kHz with sinusoidal excitation to $B_{max} = 0.2$ T, if the loss factor is 5×10^{-6}. The density of ferrite is approximately 5 g/cc.

9 (**Section 5.3.3**). Use the data in Fig. 5.15 to find values for μ'_r, μ''_r, tan δ, and the loss factor (tan δ)/μ_r as follows. Find the values at $f = 1$ MHz and at 80 MHz for the polycrystalline ferrite $Ni_{0.8}Zn_{0.2}Fe_2O_4$. (It should be noted that significant reductions in losses have been made since the time of these pioneering data.)

10 (**Section 5.3.3**). A particular toroidal core of linear ferrite has a permeability $\mu_r = 5000$. Let us suppose that the permeability is due to anisotropy in the manner of Fig. 2.14, with the "easy axis" in the radial direction. If the core manufacturing procedure is changed to cause the anisotropy to double, without changing the ferrite chemistry, what effect would you expect on the following parameters.

a. Saturation induction.

b. Permeability.

c. Losses.

d. Bandwidth.

e. Other.

11 (**Section 5.4.1**). Equation 5.67 differs slightly from the original Landau-Lifshitz equation, following the modification proposed by Gilbert. Look up the original 1935 paper [11] and make a comparison of the two dynamic equations. Summarize your findings in one page or less.

12 (**Section 5.4.2**). Give a precession model explanation of Bloch wall motion if the magnetic moment within the wall is opposite to the direction shown in Fig. 5.17. That is, the domains are magnetized as shown in the figure, but J within the wall is to have a $-\hat{a}_y$ orientation that is opposite to the figure.

REFERENCES

1. E. C. Cherry, "The Duality Between Interlinked Electric and Magnetic Circuits and the Formation of Transformer Equivalent Circuits," *Proc. Phys. Soc.*, **62B**, 101–111 (February 1949). Probably the most important and elegant paper that deals with the topic. Readable, too.

2. Stephen S. Attwood, *Electric and Magnetic Fields*, Dover, New York, 1967. A rigorous treatment of field combined with a comprehensive collection of data and engineering applications for magnetic materials. Uses MKS units. First published in 1932, so recent materials as well as domain models are lacking.

3. H. Knoepfel, *Pulsed High Magnetic Fields*, North-Holland., Amsterdam, 1970. As a by-product, this book gives a comprehensive treatment of the transient interaction between magnetic fields and conductors.

4. F. Brailsford, *Physical Principles of Magnetism*, D. Van Nostrand, London, 1966. Especially good review of the eddy current anomaly, with references.

5. H. J. Williams, W. Shockley, and C. Kittel, "Studies of the Propagation Velocity of a Ferromagnetic Domain Boundary," *Phys. Rev.*, **80**, 1090–1094 (1950). A definitive study of domain wall motion, in a picture-frame core cut from single-crystal silicon iron. Established localized eddy currents as a damping mechanism even at extremely small wall velocity. The localization accounts for increased losses known as the eddy current anomaly.

6. P. D. Agarwal, "Eddy Current Losses in Solid and Laminated Iron," *AIEE Commun. Electron.*, **42**, 169–181 (May 1959).

7. I. Leliakov and F. J. Friedlaender, "An Improved Model for Flux Reversal in Ni–Fe Cores", *AIEE Commun. Electron.*, **44**, 1–4 (March 1961). Uses a model similar to (5.4.1), carried through to an analytical solution and compared with experiment.

8. J. E. L. Bishop and P. Williams, "A Comparison of Rapid Surface and Volume Magnetization Measurements on 50% NiFe Tape with Models of Eddy-Current-Limited Domain Wall Motion", *J. Phys. D: Appl. Phys.*, **10**, 225–241 (1977). This reference gives some historical perspective as well as recent new results.

9. E. Olsen, *Applied Magnetism—A Study in Quantities*, Philips Technical Library, Springer-Verlag, New York, 1966. A little (144 pages) book with mathematical models of many types, compactly given. Olsen summarizes models for core losses: Raleigh, Peterson, Steinmetz, Jordan, Legg, etc.

10. J. Smit and H. P. J. Wijn, *Ferrites*, Wiley, New York, 1959.

11. L. Landau and E. Lifshitz, "Theory of Dispersion of Magnetic Permeability in Ferromagnetic Bodies," *Phys. Z. Sowjetunion*, **8**, 153–169 (1935). Proposed damped precession as the mode of magnetization reversal. Chikazumi (Chap. 4, Ref. 1) gives an expanded interpretation of this paper and of the subsequent modifications by Gilbert and others.

12. F. B. Hagedorn, "Domain Wall Motion in Bubble Domain Materials," *A.I.P. Conf. Proc.*, No. 5, pp. 72–90 (1972).

13. R. M. Bozorth, *Ferromagnetism*, Von Nostrand, New York, 1951.

14. J. K. Watson and C. T. Leis, "*Analog Approximations of Transient Flux Diffusion,*" *IEEE Trans. Magn.* **MAG-7**, 304–308 (June 1971).

15. R. Becker, "Dynamics of the Bloch Wall and the Permeability at High Frequencies," Proc. Grenoble Conf. on Ferromagnetism, July 3–7, 1950.

16. J. F. Dillon, Jr., "Domains and Domain Walls," in G. T. Rado and H. Suhl, Editors, *Magnetism*, Academic Press, 1963. Vol. 3, Ch. 9, pp. 415–464.

6.
Electronic Applications with Cores

6.1   GUIDE TO CHAPTER 6

This chapter consists of examples and circuits that draw on ideas from some of the earlier chapters. The background of Chapter 1, plus Sections 2.2, 2.3, and 3.1, is adequate for most of the applications, although ideas from Section 3.3 and Chapter 5 are used in some cases. In my course I have found it useful to work through selected examples from Chapter 6 as early as possible, to illustrate the concepts that are being developed.

The core memory (Section 6.2) and the lamp ballast (Section 6.3.2) are accessible after Section 2.3, whereas the d–c to d–c converter (Section 6.4.4) also uses the wire size data of Section 3.1.3. The choke-input filter (Section 6.3.4) may be used to support the airgap ideas of Section 3.3, whereas the high-Q coil (Section 6.3.3) also draws on Section 5.3.

6.2   FERRITE CORE MEMORY

Several different technologies have been used to implement random-access storage for digital computers. This section outlines the principles of operation of the ferrite core memory, a technology that totally dominated the market for nearly two decades and is still important, although no longer dominant.

Two of the four properties of the core material and shape that are relevant to this application are apparent from the square B–H loop of Fig. 6.1. First, it is vital to the memory function that the B–H characteristic be double-valued for $H = 0$, with a significant remnant flux density $\pm B_r$. Ideally the characteristic will have a fairly flat top with $B_r/B_s \approx 1$. A second important property of the square-loop material is that the sides of the B–H loop be nearly vertical and that the corners be square. These factors define the threshold value of H-field necessary to switch the direction of magnetization of the core. The coincident-current technique exploits this nonlinear magnetic property to select the one desired core from a planar array of cores. A third important property is the toroidal shape of the core. A toroid is a closed-flux structure that couples efficiently to currents through the center and inefficiently to fields from external currents. The fourth property of importance to high-speed memory is the material and geometrical property of a small switching coefficient (Section 5.2.2), which permits the sense of the magnetization of the core to be reversed from clockwise to counter-clockwise, or vice versa, in a very short time.

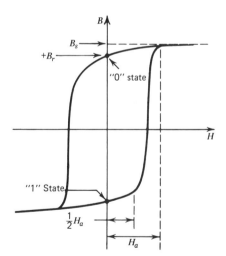

Figure 6.1 Representative B–H characteristics of a ferrite memory core. The two remanent states $\pm B_r$ represent the binary numbers 0, 1. The well-defined loop width is used to select the specific core for interrogation.

6.2.1 Overview of Ideal Operation

The usual configuration of a core memory consists of a stack of identical memory planes. The plane is the basic element of memory organization and is described below in some detail. For now, the core plane consists basically of a set of small wires n_x in the x-direction and another set n_y in the y-direction, threaded through tiny ferrite cores. Each core is linked by one x- and one y-direction wire, making a total of $n_x n_y$ cores in the plane. This large number (usually of the order 2^{10} to 2^{14}) corresponds to the number of memory storage locations or addresses. Each memory address designates a different core, which is selected by the one specific pair of x- and y-conductors that intersect in and pass through the core of interest. A third wire, the sense winding, passes through every core of the plane to sense a flux change that may take place at any core. In the overall organization of the memory stack, each plane stores one bit (binary digit), so that the number of planes in the stack is the same as the bit length of the stored numbers.

Figure 6.2 shows the read operation for a 4-bit number. A single core of each plane is interrogated by the coincidence of the x- and y-currents. The field thereby generated is sufficient to switch the selected core and is in the direction that sets the core into the "0" state (Fig. 6.1). Depending on the bit previously stored, the core may be in either the "0" or the "1" state, so that a core reversal may or may not take place.

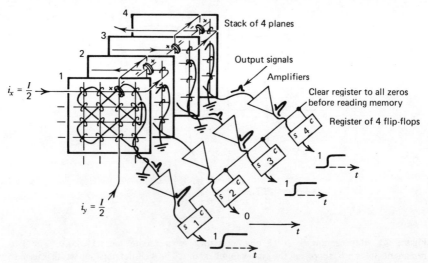

Figure 6.2 Organization of a coincident-current core memory illustrated for a 4-bit memory word.

If the total applied current causes a reversal of the selected core, a voltage pulse will be induced in the sense winding of the plane. After amplification (and time selection, not shown) the pulse from each plane is used to set the corresponding flip-flop in the memory data register. The prior magnetic state of the selected core has thereby been transduced to a flip-flop state as an electrical or logical voltage level. This read operation, followed by a rewrite operation, represents a total memory cycle.

Ideal Core Model. The selection and the reversal of a core by coincident currents can be understood by first considering the ideal geometry of a single toroidal core of rectangular cross section, perfectly centered on a long wire of small area (Fig. 6.3a). The field due to a current in the wire is inherently nonuniform as $H = I/2\pi r$ (Fig. 6.3b). If a core switches uniformly at a field strength H_0, as in Fig. 6.4a, the current required to develop that field strength will vary with radius as $I = H_0 2\pi r$. The corresponding core characteristic would be somewhat sheared or tilted, with two critical values of current

$$I_1 = H_0 2\pi r_1 \quad \text{and} \quad I_2 = H_0 2\pi r_2. \tag{6.1}$$

The two critical values correspond to the value of field strength H_0 at the inside and outside radii, respectively. Commercial memory cores

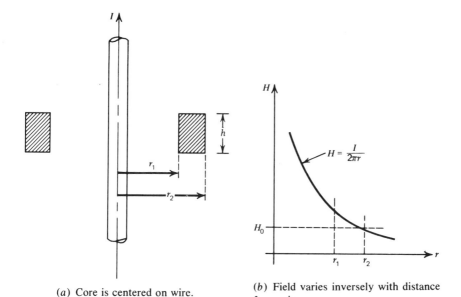

(a) Core is centered on wire.

(b) Field varies inversely with distance from wire.

Figure 6.3 Ideal geometry of a single core on a current-carrying wire.

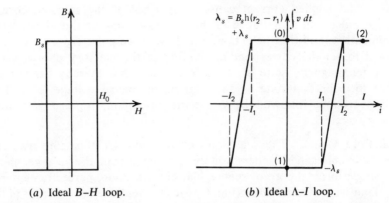

(a) Ideal B–H loop.   (b) Ideal Λ–I loop.

Figure 6.4 A perfectly rectangular material property yields a slightly sheared core characteristic with break points at I_1, I_2 defined by (6.1).

usually have radii in the ratio

$$\frac{r_2}{r_1} \approx 1.6, \tag{6.2}$$

which is consistent with coincident-current addressing.

Coincident-current core selection is achieved by driving one selected x- and one y-address line each with current

$$i_x = i_y = \left(\frac{I}{2}\right) < I_1 \qquad I > I_2. \tag{6.3}$$

The value of drive I can be readily chosen with some margin, since $I_2/I_1 \approx 1.6$ as determined by (6.1) and (6.2). Ideally the half-select current $I/2$ will not disturb any core on either line, except where the x- and y-currents add at the core of intersection. In practice there is always some disturbance, described subsequently as noise.

EXAMPLE A

Suppose a 20-mil ferrite memory core has dimensions O.D./I.D./ht = 0.020/0.012/0.005 in. and a material coercivity $H_0 = 6$ Oe. Find I_1, I_2 and choose drive current I for equal margins ϵ such that $I_1 - (I/2) = \epsilon = I - I_2$.

ANSWER. $H_0 = 1500/\pi$ A/m, $I_1 = 0.4572$ A, $I_2 = 0.762$ A. For equal margins $I = \frac{2}{3}(I_1 + I_2) = 0.8128$ A and $\epsilon = \frac{1}{3}(2I_1 - I_2) = 0.0508$ A.

Destructive Read.   Let us now suppose that a pulse of current I, defined by (6.3), is applied to "read" a core. A description of the reversal process follows, using the convention of Fig. 6.4b in which a positive current pulse I will drive a core to state 2, either from the "0" state or from the "1" state. In either event the final state of the core will be "0" after the pulse, so this procedure is called a "destructive readout" (DRO). The two initial states correspond to clockwise (CW) or counterclockwise (CCW) core saturation, which in turn correspond to the direction of the most recent pulse of current $I > I_2$ through the core.

In Fig. 6.5 the "0" state is shown as CW core magnetization, which is the same as the H-field due to a positive read current. When a total read current I is applied, the operating point in Fig. 6.4b that describes the core state is assumed to move horizontally to the right along the positive saturation line, causing a small flux change $(B_s - B_r)S_c$, which is neglected by the model of a perfect core with $B_r = B_s$. A binary "1" state is stored as a CCW sense of core magnetization. A positive read current I causes a reversal of the core, which begins at the inside radius of the core and proceeds outward.

The time derivative of the changing flux is equal to the voltage induced on the wires through the core, specifically including the sense winding, which passes through all the cores in the plane.

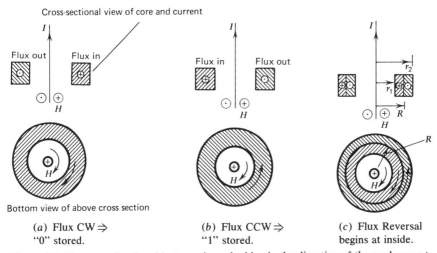

Cross-sectional view of core and current

Bottom view of above cross section

(a) Flux CW $\Rightarrow$
"0" stored.

(b) Flux CCW $\Rightarrow$
"1" stored.

(c) Flux Reversal
begins at inside.

Figure 6.5   Cross-sectional and bottom views, looking in the direction of the read current, of a ferrite memory core. (a), (b) Core states 0, 1 prior to read current. (c) An intermediate flux state as a domain wall at R, which moves outward from the inside radius.

EXAMPLE B

Suppose the ideal core of Example A reverses in 180 ns. Calculate the time average of the output voltage induced by reading a "1" assuming $B_s \simeq 0.3$ T.

ANSWER.   Since $\int v\, dt \doteq \Delta\Lambda = 2B_s S_c$, $\langle v \rangle = 2B_s S_c/\tau$, where $S_c = \frac{1}{2}(0.020 - 0.012)(0.005)(2.54 \times 10^{-2})^2 = 1.29 \times 10^{-8}$ m^2. The average voltage is thus 43 mV. The experimental voltage waveform is approximately triangular, so the calculated peak voltage is 86 mV, about twice the typical measured values.

Reversal Process.   The predominant mechanism of core reversal has been identified experimentally as domain wall motion. The flux reversal first takes place at the inside radius of the core, resulting in the creation or nucleation of a domain wall. The wall then moves outward as the reversal progresses (Fig. 6.5c). It is likely that the field required to move an existing domain wall is less than the field required to nucleate the wall initially. The ideal core model (Fig. 6.4) is inaccurate in that it omits the distinction between nucleation field and the field required to move the wall outward.

It can be noted from Fig. 6.4b that the core is driven outside the hysteresis loop by a current $I > I_2$. It has been found that reversal is faster if I is larger. In the interest of fast core memories, it is highly desirable for the reversal to take place quickly. During the development of square-loop ferrites for cores, the materials were compared experimentally by measuring reversal time τ as the applied field H was varied. The switching coefficient

$$S_w = \tau(H - H_0) \qquad \text{for} \quad H > H_0 \qquad (5.47)$$

can be deduced from a graph of the experimental data, for example, see Fig. 6.6. A smaller value of S_w is more desirable because it means lower reversal time for less drive field.

A great deal has been learned about domain wall motion since the early days of ferrites. Nowadays we recognize that the theoretical meaning of switching coefficient is not very clear because it includes the material parameters of wall mobility as well as the distance $(r_2 - r_1)$ moved by the wall. It is possible to calculate the reversal time for the ideal core model using the equation for domain wall velocity v and mobility m

$$v = m(H - H_0) \qquad \text{if} \quad H > H_0. \qquad (5.75)$$

Let us assume a domain wall at R as in Fig. 6.5c, hence $v = dR/dt$ and

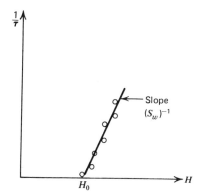

Figure 6.6 Measured values of core reversal time vary inversely with drive field in terms of switching coefficient $S_w = \tau(H - H_0)$.

$H = I/2\pi R$ at the wall. After these substitutions, (5.75) leads to

$$\int_0^\tau m \, dt = \int_{r_1}^{r_2} \frac{dR}{H - H_0} = \int_{r_1}^{r_2} \frac{2\pi R \, dR}{I - H_0 2\pi R}, \qquad (6.4)$$

which is similar to an integral table entry

$$\int \frac{x \, dx}{ax + b} = \frac{1}{a^2} [ax + b - b \log_e(ax + b)], \qquad (6.5)$$

where $a = -H_0 2\pi$ and $b = I$.

After (6.5) has been used, (6.4) becomes

$$m\tau = \frac{1}{2\pi H_0^2} \left[I \log_e \left(\frac{I - I_1}{I - I_2} \right) - (I_2 - I_1) \right], \qquad (6.6)$$

where I_1 and I_2 are defined by eq. (6.1).

EXAMPLE C

Solve (6.6) for the core of Example A, then deduce the apparent wall mobility m if $\tau \approx 180$ ns. Estimate the validity of the model.

ANSWER.   Using the results of Example A for H_0, I, I_1, and I_2, $m\tau = 0.89 \times 10^{-6}$. If $\tau = 0.18 \times 10^{-6}$ s, $m = 4.95$ m^2/s·A, which seems too large to be plausible. As a test of the effect of a lower coercivity for wall motion, a recalculation of (6.6) with the same value of I but using half the previous values for H_0, I_1, and I_2 yields $m\tau = 0.26 \times 10^{-6}$. This results in $m = 1.44$ m^2/s·A, which is more reasonable but still larger than mobility data given by Greifer [1].

6.2.2 PRACTICAL MEMORY CONFIGURATIONS

Read-Rewrite Cycles. As mentioned earlier, the most practical and competitive read arrangement for core memories is destructive, but this means that the next state of a core is always zero after reading. In the case of memories for computers it is usually necessary for the information to be retained, however, so a read operation is followed by a rewrite into the same core location. The rewrite operation differs from read in two ways. First, the x- and y-direction currents are directed through the selected core in the opposite sense, negative from Fig. 6.5. Second, the total effect of the two currents must be locally controlled for each core plane. Provision must be made for the selected core to be either kept in the "0" state or else reset to the "1" state, depending on whether a "0" or a "1" was just read from the core in question. The prior state of the core was retained in the corresponding state of the memory data register (Fig. 6.2); thus the old information is still available. By a digital logic operation, the core is reset or not reset, when the flip-flop is "1" or "0", respectively.

Other types of memory cycle are readily achieved with the same basic circuits. For instance, the initial storage of data into memory can be achieved by a clear-write cycle. A clear-write sequence is almost identical to a read-rewrite cycle, except that the memory data register flip-flops are set by data from the computer. The "read" operation is used merely to clear the cores to zero, to be able to accept the new data during the "rewrite" operation. As another example, a read-modify-write is almost identical to a read-rewrite cycle, except for additional time between the two operations. During that interval of time before the rewrite sequence, the computer is allowed to read the memory data register and alter its contents.

The operations just described have been achieved by several different configurations of core plane wiring. Three of the most common arrangements are discussed below.

3-D, 4-Wire Array. The 4-wire system is so called because 4 wires pass through each core of a memory plane. The 3-D notation indicates that there is two-dimensional x- and y-address decoding in addition to the rewrite logic that occurs at each plane, considered to be the z-direction. The 3-D, 4-wire was used in the first decade of the technology, before better semiconductors made feasible the 3-wire technologies. The 4-wire system is easiest to understand because each wire is associated with only one function.

Figure 6.7 shows a 4-wire arrangement for a 4×4 plane. Practical

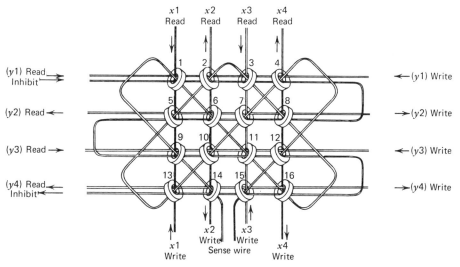

Figure 6.7 A 4-wire core plane.

$n \times n$ planes may have $n = 32$, 64, or even 128 and are addressed by an address register of $2 \log_2 n$ bits. Careful examination of the wires of Fig. 6.7 reveals the following:

1. n x-Address wires, each of which passes through n cores.
2. n y-Address wires, each of which passes through n cores.
3. One sense wire, which passes through all n^2 cores.
4. One inhibit wire, which passes through all n^2 cores.

Referring to Fig. 6.7, the n-wires in the x-direction, and the n-wires in the y-direction are used for selecting the specific core for reading or writing. To a single one of the x-wires and to a single one of the y-address lines a current of $I/2$ is applied. The core at the intersection is selected by the field due to the total current of $I > I_2$ that passes through it. The wire with the distinctive diagonal path in Fig. 6.7 is the line that senses the flux change on any selected core in the plane. The purpose of its meandering path is to cancel the interference pulses from half-selected cores. The fourth wire is the inhibit wire, which runs parallel to the y-direction, up one column and down the next as it links all the cores of the plane. The inhibit wire provides the means during the rewrite sequence of controlling whether a "0" or a "1" is written. A current pulse of $I/2$ serves to cancel the effect of the y-address current, so that the selected core remains in the cleared or "0"-state. Otherwise, with

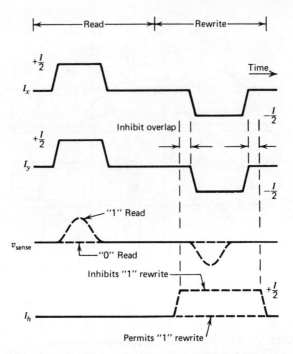

Figure 6.8 Ideal signal waveforms for a 3-D, 4-wire memory.

zero inhibit current, the selected core is reset to the "1" state by the x- and y-currents. Ideal waveforms of Fig. 6.8 illustrate the relative timing of the various signals.

3-Wire Systems. Several alternative core stack configurations have been devised in an attempt to reduce costs or memory cycle time or both. In the 1960s improvements in ferrite core technology made possible smaller cores, progressing from O.D./I.D. dimensions of 80/50 mils to 50/30, 30/18, 20/12, and even smaller. The reduction in size helped to relieve the temperature rise due to core losses by increasing the surface -to-volume ratio. In addition, smaller cores require less drive current and can be reversed more quickly for faster memory performance. It is harder to thread four wires through the smaller cores, but there have emerged several designs that use fewer wires. The principles of two 3-wire systems are indicated below.

The 3-D, 3-wire stack configuration (Fig. 6.9) combines the functions of read and inhibit on the same wire. The wire is arranged so that its center is available in addition to the two ends. During the read operation, the signal is read at the wire ends by a special differential amplifier with

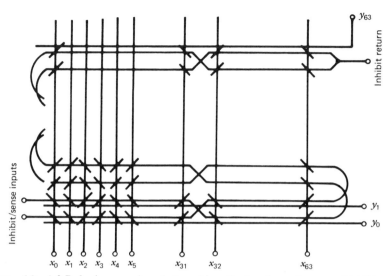

Figure 6.9 A 3-D, 3-wire core plane that combines the functions of sense and inhibit on the same center-tapped wire. The cores are oriented in a double-box pattern. (From Elder and Norman [6]. Reprinted with permission of Ampex Corporation, Redwood City, California. Reprinted with permission also from the November 1967 issue of *Computer Design* magazine. Copyright Computer Design Publishing Corp.)

the property of a fast recovery from large common-mode signals. During the rewrite operation an inhibit current of twice the usual value is driven into the center connection and divides equally into each half of the winding. This inhibit/sense configuration also must possess the property that the read signal is not obscured by noise pulses from half-selected cores. The noise cancellation is achieved by the double-box core orientation (Fig. 6.9), which may be compared with the single-box core orientation and the diagonal sense winding of Fig. 6.7.

It is interesting to note that a significant fraction of the cycle time of a conventional core memory is required for the inductive lines to recover electrically from the large pulses of drive current. The inhibit line has the slowest recovery because it is longest and passes through more cores. The 3-D, 3-wire configuration reduces the net inductance of the inhibit line substantially, whereas the 2 1/2-D, 3-wire configuration eliminates the inhibit wire altogether.

The 2 1/2D, 3-wire core memory eliminates the need for the inhibit function by controlling one of the address lines during rewrite. The read is achieved by the usual coincidence of x- and y-address currents, but the rewrite is done differently. The rewrite current on one line, say the y-direction, is locally controlled for each core plane in order to rewrite a

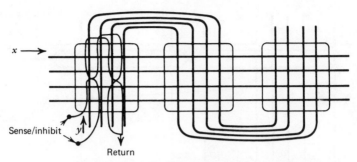

(a) 3-D, 3-wire: both address lines thread all planes.

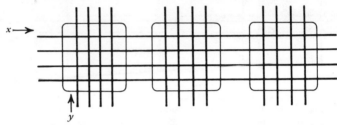

(b) 2 ½-D, 3-wire: only x-address threads all planes, y-address is
locally controlled on rewrite.

Figure 6.10 Comparison of address wiring of core planes in a stack for two 3-wire
systems.

"1" or to retain the core in its zero state. Figure 6.10 compares an
unfolded core stack for the 3-D and the 2 1/2-D configurations. The
elimination of the inhibit wire, and the short y-address lines, serve to make
the 2 1/2-D system faster, however there is a need for more support
electronics. Finally, the pattern of core orientation in the plane can be
simpler for 2 1/2-D. The cores can be oriented parallel to one another along
the drive and sense wires, with closer core spacing than for the 90° box
arrangements. The closer spacing results in shorter sense wires, which
leads to less attenuation of the signal on the sense lines.

6.2.3 Noise

The ideal core model of Section 6.2.1 assumed that read current pulses
$(I_x + I_y = I)$ induce an output signal of either a "pulse" or "no pulse,"
depending on whether the selected core reversed polarity. It was further
assumed that the half-select currents $(I_x = I_y = I/2)$ would have no effect
on any cores other than the core of interest. In fact, however, the
hysteresis data for cores depart significantly from the ideal rectangular

shape, and considerable attention must be given to the cancellation of unwanted voltage responses. Ingenious solutions to this problem are ultimately responsible for making core memories work successfully.

Three categories of spurious responses have been identified inside a core stack.

1. Capacitive coupling between windings, so that a component of the output is a response to input voltage transients.
2. Magnetic coupling between windings so that a component of spurious output is due to input current transients.
3. A component of spurious output due to the response of nonideal cores to half-select currents.

It has been found that the first two components of spurious response can be reduced adequately by design, with careful attention to voltage and current waveforms, winding geometry, and winding symmetry, and by sensing only the differential component of the signal. The minimization of the response to half-select currents merits some further comments.

The occurrence of half-select currents of alternating polarity, applied to a not quite ideally square-loop core, causes a minor hysteresis loop to be traversed. Such a minor loop can be near either polarity of saturation, with the result that either state, "1" or "0" may be further characterized as "disturbed" or "undisturbed" (Fig. 6.11). The disturbed states are imprecisely defined, since a detailed history of half-select currents

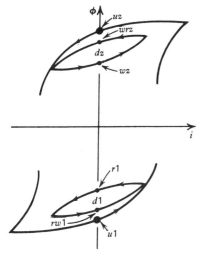

uz is an undisturbed "0".
wz is a "0" after disturbance by a write $I/2$.
wrz is wz after further disturbance by a read $I/2$.
dz is either wz or wrz.

$u1$ is an undisturbed "1".
$r1$ is a "1" after disturbance by a read $I/2$.
$rw1$ is an $r1$ after further disturbance by a write $I/2$.
$d1$ is either $r1$ or $rw1$.

Figure 6.11 Each of the two states of a memory core, "1" or "0", can be further described as "undisturbed" or "disturbed."

would need to be known. They share one characteristic that distinguishes them from the undisturbed states: an inelastic or irreversible flux change has taken place because of a demagnetizing pulse of current $I/2$. The read voltage from a disturbed "1", dV_1, is therefore smaller than uV_1, and the read voltage from a disturbed "0" is larger than uV_z (Fig. 6.12). So we see that the two signal responses from a selected core, driven by current I, suffer some deterioration if the core has been subjected to the disturbance of half-select currents. Rather than discriminating between the ideal output signal alternatives of "pulse" and "no pulse," the discrimination is between "pulse" and "smaller, earlier pulse." One or the other signal from the selected core will be induced onto the sense wire of each core plane. To some extent the signals are obscured by the half-select responses on the same line.

Consider the effect of a read current of $I/2$ applied to one each x- and y-wire to read a coincident-current $n \times n$ memory. The coincident core responds with signal voltage v_s due to I and the $2(n-1)$ half-selected cores respond with spurious voltages $\pm v_\delta$ due to $I/2$. A typical signal v_s is one of the four waveforms of Fig. 6.12. The total output voltage on the sense line due to the $2n-1$ cores is

$$v_{\text{out}} = v_s + \sum_{i=1}^{2(n-1)} v_{\delta_i},\tag{6.7}$$

where the summation of delta voltages is over the cores in the row and the column of the selected core. The objective of the clever configuration of the sense wire is to cancel v_δ components by having equal

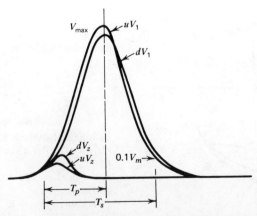

Figure 6.12 Voltage waveforms from each of the four states of a selected core: undisturbed or disturbed "1", or undisturbed or disturbed "0". The times for the peak signal T_p and for complete switching T_s are also shown.

numbers of positive and negative polarities. In practice the best cancellation that can be achieved in a square array is n delta voltages of one polarity and $n - 2$ of the other. The vital importance of the cancellation strategy becomes apparent when it is recognized that $|v_\delta|$ may be 10% of dV_1. For $n = 64$ or 128 it is clear that the memory would be inoperative without the substantial cancellation of delta voltages from rather uniform cores.

As a first approximation we may assume that the half-select delta voltages will cancel. As a second approximation we may surmise from Fig. 6.11 that the delta voltage from a half-selected "1", v_{δ_1}, may have a value slightly different from the delta voltage from a half-selected "0", v_{δ_0}. A "worst-case" data pattern therefore exists for every sense wire configuration, based on the concept of adding all the like voltages and subtracting the unlike voltages. For an array of the type depicted in Fig. 6.7, a checkerboard data pattern is worst; for example, core locations $(1, 4, 5, 8, 10, 11, 14, 15)$ might contain 1's with 0's in $(2, 3, 6, 7, 9, 12, 13, 16)$.

The reliability requirements for computer memory are almost incredible. A mean time between failures of 10 hours translates into a probability of error of the order of 10^{-12} per operation (for a 32-bit word at 200,000 memory cycles/s). Such a high level of accomplishment is a credit to the ingenuity of the many magneticians who made it happen.

6.3 INDUCTANCE APPLICATIONS

All the applications described in this section exploit the magnetic property of a linear $\Lambda - I$ core characteristic, modeled by the parameter of inductance. In some cases the linearity is achieved by use of a magnetic material with a linear $B-H$ characteristic. In other cases the linearity of the magnetic circuit may be attributed partly to an airgap that enhances the linearity of the intrinsic $B-H$ characteristic. In every example the design should avoid saturation of the magnetic core.

6.3.1 Ferrite Shielding Bead

A ferrite shielding bead is a small cylinder of linear ferrite with a hole along its axis. The beads can be simply strung onto power supply leads or onto leads of circuit components to provide high-frequency isolation. The components on either side of the bead are decoupled at high frequency, but the bead has little or no effect at low frequency. The bead provides isolation because it acts as a one-turn inductor.

One type of application uses a bead or beads, followed by a capacitor as an *LC* low-pass filter to provide attenuation in the megahertz range of frequency. Another type of application merely uses the beads alone on the leads, without added capacitance. The high-frequency isolation provided by a bead suppresses the tendency toward parasitic oscillations in the frequency range 10–100 MHz. In a third application, the beads are used to shield the wire from a hostile environment of stray magnetic fields.

It is interesting to note that the ferrite material still continues to act as an impedance, even at frequencies above Snoek's limit. In the high-frequency range the impedance is lossy rather than inductive but still provides decoupling.

Ferrite beads are available in a variety of small sizes from several manufacturers of medium permeability ferrites. One particular bead has dimensions I.D./O.D./ht = 1.2/3.5/3 mm. It is available in manganese zinc ferrite, with relative permeability of 900, which has B_{sat} that progresses from 0.34 T at $H = 800$ A/m to an eventual value $B_s \approx 0.45$ T at $H = 16 \times 10^4$ A/m.

The inductance calculated for such a bead is $L = 0.58$ μH at currents up to 1 A, using the concepts of Section 2.2.2. The field from 1.1 A of current through the bead is sufficient to cause the inside radius of the core to approach saturation; thus the inductance would be expected to decrease from 0.6 μH to a small value if the current is increased from 1 A toward 3 A.

6.3.2 Ballast for Fluorescent Lamp

When a glow discharge gas tube is driven by a supply voltage, a series impedance is usually required between the two, to limit the current. If the gas tube is a small neon indicator lamp that dissipates only a few milliwatts, a resistor is the simplest choice for the current-limiting impedance. But if the gas lamp is a fluorescent bulb that dissipates several tens of watts, an energy storage impedance is preferable to an energy dissipative resistor. In fact the common ballast for fluorescent lights is essentially an inductive reactance that limits the current from the line voltage to the nonlinear light bulb. This practical application demonstrates the use of an inductor in a circuit with waveforms that are more complicated than in the examples at the end of Chapter 2.

The example circuit (Fig. 6.13) consists of a small fluorescent lamp (24 in., 20 W) supplied through an inductor from standard U.S. line voltage.* When the circuit is turned on, the start switch is initially closed

*Long bulbs that require higher voltage than line voltage use a different kind of ballast, one that provides step-up voltage transformation as well as the series inductance function.

for a brief time, to heat the filaments in each end of the tube. After the tube has begun functioning, the filaments remain heated because they are being bombarded by gas ions in the tube. The light from the tube is given off when the fluorescent coating inside the bulb is excited by ultraviolet emission products of the glow discharge in the ionized gas. The voltage across the tube v_t is a nonuniform function of current (Fig. 6.14) that can be conveniently approximated as a square wave

$$v_t \approx V_t \, \text{sgn} \, (i) \qquad (6.8)$$

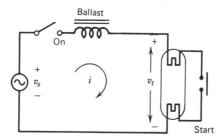

(*a*) Circuit with ballast in series with tube.

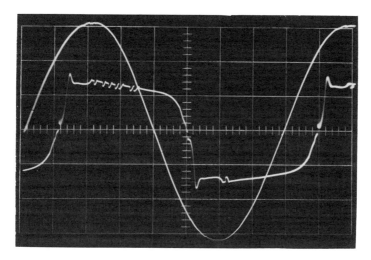

(*b*) Waveform of v_t in comparison with 115-V, 60-Hz supply voltage v_s. Scale: 50 V/div × 2 ms/div.

Figure 6.13 Circuit diagram and voltage waveforms for a small fluorescent lamp.

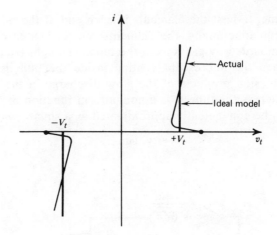

(a) Approximation of v_t used in the analysis.

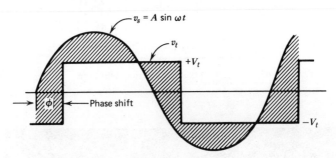

(b) Model for v_s, v_t. The ballast voltage $(v_s - v_t)$ is hash-lined.

Figure 6.14 The voltage v_t across the fluorescent tube can be approximated as a square wave of amplitude $\pm V_t$.

to aid the analysis that follows. The analysis shows (a) the phase shift ϕ by which v_t lags v_s, (b) the waveform of the current, (c) the value of Λ_s required to avoid saturation of the inductor, and (d) the value of inductance required for a specified tube wattage.

Phase Lag of v_t. According to (6.8) the polarity of v_t is controlled by the current through the tube, which lags the supply voltage because of the ballast inductance. This means that v_t will switch polarity when the current through the inductor passes through zero. For an ideal inductor

$$i(t) = \frac{1}{L} \Lambda(t) = \frac{1}{L} \int^t v_L \, dt, \tag{6.9}$$

where the inductor voltage $v_L = v_s - v_t$ is

$$v_L = [A \sin \omega t - V_t \operatorname{sgn}(\sin\{\omega t - \phi\})]. \tag{6.10}$$

The integral of (6.10) is

$$\int^t v_L \, dt = -\frac{A}{\omega} \cos \omega t - \int^t v_t \, dt, \tag{6.11}$$

which is a sinusoid, and a triangular waveform of peak value

$$\pm V_t \frac{T}{4} = \frac{\pm V_t}{4f} = \frac{\pm V_t \pi}{2\omega}. \tag{6.12}$$

A key point of the analysis follows. The peak values of (6.12) define where v_t, hence i, change polarity; therefore they define where (6.11) is zero. It follows that the two waveforms of (6.11) will touch at phase angle ϕ, where

$$\frac{A}{\omega} \cos \phi = \frac{V_t \pi}{2\omega}, \tag{6.13}$$

which leads to the result of interest

$$\cos \phi = \frac{V_t \pi}{2A}. \tag{6.14}$$

For comparison with Fig. 6.13, use of $A = 165$ V and $V_t = 70$ V yields $\phi = 48°$, which is in reasonable agreement. These values are used to illustrate the remaining analysis.

EXERCISE

Carefully sketch the waveforms v_s, v_t, v_L and the two waveforms on the right-hand side of (6.11) to satisfy (6.13).

Waveform for $i(t)$ and $\Lambda(t)$. The known values for phase shift ϕ and the amplitudes A, V_t define the waveform of $\int v_L \, dt$, which can be calculated point by point using (6.11). The result in Fig. 6.15 is shown with v_s and v_t for comparison. The peak amplitude of $\Lambda_{max} = 0.343$ V·s at 155° is the minimum design value of Λ_s for the ballast, to avoid core saturation. The same Λ_{max} value represents LI_{max}, but the inductance L is yet to be specified.

Inductance Value. In Fig. 6.15 the waveforms Li and v_t are in phase; their product is proportional to the instantaneous power in the tube. Since the calculated average value of Li is 0.207, the average power in the tube is equal to $(14.49/L)$ watts for $V_t = 70$ V. The value of in-

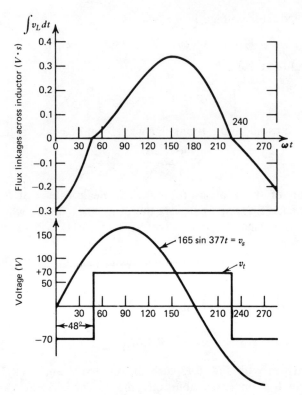

Figure 6.15 Calculated waveform of $\Lambda = Li$, compared with v_s and v_t.

ductance thereby determines the tube power; for example, $L = 0.725$ H yields an average power of 20 W according to the model.

Use of Square-Wave Supply. Because fluorescent lights are more efficient than incandescent, there has been some interest in battery-operated, portable fluorescent lamps. One design approach is to assume a square-wave supply voltage $\pm V_s$ (e.g., using a d–c to a–c inverter, Section 6.4.6, to generate the square wave from the battery) and use an inductor ballast as described earlier.

Figure 6.16 shows an idealized first cut at such a design. The details are left to a problem at the end of the chapter, since the analysis is easier than for the sinusoidal v_s. The phase angle of v_t lag is readily obtained by construction from Fig. 6.16, or from the waveforms of Fig. 6.17, as

$$\frac{T_1}{T_2} = \frac{V_s - V_t}{V_s + V_t}. \tag{6.15}$$

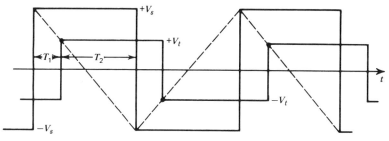

Figure 6.16 Model of the response of an ideal gas tube v_t and an inductor ballast to a square supply voltage $\pm V_s$.

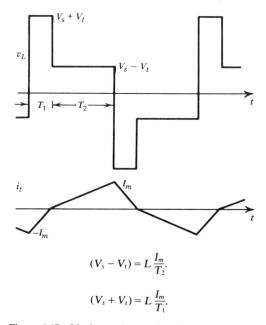

$$(V_s - V_t) = L\frac{I_m}{T_2}.$$

$$(V_s + V_t) = L\frac{I_m}{T_1}.$$

Figure 6.17 Ideal waveforms of voltage and current.

The average power in the lamp is given by

$$P = \frac{V_t I_m}{2}, \tag{6.16}$$

where I_m is the maximum of the triangular current waveform.

6.3.3 Frequency-Sensitive Circuits

Tuned Circuit. A common use of a high-Q inductor is with a capacitor in a resonant circuit. When used as a narrow bandpass filter as in Fig. 6.18a, resistor R_1 must be large, $R_1 \gg \sqrt{L/C}$, if good frequency selectivity is to be achieved. The circuit requirements for a bandpass filter are reviewed next.

Analysis of the circuit in Fig. 6.18b results in the transfer function

$$\frac{V_2}{V_1}(s) = \frac{sG_1L}{s^2LC + sL(G_1 + G_2) + 1}, \tag{6.17}$$

where $s = j\omega$ is the frequency (rads/s), $G_1 = 1/R_1$, and G_2 is the parallel loss parameter of the inductor; G_2 includes the effect of winding resistance and core losses as explained in Chapter 5 and elsewhere in Section 6.3.3. A quick examination of the extreme values of $s = j\omega$ confirms the general bandpass characteristic of (6.17), that is,

$$\left. \begin{array}{ll} \lim\limits_{\omega \to 0} \dfrac{V_2}{V_1}(\omega) \approx j\omega G_1 L & \text{low-frequency zero} \\[2mm] \lim\limits_{\omega \to \infty} \dfrac{V_2}{V_1}(\omega) \approx \dfrac{G_1}{j\omega C} & \text{high-frequency zero} \\[2mm] \dfrac{V_2}{V_1}(\omega) = \dfrac{G_1}{G_1 + G_2} & \text{pass at } \omega = 1/\sqrt{LC} \end{array} \right\}. \tag{6.18}$$

For more details in the vicinity of resonance we must examine the poles of the transfer function (6.17),

$$s^2LC + sLG + 1 = 0, \tag{6.19}$$

where $G = G_1 + G_2$. The roots of (6.19) are

$$s = -\frac{G}{2C} \pm j\sqrt{\frac{1}{LC} - \left(\frac{G}{2C}\right)^2} = -\alpha \pm j\omega_d, \tag{6.20}$$

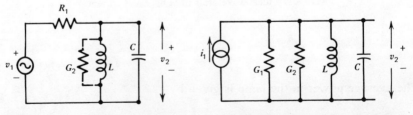

(a) Schematic of the physical circuit.

(b) Circuit after Norton transformation $i_1 = G_1v_1$.

Figure 6.18 Parallel resonant circuit used as a bandpass filter.

where the damped angular frequency is approximately equal to the undamped resonant frequency

$$\omega_d \approx \omega_r = \frac{1}{\sqrt{LC}} \qquad (6.21)$$

for high values of quality factor Q. The bandwidth between half-power frequencies (the frequencies of $1/\sqrt{2}$ amplitude, 45° phase shift) is the well-known relation

$$\Delta\omega = 2\alpha = \frac{G}{C},$$

which is shown in Fig. 6.20b as bandwidth B_2.

The Q of the circuit is

$$Q = \frac{\omega_r}{\Delta\omega} = \frac{\sqrt{C/L}}{G} = \frac{R}{\sqrt{L/C}}. \qquad (6.22)$$

Substituting (6.22) into (6.17) with $s = j\omega$ gives

$$\frac{V_2}{V_1}(\omega) = \frac{j\omega G_1 L}{1 - \omega^2 LC + j\omega\sqrt{LC}/Q}. \qquad (6.23)$$

Figure 6.19 shows the magnitude of this transfer function, calculated for $Q = 10$. For higher-Q circuits, the bandwidth $\Delta\omega$ about the resonant frequency is further decreased, (6.22), and the asymptotic response of the skirts of the curve are further suppressed in proportion to Q. For these reasons it is of interest to design coils of high Q.

Tuning Output Capacitance. When an amplifying device possesses an output capacitance that defines a limiting gain-bandwidth factor, it is sometimes feasible to resonate the output capacitance with a parallel inductor and thereby to achieve gain in a frequency range of interest. This is the principle of a tuned amplifier.

Consider an active device modeled with a transconductance g_m and an output capacitance C (Fig. 6.20). When used with an external circuit R, the transfer function is

$$\frac{V_0}{V} = -g_m Z, \qquad (6.24)$$

where

$$Z(\omega) = \frac{R}{j\omega RC + 1}. \qquad (6.25)$$

The low-frequency gain has the magnitude $g_m R$, the bandwidth B_1 is from $0 \le \omega \le 1/RC$, so the gain-bandwidth product is g_m/C.

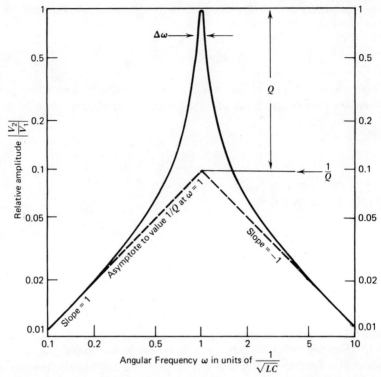

Figure 6.19 Amplitude response for (6.23) relative to the midband transfer function G_1/G, calculated for $Q = 10$.

If an ideal inductor L is now connected across the output terminal to ground, the impedance function in (6.24) is given by

$$Z(s) = \frac{Ls}{LCs^2 + GLs + 1},$$ (6.26)

which is similar to (6.17). The magnitude of gain at resonance is again given by $g_m/G = g_m R$, but the bandwidth B_2 now extends from

$$\omega_d - \frac{G}{2C} \le \omega \le \omega_d + \frac{G}{2C}$$ (6.27)

as indicated in Fig. 6.20*b*. The total bandwidth and the gain-bandwidth product remain the same in this example, which used an ideal inductor.

On the Design of High-Q Coils. The design of high-Q coils is a mixture of theory and experiment, with tradeoffs that vary with the desired frequency range and with the required power level. The following

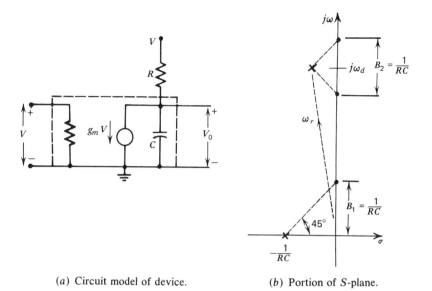

(a) Circuit model of device.   (b) Portion of S-plane.

Figure 6.20 An ideal inductor L is used to resonate the output capacitance C of an amplifying device, to move the frequency range of interest.

comments are relevant to the milliwatt power level and the frequency range well below 1 MHz.

For the audio range, it seems clear that a linear ferrite core will result in higher Q than is achievable by only an air-core coil. Consider an inductor wound on a toroidal coil form with wire of resistance r_w (Fig. 6.21). The approximate $Q = \omega L/r_w$, so a higher inductance for the same resistance will result in a greater Q. For a single layer toroid, $L \approx n^2 \mu S/l$, where $\mu = \mu_r \mu_0$ is greater than free space by the factor μ_r. This suggests

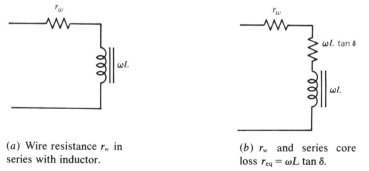

(a) Wire resistance r_w in series with inductor.

(b) r_w and series core loss $r_{eq} = \omega L \tan \delta$.

Figure 6.21 Series circuit loss model for high-Q inductor.

that a ferrite toroidal core will be superior to a nonmagnetic toroidal coil form of the same size, yielding a larger inductance, therefore a higher Q, for the same winding resistance. The real part of the complex relative permeability μ_r' provides an enhancement of flux linkages in the frequency range below Snoek's limit, but at the price of the losses in the core.

The losses in cores modeled by a complex μ can be represented by a parallel resistance $R = \omega L/(\tan \delta)$ or by a series resistor $r = \omega L \tan \delta$ according to (5.54). The series model (Fig. 6.21b), leads to the definition of Q as

$$Q = \frac{\omega L}{r_w + \omega L \tan \delta},$$
(6.28)

which is plotted in Fig. 6.22 for an example coil. At low frequency the Q is limited by the resistance of the winding, so the largest wire (AWG 20) was chosen for which the required 27 turns would fit through the window area of the small core. For such a low-resistance winding ($r_w = 0.015 \, \Omega$), the Q is limited by the core loss-tangent of 0.005 at frequencies above about 250 Hz. The loss tangent increases significantly above $f \sim 25$ kHz as Snoek's limit is approached for this high permeability, low-frequency material. A high-frequency, low-permeability material can be used to achieve a higher frequency response.

Effect of Stray Capacitance. A very important limitation to high-frequency inductor design is imposed by the stray capacitance within the

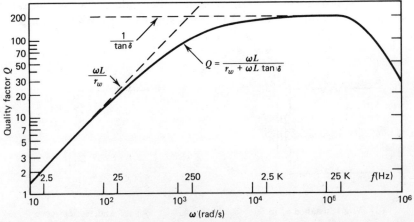

Figure 6.22 Q versus frequency calculated for a 2-mH inductor wound with large wire on a toroid of ferrite with $\mu_r \sim 5000$.

coil. An existence argument is easily given for capacitance between adjacent turns of wire, since each turn possesses some finite area in close proximity to neighboring turns. A calculation of total winding capacitance is not straightforward, is very dependent on winding geometry, and must include a Miller effect of the distributed voltage per turn. The effect of the stray capacitance is that the net inductance of a coil appears to decrease at higher frequencies of measurement. In fact, the stray capacitance can be estimated from a pair of measurements. Let C_x be the unknown stray capacitance of an inductance L, and let C_1 be the additional capacitance required to resonate L at the frequency ω_1. At the specific second frequency $\omega_2 = 2\omega_1$, let C_2 be the additional capacitance required to resonate with L. It readily follows that

$$C_x = \tfrac{1}{3}(C_1 - 4C_2), \tag{6.29}$$

which leads to the determination of the unknown value of L.

The limitation imposed by C_x is that at some frequency the inductor will be self-resonant even with no additional capacitance. Above its resonant frequency the net reactance of a coil is capacitive rather than inductive. For a given winding geometry, hence for a given value of C_x, a smaller value of L may now be preferable to extend resonance to a higher frequency. Note that the strategy is just opposite to the strategy for low-frequency, high-Q coils.

When the design of precision, reproducible inductors is necessary, the reader may refer to the airgap control technique described in Section 3.3.3. Precisely gapped, ferrite pot cores are available with permeance specified to 1% accuracy; these devices are further adjustable by using an adjustable insert. These cores are intended for use in the range of very low signal levels to ensure that the small ferrite tuning slug does not saturate.

6.3.4 Choke-Input Filter

This application concerns the design of the low-pass filter component of a d–c power supply, a component that is located immediately after the full-wave rectifier. In the particular case of high current supplies, an inductor-input circuit can perform significantly better than a capacitor-input circuit in maintaining a more nearly constant d–c output voltage as load current varies. The basic circuit functions as an $L–C$ low-pass filter that acts on the full-wave rectified input voltage. The filter is designed to pass the d–c component of the input waveform, whereas the harmonics are greatly attenuated. The description that follows consists of four parts:

1. Analysis of a simplified circuit that leads to criteria for values of L and C.
2. High- and low-current limitations.
3. Operating point on the $\Lambda - I$ curve.
4. Comparison with a capacitor-input filter circuit.

Circuit and Signal Analysis. The basic choke-input filter circuit (Fig. 6.23a) uses an inductor immediately following the rectifiers, which tends to limit the rectifier current while providing a low-loss impedance between $v_1(t)$ and $v_2(t)$. The resistor R is a simple model for the entire load on the supply, which may be a complex set of circuits, perhaps including voltage regulators. The capacitor is large so that its impedance is much less than R for the harmonics of $v_1(t)$, thereby aiding the filtering function. A large C is also useful in supplying transient load currents represented by incremental changes of R.

Straightforward frequency-domain analysis gives the transfer function

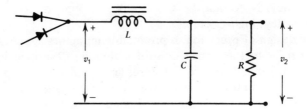

(a) Circuit for the filter component of a d–c power supply.

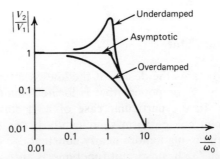

(b) Log–log plot of the magnitude of the transfer function.

Figure 6.23 Circuit and transfer function for L-input filter.

of the filter as

$$\frac{V_2}{V_1}(s) = H(s) = \frac{1}{LCs^2 + sL/R + 1},$$ (6.30)

which has the magnitude response shown in Fig. 6.23b. Disregarding for the time being the more subtle question of filter damping, the asymptotic response has a transfer function of

$$\frac{V_2}{V_1} \approx 1 \quad \text{for} \quad \omega \ll \omega_0$$ (6.31a)

$$\left|\frac{V_2}{V_1}\right| \approx \left|\frac{-1}{\omega^2 LC}\right| \quad \text{for} \quad \omega \gg \omega_0,$$ (6.31b)

where $\omega_0 = 1/\sqrt{LC}$ will be referred to as the *corner* frequency. For a given input waveform $v_1(t)$, the d–c component is transferred to the output according to (6.31a), whereas the a–c ripple components are attenuated according to (6.31b). The amount of ripple on the output voltage $v_2(t)$ is thus controlled by the LC product of the filter.

When the filter is operating within the allowed range of currents, the usual input voltage to the filter $v_1(t)$ can be closely approximated as a full-wave rectified sinusoid (Fig. 6.24). Straightforward Fourier series analysis of a full-wave rectified sinusoid of peak amplitude A gives the harmonics as

$$v_1(t) \approx \frac{2A}{\pi} \left[1 + \tfrac{2}{3} \cos 2\omega_c t - \tfrac{2}{15} \cos 4\omega_c t + \cdots + \left(\frac{-2}{n^2 - 1}\right) \right.$$
$$\left. \times \left(\cos \pi \frac{n}{2} \right) \cos n\omega_c t \cdots \right],$$ (6.32)

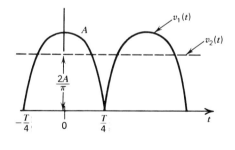
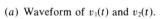
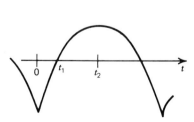

(a) Waveform of $v_1(t)$ and $v_2(t)$.

(b) Waveform of $v_L(t)$ that has zero average value.

Figure 6.24 Voltage waveforms.

where ω_c is the frequency (rads/s) of the input sinusoid before rectification. In addition to the d–c term, full-wave rectification produces only even harmonics of ω_c. The first and most important criterion of the power supply design is that the d–c component of $v_1(t)$, $2A/\pi$ volts past the rectifiers, must be consistent with the d–c voltage requirements. The voltage must also have enough margin to be sufficient at maximum load current. The voltage requirement is affected by the choice of transformer that supplies the rectifier (see Section 6.4.2).

The second criterion of the power supply design is that the filter must attenuate the harmonics of $V_1(\omega)$ to some specified value in the spectrum of V_2,

$$V_2(\omega) = V_1(\omega)H(\omega).$$

This means that the corner frequency of the filter should be at a much lower frequency than the harmonics of V_1,

$$2\omega_c \gg \omega_0, \tag{6.33}$$

so the harmonics of V_1 will be attenuated according to (6.31b). Whatever criterion is allowed for harmonic content of V_2 therefore specifies the attenuation required of the filter, which in turn indicates the approximate numerical value of LC product for the filter. If the damping factor of the transfer function is not a consideration, the value of either L or C may be chosen somewhat arbitrarily, using the required LC product to deduce the other. However a further constraint may be imposed by a requirement on filter damping so that both L and C are specified.

In some applications the relative damping of the filter may be important. The transfer function of a highly underdamped filter will have a peak near ω_0 (Fig. 6.23b), which can be excited by periodic fluctuations of load current if their periodicity is near $2\pi/\omega_0$. In such cases one more criterion is imposed on the choice of L and C, in addition to that of (6.33). The damping of the transfer function is determined by the roots of the quadratic equation in the denominator of the transfer function, (6.30). The roots are given by

$$s = -\frac{1}{2RC} \pm \sqrt{\left(\frac{1}{2RC}\right)^2 - \frac{1}{LC}} \tag{6.34}$$

and are underdamped, critically damped, or overdamped as the expression under the radical is negative, zero, or positive, respectively. For instance, if a filter is designed to be critically damped, the capacitor value of

$$C = \frac{1}{2\omega_0 R} \tag{6.35}$$

is obtained from (6.34).

Current Limitations. The analysis thus far has neglected the effect of the resistance of the inductor windings, the voltage drop across the rectifiers, and the resistance of the windings of the transformer that supplies the voltage to the rectifiers. These various factors constitute the effective output resistance of a power supply, therefore define in a straightforward manner how the d–c output voltage will vary with d–c load current. The a–c output impedance of the transformer should also include the transformer leakage inductance, which is a concept developed in Section 6.4.1. The low-current and high-current limitations are more subtle effects described below.

The minimum load current for normal operation of the L-input filter is that value of d–c current which is just equal to the peak amplitude of alternating current through the inductor. In Fig. 6.25a the total inductor current is approximately

$$I_L \approx I_{DC} + I_p \sin 2\omega_c t, \qquad (6.36)$$

where $I_{DC} = (2A/\pi)/R$ and $I_p = (2A/\pi)\frac{2}{3}/2\omega_c L$ under the assumption that $R \gg 1/\omega C$. For I_L to be always unidirectional, the load current must always exceed I_p,

$$I_{DC} \geq I_p, \qquad (6.37)$$

from which there follows a maximum value of R for normal circuit operation

$$3\omega_c L \geq R. \qquad (6.38)$$

If the requirement of (6.38) is not met, the d–c output voltage V_2 will rise above $2A/\pi$ toward a value of A, qualitatively as indicated in Fig. 6.25b.

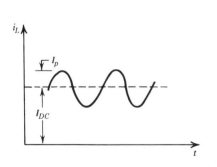

(a) Inductor current as the sum of I_{DC} plus $I_p \sin 2\omega_c t$.

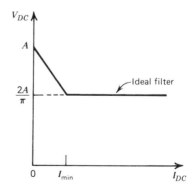

(b) For $I_{DC} < I_{min}$, the d-c output voltage $A \geq V_{DC} \geq 2A/\pi$.

Figure 6.25 Conditions that define the minimum d-c load current for normal filter operation.

In the low-current range neither of the waveforms above nor the analysis is valid. The circuit behaves somewhat as a C-input filter, but the analysis and waveforms are far messier.

In the normal range of currents, the inductor current must be unidirectional as required by the series rectifiers. It may be observed in passing that the inductor current commutates quickly from one rectifier to the other at the instants of time in Fig. 6.24a designated by $\pm T/4$. One diode rectifier turns on as the other turns off, so the total inductor current remains essentially constant during the transition. The concept of current commutation is brought out more clearly in Section 6.3.5.

It is possible that the maximum d–c current rating for an inductor may be limited by the current-carrying capacity of the wire with which the inductor is wound, but the limitation of present interest is that of core saturation. A piecewise-linear inductor (Fig. 6.26), saturates at a current given by

$$\Lambda_{\text{sat}} = LI_s. \tag{6.39}$$

Equation 6.39 suggests that the current rating of an inductor can be extended by decreasing the inductance, for example by increasing the airgap of the core as in Fig. 6.26.

It should not be inferred that the ideal inductor for the power supply application necessarily should have a linear $\Lambda - I$ characteristic as in Fig. 6.26. Alternatively, it may be preferable in many cases for L to increase substantially for low values of I_{DC}, in order that I_{min} of Fig. 6.25 can be as low as possible. Such an inductor is called a *swinging choke*. A

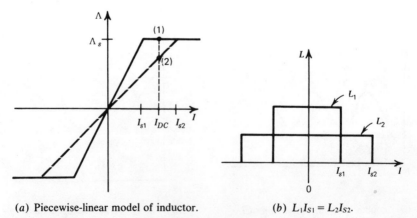

(a) Piecewise-linear model of inductor.   (b) $L_1 I_{S1} = L_2 I_{S2}$.

Figure 6.26 Inductance can be traded for current rating by increasing the airgap in the magnetic circuit.

swinging choke can reduce the amount of current to be wasted in a "bleeder" resistor, connected in parallel with the load for the case that load current may decrease to zero.

The Λ–I Operating Point. A choke-input filter operates in a region on a Λ–I graph that has two components, an average value and a fluctuation about that average. The average flux linkage $\Lambda_A = LI_{DC}$ corresponds to the specific $\int v_L \, dt$ that develops during the initial transient when power supply is first turned on. A steady-state fluctuation $\Delta\Lambda$ is inherent in the waveform for $v_L(t)$ (Fig. 6.24b).

Consider the response of the filter to a step input of voltage

$$v_1(t) = B_0 u(t), \tag{6.40}$$

where $B_0 = 2A/\pi$ and $u(t)$ is a unit step function. For simplicity, let us assume that the filter transfer function is critically damped such that

$$\alpha = \frac{1}{2RC} = \frac{1}{\sqrt{LC}} = \omega_0 \tag{6.41}$$

as determined by (6.34). In that case the Laplace transform of v_2 can be obtained by conventional circuit analysis as

$$V_2(s) = \frac{\alpha^2 B_0}{s(s + \alpha)^2} \tag{6.42}$$

so that the time response is

$$v_2(t) = B_0 u(t)[1 - e^{-\alpha t} - \alpha t e^{-\alpha t}]. \tag{6.43}$$

The transient voltage across the inductor is therefore

$$v_L = v_1 - v_2 = B_0 e^{-\alpha t}(1 + \alpha t)u(t), \tag{6.44}$$

which can be integrated to yield the result of interest

$$\Lambda_A = \int_0^\infty v_L \, dt = \frac{2B_0}{\alpha} = 2B_0 \sqrt{LC}, \tag{6.45}$$

where (6.41) was used to get the final expression on the right. The result is also equal to $\Lambda_A = LI_{DC}$ since $I_{DC} = B_0/R$, which was the result to be demonstrated. What this means is that Λ_A does not correspond to some explicit number of lobes of the input voltage waveform, but instead corresponds to the transient of the average of the input voltage.

Figure 6.27 is an interpretation of the foregoing result. Let us suppose the input voltage to the filter is turned on at $t = 0$, as a full-wave rectified sine wave with successive lobes at intervals of $T/2$. The integral of such a waveform can be done by inspection for each successive lobe, each of which yields an offset negative cosine half-cycle. The result in Fig. 6.27b

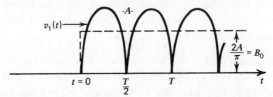

(a) Transient input voltage $v_1(t)$ and the average value $B_0 u(t)$.

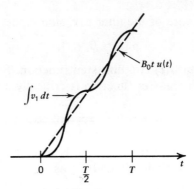

(b) Integrals of voltage waveforms.

Figure 6.27   The integral of a series of half-sine waves is a series of negative half-cosine waveforms linked together. The latter has the general character of a ramp with fluctuations.

shows that $\int v_1 \, dt$ has a qualitative resemblance to a ramp waveform $t B_0 u(t)$, but differs from the ramp by $\pm$ fluctuations, described next. The integral of $v_L(t)$ can be deduced from the same figure.

The steady-state fluctuation of $\Delta\Lambda$ is readily calculated from the waveform of $v_L(t)$. In Fig. 6.24b, the peak amplitude is

$$\Delta\Lambda_p = \int_0^{t_1} v_L \, dt = A \int_0^{t_1} \left(\sin \omega t - \frac{2}{\pi} \right) dt, \qquad (6.46)$$

where $\theta_1 = \omega t_1$ is the angle at which $\sin \theta_1 = 2/\pi$. Carrying out the integration of (6.46) leads to

$$\Delta\Lambda_p = -\frac{A}{\omega} \left(\frac{2\theta_1}{\pi\omega} + \cos \theta_1 - 1 \right) \qquad (6.47)$$

which leads to the negative peak value

$$\Delta\Lambda_p = -\left(\frac{2A}{\omega} \right) \times 0.1052568. \qquad (6.48)$$

The fraction in parentheses in (6.48) is the area under one lobe of $v_1(t)$, of which the total peak-to-peak fluctuation $\Delta\Lambda$ is about 21%. The quantitative result (6.48), if divided by L, is an alternative derivation of the peak value of current fluctuation for which I_p of (6.36) is an approximation, valid within 1%.

Simple Capacitor Filter for Comparison. For low-current d–c power supplies of moderate performance, a simple smoothing filter results from merely connecting a capacitor across the load, resistor R of Fig. 6.28. Without the capacitor, the output voltage would be a full-wave rectified sinusoid, as in Fig. 6.27a for $t > 0$. With a capacitor of appropriate value, the output voltage waveform can be considerably smoother (Fig. 6.28b). During time interval t_1 of each half-cycle, the capacitor is charged through the diode rectifier toward the peak value A of the full-wave rectified voltage. During time interval t_2 the diodes are reverse

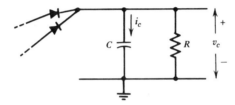

(a) Capacitor-input circuit.

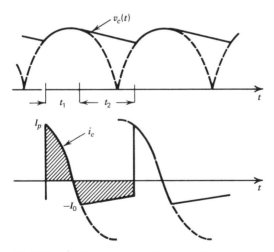

(b) Voltage and current waveforms for the capacitor.

Figure 6.28   A single-capacitor filter for a d-c supply.

biased and the load current is supplied from the capacitor. The capacitor current in either interval is given by

$$i_c = C \frac{dv_c}{dt}, \tag{6.49}$$

but the capacitor voltage v_c is defined differently for each time interval, as segments of the functions

$$\begin{aligned} v_c &\approx A \sin \omega t & \text{during } t_1 \\ v_c &\approx A e^{-t/RC} & \text{during } t_2, \end{aligned} \tag{6.50}$$

neglecting the resistances of the source and the diode.

The current waveform that results from applying (6.49) to (6.50) is shown in Fig. 6.28b. In steady-state operation the integral of the charging current during t_1 is equal to the integral of the discharge current during t_2 so the two cross-hatched areas in Fig. 6.28b are equal. If the RC time constant is long compared with the half-period $T/2$, then t_2 will be much longer than t_1 and the peak charging current will be approximately

$$I_p \approx 2 I_{DC} \frac{t_2}{t_1}. \tag{6.51}$$

Thus it can easily happen that the diode current has peak values that are an order of magnitude greater than the average load current. On the other hand if the time constant is short—for instance, if RC approaches the minimum practical value of about $T/2$—the output voltage has a large sawtooth waveform component. The average output voltage is correspondingly less than the peak amplitude A.

The disadvantages of the circuit are that the d–c output voltage decreases and the undesirable sawtooth ripple in the output voltage increases as load current increases. The simplicity of the circuit is attractive. The resistor R can be replaced by a single-chip voltage regulator circuit to make an attractive, simple, low-current supply.

6.3.5 Switching Regulator

A regulator for a d–c voltage supply consists of a controller and a controlled impedance. In many applications the controlled impedance is a series element as in Fig. 6.29, arranged to absorb the difference voltage $(V_{in} - V_{out})$ between an unregulated input and the regulated output voltage. A switching regulator provides the required attenuation with high power efficiency by using electronic switches together with passive reactive elements.

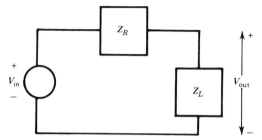

Figure 6.29 A series regulator represented as a regulated impedance Z_R between an unregulated supply voltage V_{in} and the load impedance Z_L.

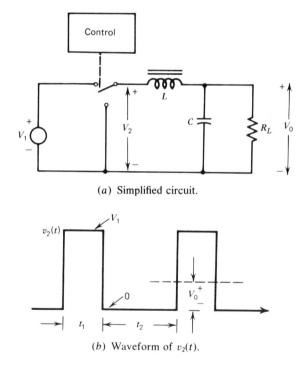

(*a*) Simplified circuit.

(*b*) Waveform of $v_2(t)$.

Figure 6.30 Model of a switching regulator as an ideal switch followed by a low-pass LC filter. The switch connects the filter input either to the unregulated V_1 or to ground. The schedule of switching is controlled so that the time average of $v_2(t)$ is the desired output voltage (6.52).

The principle of operation of a switching regulator (Fig. 6.30) can be explained as follows. The device consists of a controlled switch and an LC low-pass filter. The filter is intended to pass the d–c component V_0 of its input voltage $v_2(t)$. The switch defines the time average of $v_2(t)$

within each time period $T = t_1 + t_2$ as

$$V_0 = \frac{V_1 t_1}{t_1 + t_2} = V_1 f t_1, \tag{6.52}$$

where V_1 is the unregulated input voltage.

In the usual mode of operation, the total period of operation $T = 1/f$ is fixed at a duration short enough to permit small values of L and C to be used. The control is accomplished by varying the pulse width t_1 to maintain the output voltage constant according to (6.52).

Waveforms and Design Equations. The voltage across the inductor can be deduced in the usual way by subtraction, $v_L = v_2 - V_0$, with the result shown in Fig. 6.31 as a rectangular waveform. It has been assumed for convenience that V_1 is a constant d–c value. The current in the inductor therefore has a periodic waveform of $\pm$ ramps about the average value I_{DC}. The peak-to-peak excursion of current can be deduced from the inductor voltage waveform

$$L\Delta i = (V_1 - V_0)t_1 = V_0 t_2. \tag{6.53}$$

The d–c component of current flows entirely through the load, whereas the ramp components are taken primarily by the capacitor. It follows

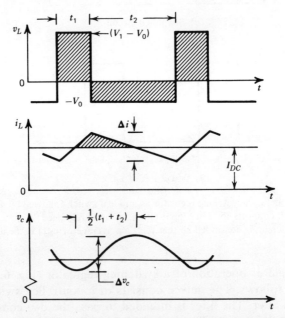

Figure 6.31 Waveforms of inductor voltage and current and of capacitor voltage.

from the basic capacitor equation

$$\Delta v_c = \frac{1}{C} \int i \, dt \tag{6.54}$$

that a ramp of current, $i \propto \pm t$, will cause a parabola of voltage, $\Delta v_c \propto \pm t^2$. These considerations lead to the following expression for the peak-to-peak fluctuation of capacitor voltage:

$$\Delta v_c = \tfrac{1}{2}(1/C)(\Delta i/4)(t_1 + t_2) \tag{6.55}$$

The hash-lined triangle of charge under the waveform for i_L (Fig. 6.31) was used to write (6.55). The design equations for the switching regulator consist of (6.52), (6.53), and (6.55) or equivalent formulas that are readily found by manipulation, for example,

$$L = \frac{V_1 - V_0}{f \Delta i} \frac{V_0}{V_1}; \qquad C = \frac{V_1 - V_0}{8L f^2 \Delta v_c} \frac{V_0}{V_1}. \tag{6.56}$$

Current Commutation. In a practical circuit the ideal switch of Fig. 6.30a is replaced by a transistor and diode combination as in Fig. 6.32. It must be noted that the transistor is different from the "pass" transistor of a conventional linear regulator, which is essentially an emitter-follower connection. The transistor of Fig. 6.32 is controlled as a switch, therefore is either cut off or saturated on with negligible collector-to-emitter voltage. Depending on the transistor state, the inductor current is supplied either by the transistor or through the diode.

During time t_1 when the transistor conducts the inductor current, the collector voltage is

$$v_2(t) \approx V_1 - V_{ec} \approx V_1 \qquad \text{during } t_1, \tag{6.57}$$

which is the voltage on the left-hand side of the inductor (Fig. 6.32). At the end of t_1, the controller turns off the transistor, which would

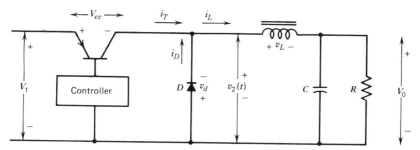

Figure 6.32 Realization of the ideal switch of Fig. 6.30a using a transistor and diode.

decrease i_L if it were not for diode D. The tendency of the inductor current to decrease causes v_L to surge toward a negative value, but in fact diode D begins to conduct and v_2 takes the value

$$v_2(t) = -v_d \approx 0 \qquad \text{during } t_2. \tag{6.58}$$

As a result, the inductor current i_L undergoes no discontinuities. It is supplied by V_1 for a period t_1, and is sustained through the diode for t_2. The average output current exceeds the average input current by the same ratio

$$\frac{t_1 + t_2}{t_1} = \frac{I_{\text{out}}}{I_{\text{in}}} \tag{6.59}$$

by which the voltage is stepped down, (6.52). It follows that the average input power is equal to the average output power for this ideal model of a switching regulator.

6.4 TRANSFORMERS

Chapter 1 treated a magnetic core with turns of wire wound upon it, pointing out that the properties of the magnetic core are manifest as electrical properties at the one winding. The emphasis on magnetic materials was continued in Chapters 2 through 5 by examining further details of B and H and of dynamic losses. Now a second set of turns is wound on the same core, and our interest centers on the relationship between the voltages and currents on the two windings, referred to as primary and secondary windings. For the sake of simplicity the present treatment omits the effects of core losses, developed in Chapter 5.

In most transformers of interest the magnetic flux is largely confined to the core, to which both windings are well coupled. In many cases the current required to excite the core is a small fraction of the load current that passes through the transformer. Such transformers operate with high efficiency to raise or lower the voltage in proportion to the ratio of turns, $V_2/V_1 = n_2/n_1$. In the area of electrical-mechanical analogs, the step-up or step-down of currents (and voltages) by a transformer is analogous to the transformation of forces (and translational velocities) by the action of a lever. The length of the lever arm on either side of the fulcrum is analogous to the number of turns on either side of the core.

Two basic properties of transformers are exploited in many straightforward applications: (*a*) the transformation property of step-up or step-down, viewed as voltage- or current- or impedance transformation, and (*b*) the property of electrical isolation between the primary and secondary windings. The following presentation begins with some elementary ideas that underlie transformer design, then gradually develops more subtle properties from the functional viewpoint of the application.

6.4.1 Elementary Properties of Transformers

The basic principles of transformer operation can be explained by applying Ampere's circuital law to the 3-winding transformer of Fig. 6.33:

$$n_1 i_1 + n_2 i_2 + n_3 i_3 = \oint \bar{H} \cdot d\bar{l} \approx Hl, \tag{6.60}$$

where l is the path length of the flux in the core. Before writing (6.60), care was taken to define a dot-mark convention for each winding such that a current entering the dot-marked end would cause the same sense of core flux as shown. It also follows for Fig. 6.33 that if ϕ is increasing with time, the voltage polarity for each winding will be positive at the dot-marked end. For this particular circuit, the actual currents i_2 and i_3 have the opposite polarity to that used in (6.60). Windings 2 and 3 merely supply load impedances, so that the currents flow *out of* the dotted ends at the same time that excitation current i_1 flows *into* the dot-marked terminal of winding number 1, the so-called *primary* winding. The primary current from (6.60) consists of three components

$$i_1 = \frac{Hl}{n_1} - i_2 \frac{n_2}{n_1} - i_3 \frac{n_3}{n_1}$$

$$= \frac{Hl}{n_1} + \left(\frac{v_2}{R_2}\right) \frac{n_2}{n_1} + \left(\frac{v_3}{R_3}\right) \frac{n_3}{n_1}. \tag{6.61}$$

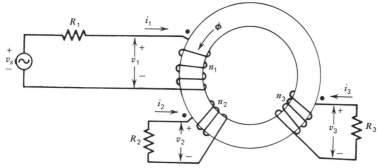

Figure 6.33 An elementary transformer with three windings n_1, n_2, n_3. The dot marks on the windings indicate the relative polarity of the voltages. Resistors R_1, R_2, R_3 include the resistance of the windings.

The first term represents the magnetic potential required to excite the core. In fact the first term may consist of several components given previously as piecewise linear equations (1.12) and (1.13). The present treatment can be extended to include core losses by retaining and generalizing the first term. The next two terms of (6.61) represent components of primary current that result from load resistors R_2 and R_3. For an efficient transformer the core component of primary current is a great deal smaller than the load component, perhaps 1 or 2 orders of magnitude, and sometimes can be neglected. It may be noted in (6.61) that i_2 and i_3 each has an effect on i_1 by the respective turn ratios n_2/n_1 and n_3/n_1, but the two currents do not explicitly affect each other. They may affect each other implicitly by loading down the primary circuit, and this possibility is examined subsequently.

If the flux is equal for each of the windings of Fig. 6.33, and also its time derivative, the induced voltages will all be related by Faraday's law*

$$\frac{d\phi}{dt} = \frac{v_1}{n_1} = \frac{v_2}{n_2} = \frac{v_3}{n_3}. \tag{6.62}$$

Equation 6.62 is the transformer equation for voltages, as the right-hand terms of (6.61) represent the transformation of currents. Equation 6.61 can now be rewritten using v_1 as

$$i_1 = \frac{Hl}{n_1} + \frac{v_1}{R_2}\left(\frac{n_2}{n_1}\right)^2 + \frac{v_1}{R_3}\left(\frac{n_3}{n_1}\right)^2, \tag{6.63}$$

which shows the effect on the primary current of secondary load admittances. It is to be noted that a resistor R_x in a secondary circuit has an effect equivalent to a resistor of $a^2 R_x$ in the primary circuit, where a is the turns ratio $a = n_1/n_x$. Figure 6.34 shows circuit models for (6.61) and (6.63); in the latter circuit the load impedances are transformed to the primary side of the transformer.

EXAMPLE D

(a) Suppose a transformer with primary and secondary turns n_1, n_2 is wound on a core modeled by a linear permeance P_c. Find the core

---

*An alternative derivation of (6.62) can be given in a manner parallel to Ampere's circuital law (Section 3.1.2), where in the present case we begin with Maxwell's curl equation $\bar{\nabla} \times \bar{E} = -d\bar{B}/dt$. Writing the integral over the area of the core, but using Stokes' theorem on the left-hand side gives the result $\oint \bar{E} \cdot d\bar{l} = -(d\phi/dt)_{encl}$, which is analogous to (3.15). The left-hand side is the voltage induced per turn, which is the integral of the electric field around the periphery of the core.

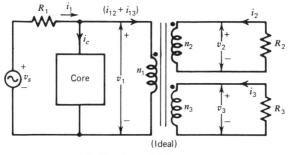

(a) Circuit model for (6.61).

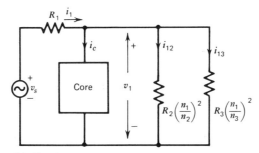

(b) Circuit model for (6.63), with R_2, R_3 reflected in the primary circuit.

Figure 6.34 Two equivalent circuit models for the transformer of Fig. 6.33. The rectangle represents the core function of (i_c, v_1), which may be modeled as (1.13).

function and its circuit model as it appears from the primary windings and from the secondary.

(b) Repeat for a square-loop core modeled by static width H_0.

ANSWER

(a) From the primary side the core function is the magnetizing inductance $L_{11} = n_1^2 P_c$. From the secondary side the core function is $L_{22} = n_2^2 P_c$, which is the same as applying the impedance transformation relation $L_{22} = (n_2/n_1)^2 L_{11}$, see Fig. 6.35.

(b) From the primary side the core function is the current source $I_{01} = H_0 l/n_1$. From the secondary side the core appears as $I_{02} = H_0 l/n_2$, which obeys the current transformation equation $n_1 I_{01} = n_2 I_{02}$.

In summary, the discussion above has yielded equations that relate currents, voltages, and impedances on one side of a transformer to the same corresponding parameters as viewed from the other side. These

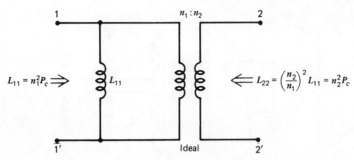

Figure 6.35 Core functions for a perfectly coupled transformer with linear core permeance P_c.

elementary, ideal relations for transformers are applicable in a great many cases without further complications. Certain limitations that arise at extremes of signal amplitude and frequency (e.g., core saturation) are taken care of by the piecewise-linear model for the core itself. Components of the core model have been described at length elsewhere in this book; the present treatment merely shows how the core function can be included as a component of primary current. Two considerations that specifically apply to transformers are now developed. The first topic is related to imperfect magnetic coupling between windings; the second concerns the modeling of complicated core shapes.

Coupling Coefficient. Transformer equations (6.62 and 6.63) were based on the assumption of equal flux linking each winding, which is known to

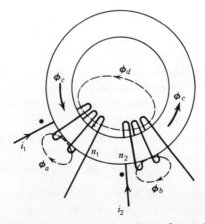

Figure 6.36 Air flux components ϕ_a, ϕ_b, ϕ_d and core flux ϕ_c in a transformer.

be true only approximately. A coefficient of coupling is defined, then is used to define a transformer leakage inductance. Only a special case is treated, that of a nonsaturating core with linear permeance.

Section 2.2.3 noted that the total flux that links a set of windings on a core may include not only the flux through the core but also flux through the air. For instance, in Fig. 6.36 the total flux that links winding 1 includes core flux ϕ_c plus two components of air flux, ϕ_a and ϕ_d. Assuming that each component of flux is proportional to the magnetic potential that causes it, the flux in winding 1 can be written in a form such as

$$\phi_1 = n_1 i_1 (P_a + P_c + P_d) + n_2 i_2 (P_c + P_d), \tag{6.64}$$

where each P is a specific component definition of permeance. The sole purpose of (6.64) is to clarify the following compact notation:

$$\phi_1 = n_1 i_1 P_{11} + n_2 i_2 P_{12} \tag{6.65a}$$

$$\phi_2 = n_1 i_1 P_{21} + n_2 i_2 P_{22}. \tag{6.65b}$$

In the absence of air flux, all the permeances in (6.65) are equal to the core permeance P_c. Multiplying (6.65a) and (6.65b) by n_1, n_2, respectively, leads to the following volt·ampere equations for the two windings

$$\int v_1 \, dt = n_1 \phi_1 = i_1 L_{11} + i_2 L_{12} \tag{6.66a}$$

$$\int v_2 \, dt = n_2 \phi_2 = i_1 L_{21} + i_2 L_{22}, \tag{6.66b}$$

where

$$\begin{array}{ll} L_{11} = n_1^2 P_{11}, & L_{22} = n_2^2 P_{22}, \\ L_{12} = n_1 n_2 P_{12}, & L_{21} = n_1 n_2 P_{21}. \end{array} \tag{6.67}$$

Equations 6.66 and 6.67 are the results of interest, which lead to the model of Fig. 6.37a. It is to be noted that $L_{12} = L_{21}$ from the reciprocity theorem of circuit theory, which thereby defines the mutual inductance $M = L_{12} = L_{21}$ of two coupled coils.

It is convenient to define a single coupling coefficient k for the transformers*

$$k = \frac{M}{\sqrt{L_{11} L_{22}}} \tag{6.68}$$

*Some authors define two coupling coefficients, $k_1 = P_{21}/P_{11}$ and $k_2 = P_{12}/P_{22}$ as the ratio of mutual flux to self-flux produced by the ampere·turns of each winding. It follows that $k = \sqrt{k_1 k_2}$.

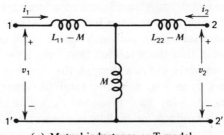

(*a*) Mutual inductance or T-model.

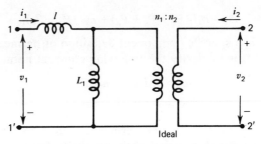

(*b*) Physical model with one leakage inductance.

Figure 6.37 Two equivalent models for a transformer, each of which permits the definition of leakage inductance. The physical model is usually preferred by magnetics designers.

with values that range between zero and unity. For perfectly coupled coils $k = 1$ and

$$M = \sqrt{L_{11}L_{22}} = n_1 n_2 P_c \qquad \text{for} \quad k = 1. \tag{6.69}$$

For tightly coupled coils with $n_1 \neq n_2$, it follows that one or the other inductances of Fig. 6.37*a* will be negative

$$\begin{aligned}(L_{11} - M) &\approx n_1 P_c (n_1 - n_2) \\ (L_{22} - M) &\approx n_2 P_c (n_2 - n_1).\end{aligned} \tag{6.70}$$

The negative inductance has no physical significance, being merely a consequence of the circuit equations for voltage step-up or step-down.

Because of the physical unreality of negative inductance, most magnetics designers prefer a more physical model as in Fig. 6.37*b*, which is a modification of Fig. 6.35 by the addition of a leakage inductance in the transformer primary. If a more detailed analysis is required, the leakage inductance l can be split into primary and secondary parts

$$l = l_1 + l_2 \left(\frac{n_1}{n_2}\right)^2, \tag{6.71}$$

a refinement that is omitted from the present treatment.

Let us now force the equivalence of the two circuit models of Fig. 6.37, by requiring the inductances measured at terminals 1–1' to be equal. With terminals 2–2' open circuit,

$$l + L_1 = L_{11} - M + M = L_{11}, \tag{6.72}$$

whereas with terminals 2–2' shorted together

$$l = L_{11} - M + \frac{M(L_{22} - M)}{M + L_{22} - M} = L_{11} - \frac{M^2}{L_{22}}.$$

But from (6.69) $M^2 = k^2 L_{11} L_{22}$, so that

$$l = L_{11}(1 - k^2) = L_{11}(1 + k)(1 - k). \tag{6.73}$$

Therefore

$$L_1 = k^2 L_{11}. \tag{6.74}$$

EXAMPLE E

Find L_1 and l for the physical model of Fig. 6.37b given a typical $k = 0.99$.

ANSWER. $l \approx 0.02 L_{11}$ and $L_1 = 0.98 L_{11} \approx L_{11}$ within the usual accuracy of measurement for a slightly hysteretic core.

Duality in Transformer Modeling. The topological dual of a circuit is one in which nodes are replaced by loops and vice versa, currents are replaced by voltages, and impedances are replaced by their reciprocals. Duality is an important tool in the development of electrical models of magnetic circuits. The following presentation consists of four steps:

1. Illustration of the duality principle using an electric circuit example.
2. Explanation of the circuit equations.
3. Use of duality in developing electric circuit models for two different magnetic circuits,
4. Summary of the procedure for magnetic circuits.

Consider the two electric circuits of Fig. 6.38, which are duals of each other. Construction of dual circuit (Fig. 6.38b) from the original (Fig. 6.38a) consists of the following procedure.

1. Put a reference dot (ⓐ and ⓑ) inside each loop of the original figure and a reference dot ⓚ outside. These three points will become the nodes of the dual circuit.

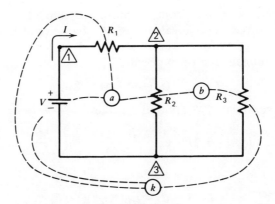

(a) Original circuit with loops (a), (b) and reference (k).

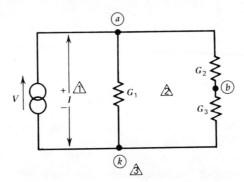

(b) Dual circuit with nodes (a), (b) and (k).

Figure 6.38 Procedure for constructing duals of circuits.

2. Draw a line between any two nodes of the original circuit to pass through one and only one circuit element,—for example, from (a) to (b) passing through R_2. Construct the corresponding dual element between the same two nodes of the dual circuit,—for example, G_2 from (a) to (b).

Repeat the same procedure for each element of the original circuit, drawing I's for V's, G's for R's, and so on.

The voltage equation for Fig. 6.38a is

$$V = I\left(R_1 + \frac{R_2 R_3}{R_2 + R_3}\right),$$ (6.75)

which can be readily rewritten as the current equation

$$I = V\frac{R_2 + R_3}{R_1 R_2 + R_1 R_3 + R_2 R_3}.$$

The latter is also equal to

$$I = V \frac{G_1(G_2 + G_3)}{G_1 + G_2 + G_3},$$ (6.76)

which is the result of writing a dual equation for the dual circuit of Fig. 6.38b. The dual equation for a dual circuit is equivalent to the original equation. The dual equation may be written by treating I as a voltage, V as a current, and the G's as resistors; thus G_1 is in parallel with the series combination $(G_2 + G_3)$.

The duality procedure is now used to develop an electrical model for magnetic circuits. The first example develops the circuit model for an inductance wound on a linear core with an airgap, shown step by step in Fig. 6.39. The inductor-core configuration is in Fig. 6.39a, and the analog reluctance circuit is Fig. 6.39b (which is the same as Fig. 3.32). Conventional analysis of Fig. 6.39b gives the flux as

$$\phi = \frac{ni}{R_m + R_g};$$ (3.84)

from which the inductance is

$$L = \frac{n\phi}{i} = \frac{n^2}{R_m + R_g}.$$ (6.77)

The dual of Fig. 6.39b is constructed in Fig. 6.39c, for which the dual equation is

$$\phi = \frac{ni P_m P_g}{P_m + P_g}.$$ (6.78)

Equation 6.78 is equivalent to (3.84), since each permeance is reciprocal reluctance (i.e., $P_m = 1/R_m$), which concludes the algebraic example. The remaining parts of Fig. 6.39 show two intermediate steps between the dual of the analog magnetic circuit and the final electrical model (Fig. 6.39f). The intermediate steps consist of scaling by n^2, which converts the circuit of (ϕ vs. ni) into (λ vs. i), and finally recognizing that v is the time derivative of λ. The intermediate steps are useful to include in transformer modeling, to keep track of whether the circuit model is scaled to the primary or secondary impedance level.

The next duality example, adapted from the pioneering paper by E. C. Cherry [10], also establishes the credibility of the physical model (Fig. 6.37b) for a transformer with leakage inductance. Figure 6.40 shows the sequence of steps from the transformer pictorial to the final electrical circuit model. Figure 6.40a gives three components of flux: the main component ϕ in the core, and leakage components ϕ_1 and ϕ_2 at the respective windings. Secondary current i_2 is shown coming out of the

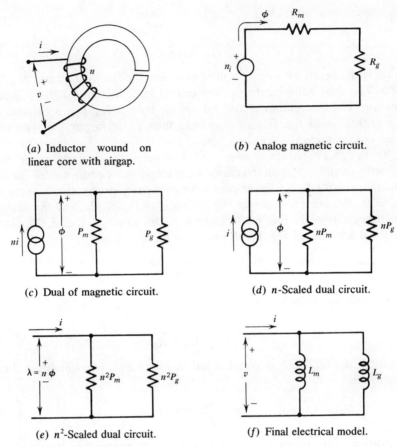

(a) Inductor wound on linear core with airgap.

(b) Analog magnetic circuit.

(c) Dual of magnetic circuit.

(d) n-Scaled dual circuit.

(e) n^2-Scaled dual circuit.

(f) Final electrical model.

Figure 6.39   Step-by-step development of electrical circuit model for inductor.

dot-marked terminal, consistent with the polarity of $v_2 = i_2 Z_L$. The leakage fluxes in Fig. 6.40b are modeled with the aid of reluctances R_1, R_2 to indicate the flux paths. As a subtle point it can be noted that in coil 1, ϕ and ϕ_1 have the same polarity, since both are caused by i_1. However in coil 2, ϕ and ϕ_2 have opposite polarity, since one flux is the cause of i_2 and the other is the result of i_2. The circuit in Fig. 6.40c is the dual of Fig. 6.40b, constructed as explained earlier. Figure 6.40d shows the details of scaling by n_1^2, which has the effect of referring all inductances to the primary side of the transformer. The transformer leakage inductance is split into two parts as in (6.71), which is a more detailed model than Fig. 6.37b.

In summary, the duality method consists of four steps for the development of an electric circuit model of a magnetic core. First, draw an analog magnetic circuit of potentials and reluctances having the same topology as the device to be modeled. Second, draw a dual of the magnetic circuit, using the graphical technique of a reference dot within

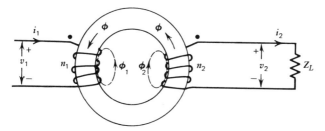

(a) Transformer wound on linear core.

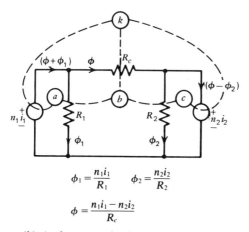

$$\phi_1 = \frac{n_1 i_1}{R_1} \qquad \phi_2 = \frac{n_2 i_2}{R_2}$$

$$\phi = \frac{n_1 i_1 - n_2 i_2}{R_c}$$

(b) Analog magnetic circuit of transformer.

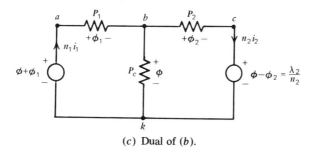

(c) Dual of (b).

Figure 6.40 Development of an electric circuit model for a transformer with leakage fluxes.

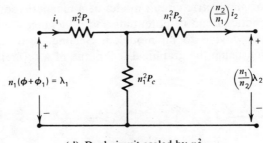

(d) Dual circuit scaled by n_1^2.

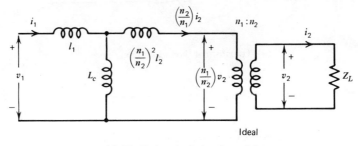

Ideal

(e) Final electrical circuit model.

Figure 6.40   (Cont'd).

each loop. The elements of the dual circuit now become permeances in a (ϕ vs. ni) relationship. Third, multiply all permeances by n_j^2, to scale the dual circuit into a (λ vs. i) relationship. Care should be taken in the choice of n_j. Fourth, replace all n^2P's by L's; this puts the circuit into its final (v vs. i) relationship. Ideal transformers may be added as necessary at auxiliary ports.

6.4.2   Some Common-Ordinary Transformers

Autotransformer.   An autotransformer is a single-winding transformer with taps on the winding that define the primary and secondary connections. The two parts of the winding are called the common winding and the series winding (Fig. 6.41a). As with conventional transformers, and autotransformer can be designed either to step up or to step down the primary voltage.

An ordinary two-circuit transformer can be connected as an autotransformer by connecting the two windings in series, provided the voltage insulation is adequate for the series winding. An interesting property of such an autotransformer connection is its capability of

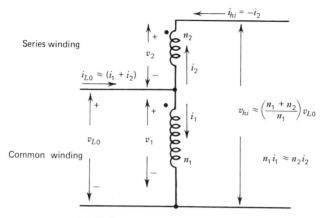

(a) Voltage and current definitions.

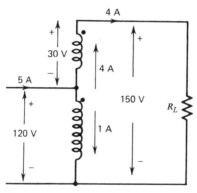

(b) An example of volt·ampere enhancement.

Figure 6.41 Autotransformer circuits.

transforming power in excess of its volt·ampere rating. For instance, suppose we have a transformer that is designed for 120-to 30 V step-down at a load current of 4 A, hence is rated at 120 V·A. If a step-up autotransformer connection is made as in 6.41b, the voltage rating is now 120-to-150 V at a load current of 4 A. The load power is therefore 600 V·A, which is 5 times the power rating of the transformer. This means that an autotransformer can offer substantial size and weight advantages compared to a conventional transformer of the same power rating. Such an autotransformer is also more efficient. The advantages are most evident when the primary and secondary voltages are in the same range. There is no great advantage when the voltage ratio of step up or step down is large.

The most evident disadvantage of an autotransformer is the direct electrical connection between primary and secondary circuits. Many applications require the primary and secondary grounds to be isolated from each other.

Variable Autotransformer. A variable autotransformer (Fig. 6.42) is a commercial product that provides a convenient and efficient source of a–c power at an arbitrary voltage. The voltage can be changed manually by moving a sliding electrical contact from one turn to the next, thereby changing the turns ratio. The turns are wound in a single layer on a toroidal core, so that the contact slides around at a fixed radius as it is moved from turn to turn. The contact is a carbon brush, similar to those used with commutators of other types. The transformer voltage-per-turn depends on the design but is often of the order of 0.5 V/*turn*. Presumably the carbon brush has enough resistance to cause no short circuit as it bridges across two adjacent turns. Yet the brush resistance must also be low, to retain a low output impedance for the transformer.

Rectifier Transformers. Either of two arrangements of transformer and rectifiers is commonly used to obtain the full-wave rectified sinusoids required by d–c power supplies. Section 6.3.4 described two alternative filters for such supplies, assuming the existence of one of the circuits of Fig. 6.43. The circuits work as follows, assuming a load resistor R and neglecting the leakage reactance of the transformers for the sake of simplicity.

The transformer in the circuit of Fig. 6.43a has a turns ratio $n_1 : 2n_2$

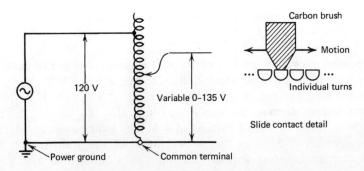

Figure 6.42 A variable-ratio autotransformer provides an efficient way to vary the a–c voltage from the power line. For safety's sake, the common terminal of the transformer should be connected to the power line ground as shown.

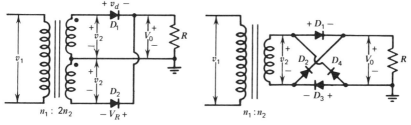

(a) Center-tapped secondary of $2v_2$.   (b) Single secondary v_2 followed by bridge rectifier.

Figure 6.43 Two conventional circuits for single-phase, full-wave rectification. The output voltage V_0 is approximately the same for each circuit.

followed by diodes $D1$, $D2$ that alternate in conduction. The transformer center-tap is usually grounded. Diode $D1$ conducts when v_2 is positive as shown, so the output voltage is

$$V_0 = v_2 - v_d, \tag{6.79}$$

where v_d is the forward voltage drop across the diode. At that time $D2$ is nonconducting, with an inverse voltage

$$V_R = V_0 + v_2. \tag{6.80}$$

On the following half-cycle the polarity of v_2 is negative, so that diode $D2$ conducts and $D1$ is reverse-biased.

The transformer of Fig. 6.43b has a turns ratio $n_1 : n_2$ followed by a bridge rectifier. The diode bridge functions essentially as a reversing switch. Diodes $D1$ and $D3$ conduct on the positive half-cycle when the output voltage is

$$V_0 = v_2 - 2v_d, \tag{6.81}$$

which is slightly less than (6.79). At that time $D2$ and $D4$ are nonconducting, with an inverse voltage on each of

$$V_R = v_2 - v_d = V_0 + v_d, \tag{6.82}$$

which is only about half of (6.80).

There is little substantive difference between the two circuits that would make either one obviously superior to the other in all respects. The circuit of Fig. 6.43a has twice as many secondary turns; but since each winding carries current only on alternate half-cycles, the wire size can be smaller for the same average current density. For a brute force high-current supply, if the transformer winding resistance is a more significant limitation than the extra diode, the circuit of Fig. 6.43b may be preferable.

Current Transformer. The principle of a current transformer is illustrated in Fig. 6.44, where the secondary winding of the transformer is terminated in a short-circuit. The secondary current is a measure of the primary current as,

$$i_2 = \frac{i_1}{n} = \frac{I_{ac} - i_c}{n} \approx \frac{I_{ac}}{n}, \qquad (6.83)$$

where i_c is the current required to energize the core and I_{ac} is the line current to be measured. The secondary voltage, ideally zero, is given by the small secondary resistance $v_2 = i_2 r$. The primary voltage is $v_1 = v_2/n$ for the $1:n$ transformer in Fig. 6.44b, which ought to be a very small voltage indeed. Such a configuration is the conventional way of measuring large line currents.

If the secondary winding of a current transformer is left open-circuit, the resulting catastrophe can be described as follows. The magnetic potential in the transformer $n_1 I_{ac} = I_{ac}$ would no longer be canceled by the opposing secondary ampere·turns $n i_2$, so the full line current would be available to excite the core, thereby to induce a significant primary voltage v_1. The step-up voltage transformation $1:n$ would induce a very large secondary voltage $v_2 = n v_1$.

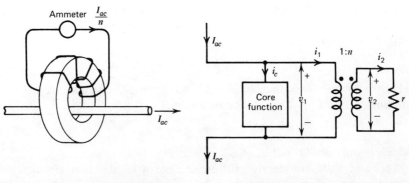

(a) A wire that carries an a-c current   (b) Circuit model of (a).
to be measured is passed through an
n-turn core.

Figure 6.44 A current transformer is a $1:n$ turn transformer with the secondary shorted through an ammeter.

6.4.3 Frequency Limitations and Broadbanding

This section concerns the limitation of frequency response that results from the interaction between the transformer inductances and the impedances of the signal source and the load. The interactions consist of R/L relationships that define critical frequencies using conventional circuit analysis.

Omitted from the present treatment are other effects that in fact may be dominant in some applications. For instance, core saturation is a low-frequency limitation that was described in Chapter 2. Other high-frequency limitations may be imposed by the high-frequency limitation of the core material as Snoek's limit (Chapter 4) or by excessive losses of the core (Chapter 5). Finally, the capacitance of the transformer windings may be a limitation. A clever transformer circuit is described that uses twisted-pair windings to achieve broadband response, using to advantage the stray capacitance between windings.

Effect of Transformer Inductances. The following analysis shows that the magnetizing inductance limits the low-frequency response of a transformer by gradually shorting out the source voltage. The leakage inductance limits the high-frequency voltage transfer function by its additional series impedance.

The circuit in Fig. 6.45 represents a voltage source V_1, with Thévenin output resistance r, which is coupled to load resistance R_L through a transformer of turns ratio n_1/n_2. The resistances of the transformer winding are omitted for simplicity but can be considered as included in r and R_L. Figure 6.45b shows the circuit model to be analyzed, where l and L are the leakage and magnetizing inductances of the transformer, respectively. Figure 6.37 can be referred to as an intermediate step in the development of the model. The voltage $V_2' = (n_1/n_2)V_2$ is proportional to

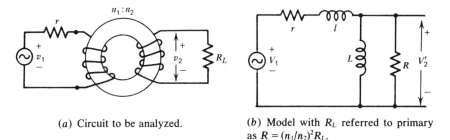

(a) Circuit to be analyzed.   (b) Model with R_L referred to primary
                                           as $R = (n_1/n_2)^2 R_L$.

Figure 6.45 Model of a transformer circuit that couples a voltage source to a load.

the actual output voltage. The voltage transfer function in the frequency domain is

$$\frac{V_2'}{V_1}(s) = \frac{sL/r}{s^2 lL/rR + s(L/r + L/R + l/r) + 1},$$ (6.84)

which is evidently a bandpass function, but the details are obscure at first glance. The following alternative approach is a valid approximation if $l \ll L$.

The three simple circuits of Fig. 6.46 follow from the assumption that $j\omega l$ is a small series impedance that is negligible at low frequencies and that $j\omega L$ is a large parallel impedance that has negligible effect at high frequency. Figure 6.46a omits both inductances in an intermediate range of frequency, where the voltage transfer function is approximately

$$\frac{V_2'}{V_1} = \frac{R}{R + r}.$$ (6.85)

From Fig. 6.46b the low-frequency transfer function is

$$\frac{V_2'}{V_1}(s) = \frac{sL/r}{\tau_1 s + 1} = \frac{R}{R + r} \frac{s}{s + 1/\tau_1},$$ (6.86)

where the low-frequency time constant $\tau_1 = L/R'$, and $R' = rR/(r + R)$. The lower limit of the midfrequency range is therefore at $\omega_1 = 1/\tau_1$

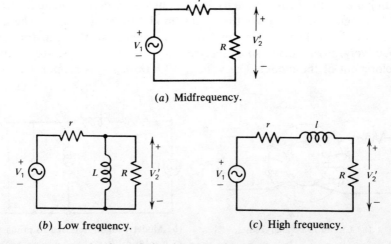

(a) Midfrequency.

(b) Low frequency.   (c) High frequency.

Figure 6.46 Approximations of the circuit of Fig. 6.44 for three ranges of frequency, assuming $l \ll L$.

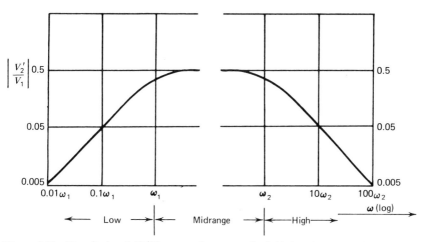

Figure 6.47 Magnitude of V_2'/V_1 versus frequency (rads/s) for the composite of (6.85)–(6.87).

rads/s. The high-frequency transfer function, from Fig. 6.46c, is

$$\frac{V_2'}{V_1}(s) = R/(R + r)(\tau_2 s + 1) \qquad (6.87)$$

where the high-frequency time constant $\tau_2 = l/(R + r)$ defines the upper limit of the midfrequency range at $\omega_2 = 1/\tau_2$. A combination of the three simple analyses yields the magnitude Bode plot (Fig. 6.47), where it is assumed that $r = R$. That criterion is consistent with the use of a transformer to match a load to the output resistance of a source, for maximum power transfer.

A qualitative extension of the results above can be made, to include the effect of core loss at high frequency. Chapter 5 modeled the core loss using a parameter G_e in parallel with L, which would also be in parallel with R in the present case. For constant output voltage, it can be argued that conductance G_e will increase with frequency in proportion to f^x, where $1 < x < 2$. The effect will be that R is shunted more and more at high frequency, which will reduce the term $R/(R + r)$ in the three transfer functions above.

A time-domain analysis of the circuits in Fig. 6.46 results from assuming v_1 to be a step function of voltage

$$v_1(t) = V_1 u(t). \qquad (6.88)$$

The rise time of $v_2'(t)$ is limited by the high-frequency time constant τ_2 as

$$v_2'(t) = V_1 \frac{R}{r+R}(1 - e^{-t/\tau_2})u(t), \tag{6.89}$$

which appears to approach $V_1 R/(r+R)$ as a final value. However the step response of the low-frequency circuit (Fig. 6.46b) is

$$v_2'(t) = V_1 \frac{R}{r+R}(e^{-t/\tau_1})u(t), \tag{6.90}$$

which shows that the final value will collapse exponentially along the low-frequency time constant τ_1. An input pulse of duration T,

$$v_1(t) = V_1[u(t) - u(t - T)],$$

where $\tau_2 \ll T \ll \tau_1$, would generate a response as in Fig. 6.48, assuming quiescent initial and final conditions.

As a final observation, it should be noted that the high-frequency limitation imposed by the leakage inductance was a limitation on the *voltage* transfer ratio V_2'/V_1. At first glance, the foregoing results may seem to be inconsistent with the facts concerning loosely coupled transformers that are used in tuned amplifiers, the intermediate-frequency (I–F) amplifiers in radio and television communication circuits. The coupling coefficient k for such transformers is low and variable, so the condition $l \ll L$ is not true. The answer is that I–F transformers are driven by high-impedance circuits modeled as current sources, rather than by voltage sources. The high-frequency response of transfer function V_2/I_1 is unaffected by the series impedance $j\omega l$.

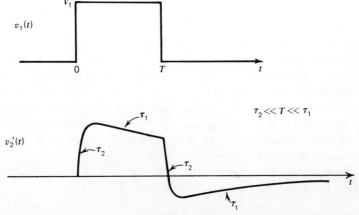

Figure 6.48   Calculated response of a transformer circuit to an input pulse of duration T.

A Broadband Balun Transformer. The circuit described here is typical of a class of circuits that have come to be very widely used for impedance matching at high frequency. The typical bandwidth for a single circuit may be from 0.2 to 100 MHz. The impedance transformation ratio of 1:4 is described for a voltage step-up transformer of turns ratio 1:2. Several alternative arrangements are described in the references [11–14]. Some circuits have been reported for use at transmitter outputs, at a kilowatt of transmitted power.

The circuit in Fig. 6.49 is basically an autotransformer with the primary and secondary wound together in a twisted-pair or bifilar arrangement. There are two cooperative effects that enhance the coupling between input and output. At the low end of the frequency range the most significant coupling is the conventional magnetic coupling of a step-up transformer (Fig. 6.49c) with a turns ratio $n:2n$. The turns ratio provides an impedance match of source resistance R_S to load resistance $R_L = 4R_S$. At the high end of the frequency range the coupling is due mostly to the line-to-line coupling of the windings as a transmission line transformer (Fig. 6.49b). This means the total voltage at point $1'$ will consist of a component that is propagated down the winding from point

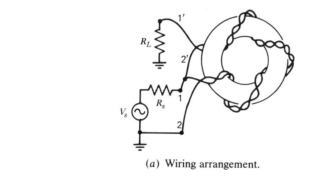

(a) Wiring arrangement.

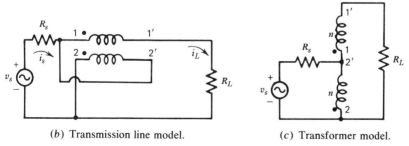

(b) Transmission line model.   (c) Transformer model.

Figure 6.49   Schematic and models for broadband balun.

1, and a second component that is coupled across from point 2' through the line-to-line capacitance between the two windings. The impedance transformation is a result of the parallel connection of the transmission lines at the source, where 1 and 2' are connected together, and their series connection at the load. The latter can be thought of as somewhat similar to a Miller effect on the impedance from 1' to 2'. At matched conditions we find

$$R_S = \frac{z_0}{2} \quad \text{and} \quad R_L = 2z_0, \tag{6.91}$$

where z_0 is the characteristic impedance of the transmission line.

The design criteria for bandwidth include the designation of low-frequency and of high-frequency limits. Applying (6.86) and assuming matched impedance, the low-frequency limit ω_1 is at

$$\omega_1 = \frac{R_S}{2L} \quad \text{rads/s}, \tag{6.92}$$

where $L = n^2 P_c$ is the magnetizing inductance. The required value of inductance is thereby deduced from R_S and ω_1, but we are not yet ready to specify the number of turns. It seems to be common practice to use a small toroidal core of a ferrite material that possesses high permeability at ω_1. It is not necessary for the bandwidth of the core material to extend to the required upper-frequency limit for the transformer, since the high-frequency performance of the circuit is dictated by transmission line considerations.

The high-frequency specification defines the maximum length of the transmission line windings, to ensure that the phase shift of the propagated signal will not exceed some specified angle. A phase angle less than 45° means that the length z of the transmission line must not exceed $\frac{1}{8}$ wavelength

$$z \simeq \frac{\lambda}{8} = \frac{v}{8f_2}, \tag{6.93}$$

where f_2 is the specified maximum frequency. In (6.93) v is the characteristic velocity of propagation of the transmission line, which must be determined experimentally for the wire configuration of interest. It may be noted that velocity and impedance of transmission lines are characteristic quantities given by

$$v = \frac{1}{\sqrt{lc}} \quad \text{and} \quad z_0 = \sqrt{\frac{l}{c}}, \tag{6.94}$$

where l and c are inductance and capacitance per meter of length, respectively.

A major aspect of the design is concerned with devising a configuration for the transmission line windings with a value for z_0 that will satisfy (6.91). The characteristic velocity may then be measured; this allows the designer to use (6.93) to determine the length of the line. A typical value for v is in the range of 1 to 2×10^8 m/s; thus for $f_2 = 100$ MHz, for example, the maximum length z would be 12.5 to 25 cm. The wire area and the length of the transmission line are the additional items of information that are needed to select the core geometry and to specify the number of turns.

Several surprising aspects of balun transformers can be pointed out. In a normal transformer configuration, components of the stray capacitance of the windings would react with L to cause spurious resonances. The bifilar twisted pair arrangement actually enhances the line-to-line capacitance and uses it to advantage in the transmission line mode of coupling. Furthermore, the transmission line coupling provides bandwidth above the frequency limit of the core. The symmetry of the windings virtually eliminates leakage inductance, thereby the restriction of (6.87). Finally, the high efficiency and the high volt·ampere ratings of autotransformers are additional advantages of the circuit. The present autotransformer can supply to the load just twice the volt·ampere rating of the transformer.

6.4.4 Transformers Driven by Transistors

This section introduces some principles of the design of pulse circuits using transistors and transformers. A description of three circuits follows a brief review of the necessary circuit properties of bipolar junction transistors. The first circuit, a d–c to d–c converter for power supply applications, uses a square-loop, tape-wound core in a magnetically coupled astable multivibrator circuit. The second circuit is a basic tutorial on the use of a transistor to drive an inductive pulse transformer. Two different modes of circuit operation are explained. The third circuit is a gated blocking oscillator, a source of low-impedance pulses of short duration. Previously, Section 6.4.3 has explained how transformer circuits are sensitive to the impedance of the signal source and load. The present applications extend Section 6.4.3 by demonstrating the use of transistors as variable-impedance elements to drive transformers.

Terminal Properties of Transistors. The circuits that follow use *NPN* bipolar junction transistors in three different bias modes: cutoff, biased ON in the normal linear mode, and saturated ON. The three regions of operation can be explained by reference to Fig. 6.50. It is assumed that the reader is basically familiar with transistor operation and is aware that the transistor consists of two *PN* junctions, appearing in Fig. 6.50*a* as two back-to-back diodes. In the cutoff region, both diodes are reverse biased and no current flows. A circuit model for cutoff is not shown because it is trivial, consisting merely of open circuits between the base, emitter, and collector terminals.

In both ON states the base-emitter junction is forward biased, so that conventional current i_E flows from the emitter terminal. Base and collector currents also flow and are related to emitter current by

$$i_B + i_C = i_E. \tag{6.95}$$

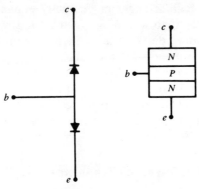

(*a*) Two back-to-back diodes.

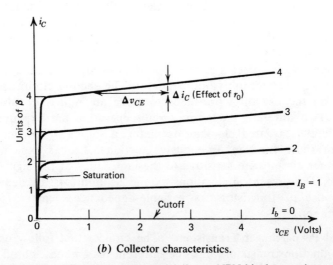

(*b*) Collector characteristics.

Figure 6.50   Elementary circuit models for an *NPN* bipolar transistor.

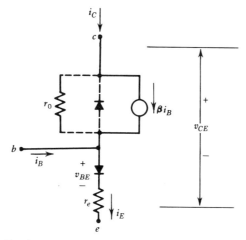

(c) Circuit model for the normal mode of operation.

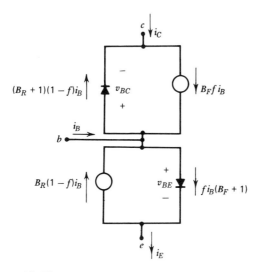

(d) Ebers–Moll model of saturated transistor.

Figure 6.50   (Cont'd).

The base-collector junction is reverse biased in the normal linear region of operation, which means that the collector-to-emitter voltage v_{CE} is positive. In the saturated region both junctions are forward biased, so that v_{CE} is a small positive voltage that is the difference of the two junction potentials. The impedance levels of the two ON states differ significantly.

Transistor saturation is a low-impedance conducting state, the almost vertical line on the left-hand side of the collector characteristics (Fig. 6.50b). A simple circuit model for saturation is a short-circuit from collector to emitter, possibly including a small series saturation resistance r_s as an optional refinement. A transistor used as an off-on switch is driven between cutoff and saturation by base-to-emitter input signals that turn off or on the base-emitter diode. The saturated state is achieved by turning on the base-emitter junction solidly with a large current. In saturation the collector current in (6.95) is limited by the external components of the collector circuit; thus i_C is independent of i_B. That characteristic is the basic property of transistor saturation. A detailed model for the distribution of current in a saturated transistor is given subsequently.

The linear incremental mode of transistor operation is a high-impedance conducting state in which the collector current term of (6.95) is strongly dependent on base current

$$i_C = \beta i_B + \frac{v_{CB}}{r_0} \approx \beta i_B. \tag{6.96}$$

This equation represents collector characteristics fairly well (Fig. 6.50b). For present purposes the voltage-dependent component of i_C can be omitted as a reasonable approximation, but we note the existence of a finite output resistance r_0.

The incremental base input resistance can be deduced from the derivative of the ideal diode equation for current in the forward-biased emitter

$$i_E = I_S e^{qv/kT}, \tag{6.97}$$

where $v \equiv v_{BE}$, q is the charge of the electron, k is Boltzmann's constant, and T is the junction temperature (K). The derivative is

$$\frac{di_E}{dv_{BE}} = \frac{I_S q}{kT} e^{qv/kT} = \frac{i_E q}{kT}, \tag{6.98}$$

which is the reciprocal of the incremental resistance within the emitter region. The value of the resistance at room temperature is

$$r_e = \frac{kT}{q i_E} = \frac{0.026v}{i_E}. \tag{6.99}$$

With the help of (6.95) and (6.96), it follows that the apparent incremental input resistance at the base terminal at room temperature is

$$r_\pi = \frac{dv_{BE}}{di_B} = r_e(\beta + 1) = \frac{0.026v}{i_B}. \tag{6.100}$$

The currents i_E and i_B in the right-most terms of the equations above are to be interpreted as the d–c or quiescent currents in the transistor. It is a property of the exponential equation (6.97) that the incremental slope is proportional to the ordinate; thus the incremental admittance of a diode is proportional to the current through the diode.

The above commentary on incremental resistance must not overshadow the most significant property of transistor action, current amplification (6.96). A more general model defines (6.96) as current amplification in the *forward* mode, recognizing that the transistor can also be operated in the *reverse* mode merely by interchanging the emitter and collector leads. Both modes of transistor action are shown in Fig. 6.50*d*, using an operator f to designate the active mode. Forward gain β_F is selected by $f = 1$; reverse gain β_R is selected by $f = 0$. We are now in a position to recognize the model for transistor saturation as a combination of both forward and reverse modes with $0 < f < 1$.

Transistor saturation results if the collector current is constrained to a lower value than the current in the linear mode

$$i_C < \beta i_B \qquad \text{at saturation.} \qquad (6.101a)$$

A preliminary interpretation of (6.101a) can be deduced from the circuit model of Fig. 6.50*c*, which includes the base-collector diode as well as a dependent current source βi_B. In the normal linear mode of operation the b–c diode is reverse biased so that $i_C = \beta i_B$. However in the saturated mode the b–c diode is forward biased and carries a forward current to account for the inequality of (6.101a). An explicit distribution of currents can be deduced from the Ebers-Moll model (Fig. 6.50*d*). A fraction f of the total base current controls the current through the b–e junction (and the forward current generator $\beta_F f i_B$), whereas the remaining fraction $(1 - f)$ of base current controls the reverse mode of the transistor. If the transistor parameters and external currents are known, f can be determined from the expression

$$f = \left(\frac{i_C / i_B + \beta_R + 1}{\beta_F + \beta_R + 1} \right), \qquad (6.101b)$$

which follows from the solution for i_C in Fig. 6.50*d*.

D–c to D–c Converter. The type of d–c to d–c converter to be described provides a compact, economical way to develop several different voltages from the same basic power supply. Each derived voltage can be either greater or less than the supply voltage and can be isolated from it. Both these properties are a consequence of the transformer-based design of the circuit. The circuit also provides short-circuit protection.

The basic circuit uses a magnetically coupled, free-running multi-vibrator to generate a periodic square wave of voltage across a transformer, windings n_1 of Fig. 6.51. The input square wave is transformed up or down, then rectified to produce d–c outputs. The transformer primary is the center-tapped winding of $2n_1$ total turns. Multivibrator action occurs because the two secondary windings n_2 provide positive feedback to transistors Q_1 and Q_2, driving one transistor to saturation and the other to cutoff. The circuit alternates between the two states (Q_1ON, Q_2OFF) and (Q_1OFF, Q_2ON) see Fig. 6.52, to cause the same effect as if the d–c supply voltage V_s were connected across the primary with alternating polarity. The basic transformer voltage is therefore a square wave, yielding a peak amplitude on the jth winding of

$$\frac{V_s n_j}{n_1} = V_j \qquad (6.102)$$

by transformation of the primary volts-per-turn V_s/n_1. The voltage across each secondary winding can be full-wave rectified to yield the

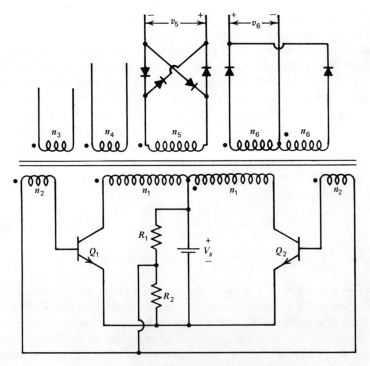

Figure 6.51 Basic circuit of the dc-to-dc converter.

final d–c output, as V_5 and V_6 of Fig. 6.51. The rectifier circuit usually is followed by a low-pass filter. The output filtering is easier than for a conventional a–c supply for two reasons: the frequency of the square wave can be higher than a–c line frequency, perhaps by 1 or 2 orders of magnitude. Second, a full-wave rectified square wave requires less filtering than a rectified sinusoid because the waveform is almost flat to start with.

The period of oscillation T for the inverter portion of the circuit is defined by the time required for the core to be driven between saturation limits. For instance during the half-period defined by the state of Fig. 6.52, the core is driven from $-\Lambda_s$ to $+\Lambda_s$ in the time that corresponds to the primary voltage integral $\int v \, dt = V_s T/2$. Equating the two relations as required by (2.31) yields the relation

$$2\Lambda_s = 2S_c n_1 B_s = \frac{V_s T}{2}. \tag{6.103}$$

This result is used twice, first to select the core and subsequently to specify the primary turns.

The recommended type of magnetic core is a tape-wound toroid of grain-oriented 50% nickel-iron alloy as described in Chapter 1. The preferred type of hysteresis loop is very square and narrow, to ensure that the magnetizing current I_0 for the core will be small and relatively constant as the core flux builds up. An inductive type of core can be used if two conditions are met. Sufficient base current must be provided to maintain transistor saturation, and a diode should be added across each transistor to handle the inductive kick that follows each change of transistor state. (The diode connection is anode-to-emitter, cathode-to-collector for each Q_1, Q_2.)

Standard sizes of commercial tape-wound cores are tabulated by core area S_c, by window area W, and the product WS_c. The window area is

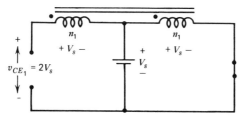

Figure 6.52 Circuit state (Q_1OFF, Q_2ON) with transistor Q_2 modeled as a short-circuit. During this state the collector-emitter voltage v_{CE} is approximately zero for Q_2 and $2V_s$ for Q_1.

the opening in the center of the toroid, which must be big enough to accommodate all the primary and secondary windings. The window area can be estimated on the basis of the total primary turns $2n_1$ as

$$W = \frac{2n_1 a_w}{k}, \tag{6.104}$$

where a_w is the wire area for the primary winding and k is the fraction of W occupied by the primary windings. For convenience W and a_w should use the same units. Standard wire tables specify a_w if the current is known; the instantaneous primary current can be determined from the total power divided by supply voltage V_s. The core selection can be made from the product WS_c, which can be found from (6.103) and (6.104)

$$WS_c = \frac{V_s T a_w}{2kB_s} \qquad \text{m}^2 \times \text{units of } a_w. \tag{6.105}$$

A typical value for k is 0.2, B_s for Orthonol® is 1.4 T, and the maximum frequency $f = 1/T$ is specified by the core manufacturer. Table 6.1 lists some typical tape-wound core geometries.

Following core selection, the number of primary turns can be determined from (6.103) and the turns of the output windings are specified by (6.102). The number of turns n_2 in the transistor base circuit, together with resistors R_1 and R_2, is determined by the transistor drive requirements. For the circuit to function, two design criteria must be met (Fig. 6.53). The d–c base voltage must forward bias the transistors during a condition of zero transformer voltage, as at the point of core saturation; thus

$$V_s b \geq V_{BE}, \tag{6.106}$$

where $b = R_2/(R_1 + R_2)$; 3 or 4 V is a reasonable value for bV_s. It is a good idea to include separate small resistors R in each base circuit (Fig. 6.53) to prevent "current hogging" during conditions of core saturation.

Second, the base current must be large enough to keep the ON transistor driven into its region of saturation, defined as $I_B > I_C/\beta$, where

$$I_B = \frac{V_s(n_2/n_1 + b) - V_{BE}}{R' + R}, \tag{6.107}$$

as shown in Fig. 6.53b. For the latter criterion the collector current I_C includes the effect of all secondary load currents and the base current, as well as the current I_0 required by the core itself.

An additional criterion is that the frequency rating of the power transistor must be very high compared to the oscillation frequency of

Table 6.1 Tape-wound core geometry tabulated by core area S_c, window area W, and the product WS_c

Areas[a]			Manufacturers' Designations				Core[b] Dimensions (in.) (Nominal)		
WS (cm⁴)	W (cm²)	S_c (cm²)	Arnold Engineering Co.	G.L. Industries, Inc.	Magnetics, Inc.	Magnetic Metals Co.	I.D.	O.D.	Height
0.132	1.76	0.076	5515	1030	50002	5	0.650	0.90	0.125
0.269	1.56	0.171	5958	1018	50076	37	0.625	1.0	0.188
0.334	4.38	0.076	4168	1060	50011	9	1.0	1.25	0.125
0.355	2.34	0.151	5502	1040	50061	79	0.75	1.0	0.250
0.355	1.56	0.227	5651	1020	50007	3	0.625	1.0	0.250
0.400	2.34	0.171	5504	1050	50106	7	0.75	1.125	0.188
0.993	4.38	0.227	4635	1080	50029	10	1.00	1.375	0.25
2.10	6.94	0.303	5387	1120	50030	13	1.25	1.75	0.250
2.65	4.38	0.605	6847	1110	50038	62	1.0	1.5	0.500
4.72	6.94	0.681	5772	1133	50425	75	1.25	2.00	0.375
11.07	18.29	0.605	4178	1160	50017	17	2.00	2.50	0.500
12.01	9.93	1.21	5320	1140	50001	15	1.5	2.5	0.500
22.14	18.29	1.21	6110	1170	50103	76	2.0	3.0	0.500
65.9	27.1	2.42	5468	1190	50042	20	2.5	3.5	1.0
446	73.7	6.05	5611	1220	50112	25	4.0	5.25	2.0
712	73.6	9.68	9260	1222	50426	78	4.0	6.0	2.0

[a]Both S_c and W are given in cm². To convert to circular mils, note that 5.067 cm² $= (2.54)^2 \pi/4$ is the same area as 10^6 c.m. The values for core area are the values for 1-mil lamination thickness, for which the manufacturer specifies $f < 4\,$kHz.
[b]The case around the core has a smaller I.D., and a larger O.D. and height.
Adapted from Johnson [17], with permission from *Electronics*.

297

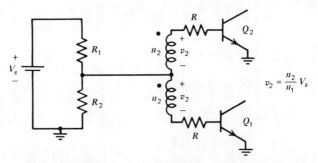

(a) The positive polarity of the feedback voltages v_2 maintains Q_2ON and Q_1OFF during a half-period.

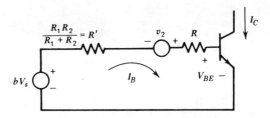

(b) Circuit model that yields (6.107).

Figure 6.53   The base circuit portion of the basic dc-to-dc converter.

the multivibrator. This serves to minimize the duration of the transient change of state at each core saturation, which is a time of circuit losses.

Inductive Pulse Transformer.   Consider the circuit of Fig. 6.54 in which an inductive pulse transformer with secondary load resistor R is driven by a transistor. A single input voltage pulse $v_1(t)$ of amplitude V_1 and duration T turns on the transistor with base current i_B. The signal amplitude and the circuit component values determine whether the transistor will drive the transformer as a current source or as a voltage source. A numerical example seems to be the best way of showing the distinction between the two modes of operation. For both illustrative cases let the model of Fig. 6.53b take the following values:*

$V_{CC} = 5$ V d–c supply
$\beta_F = 50$, forward current gain of transistor
$\beta_R = 2$, reverse current gain of transistor
$L_1 = 1$ mH primary, for instance, 20 turns at 2.5 μH/t^2

*The values were chosen to illustrate two modes of operation of the same circuit. In practice the value of R' may often be an order of magnitude smaller.

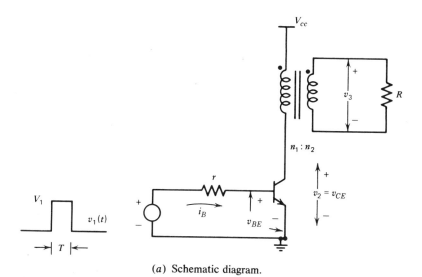

(a) Schematic diagram.

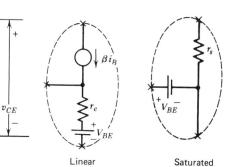

General   Linear   Saturated

(b) Alternative models of circuit during pulse.

Figure 6.54 A transistor is turned on by a pulse of duration T.

l = leakage inductance, neglect for simplicity
$T = 2\mu s$ duration of pulse
$\tau = L_1/R' = 0.4\,\mu s$ time constant
$R' = (n_1/n_2)^2 R = 2.5\,k\Omega$ referred to primary
Initial conditions: transistor cutoff, zero inductor current

For the first case, suppose the input pulse is small so that only $20\,\mu A$ of current is driven into the base. It is assumed for simplicity that the transistor responds instantaneously with $i_C = 1\,\text{mA}$ as in Fig. 6.55. Initially the collector current flows entirely through R', since the inductor current cannot change instantly from its earlier value of zero. As i_C jumps to $\beta i_B = 1\,\text{mA}$, v_{CE} drops to 2.5 V along a load line on the collector characteristics

$$v_{CE} = V_{CC} - i_C R' \tag{6.108}$$

as in Fig. 6.55b. During the 2 μs pulse, the inductor current builds up according to the transient equation

$$i_L = i_C(1 - e^{-t/\tau}), \tag{6.109}$$

which has time to reach its final value because $T = 5\tau$. At the end of the input pulse the transistor turns off, but the inductor current persists. There is a path through R' for the inductor current, which collapses according to*

$$i_L(t) = I_l e^{-t/\tau}, \tag{6.110}$$

where I_L is the initial condition at $t = 2\,\mu$s. The transient waveforms (Fig. 6.55c, 6.55d) are correlated with a path on the collector characteristics (Fig. 6.55b) at times t_1–t_4.

It follows from (6.110) that the collector will experience an *inductive back-kick* of voltage

$$v_{CE} = V_{cc} + i_L R' \tag{6.111}$$

after the pulse is over. In an alternative expression of the same idea, the current i_L is a measure of energy stored in the magnetic field of the inductor

$$\tfrac{1}{2}\Lambda i_L = \tfrac{1}{2} L i_L^2. \tag{6.112}$$

In the present circuit the decay of the magnetic energy is accomplished by a current through load resistor R in the secondary winding, described by (6.111) in terms of the effect at v_{CE}.

Let us now examine the case of transistor saturation, assuming that the input voltage is large enough to cause $i_B = 300\,\mu$A. It follows that $\beta i_B = 15\,\text{mA} > i_C$ because the initial value of i_C must obey (6.108). The maximum initial value of i_C, for $v_{CE} = 0$, is $i_C = V_{cc}/R' = 2\,\text{mA}$. These considerations confirm that the transistor saturates, thereby effectively shorting the transformer to ground. Since

$$v_L = V_{cc} - v_{CE} \approx V_{cc}, \tag{6.113}$$

---

*In this equation $t = 0$ defines the beginning of the new state of the circuit in which the equation is applicable, i.e. at the end of the pulse when the transistor turns off. This convention is called *time segmentation*.

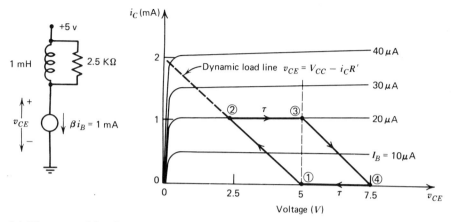

(a) Linear model of collector circuit.

(b) Operating path on collector characteristics. Points 1–4 correspond to times t_1–t_4 of (c) and (d).

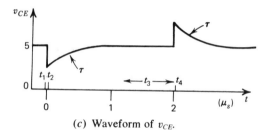

(c) Waveform of v_{CE}.

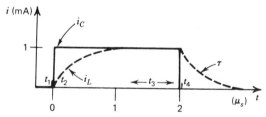

(d) Waveforms of collector and inductor currents. Times t_1–t_4 are shown.

Figure 6.55 Response of circuit to a small input pulse, neglecting finite rise time.

the inductor current increases linearly at a rate of

$$\frac{di_L}{dt} = \frac{v_L}{L} \approx \frac{V_{cc}}{L} \tag{6.114}$$

or $5\,\text{mA}/\mu\text{s}$. After $2\,\mu\text{s}$, the inductor current would only reach $10\,\text{mA}$, thus we can conclude that the transistor is saturated for the entire pulse.

The saturated transistor may be modeled (Fig. 6.56a) as essentially a short circuit from collector to emitter, through r_s of about 50 Ω. Consistently, the detailed components of current within the saturated transistor can be calculated by using the Ebers-Moll model. As the transient collector current increases from 2- to 12 mA, the corresponding value of fraction f increases from 0.1824 to 0.8113, found by using (6.101b). In any event the saturated transistor provides a low resistance connection to ground for the primary winding of the transformer.

Comparing the voltage waveforms across the transformer, $v_L = V_{cc} - v_{CE}$ of Figs. 6.56 and 6.55, we see a substantial difference, although the circuit is the same for the two cases. The difference is attributed to the impedance of the transistor driver, which acts as a high resistance in one case and as a low resistance in the other. The present example has shown the consequences in the time domain of varying the low-frequency time constant, described in the frequency domain by (6.86).

Equation 6.111 predicts the inductive back-kick following the pulse may reach 30 V, which is also consistent with the operating path 3 to 4 in Fig. 6.56b. The area under the back-kick transient is

$$\int_0^\infty v_L \, dt = I_L R' \tau = 10 \times 2.5 \times 0.4 \times 10^{-6} = 10^{-5} \text{ V·s},$$

which is equal and opposite to the area during the pulse $5 \text{ V} \times 2 \, \mu\text{s} = 10^{-5}$ V·s, as it should be to restore the quiescent state of the core to $\Lambda = 0$ at $i_L = 0$.

Control of the Inductive Back-Kick. Some transistors may not appreciate being subjected to a large voltage spike, as the 30 V v_{CE}, and may need to be protected. A damping resistor R_d can be put in series with a diode, so that current flows only during the back-kick. The combination can then be put across any winding with the effect of being in parallel with R'. Such a circuit protects v_{CE} from being driven too far above V_{cc} by the transient recovery of the inductive transformer. As the amplitude of the back-kick is decreased, the duration will be extended, to ensure that the area remains constant under the voltage waveform.

Many uses have been made of the inductive voltage kick that results from suddenly interrupting the current, typically interrupting the primary current in a step-up transformer. The spark coil for a gasoline engine is a commonplace example. Another example is a circuit described by L. T. Rees [19] which uses the inductive kick of a 1:100 step-up transformer in the power stage of a photoflash capacitor charger. The circuit pulses thousands of times to gradually charge a 480-μF capacitor to 500 V, to fire a 60-J flashbulb. The circuit timing is done with a free-running blocking oscillator.

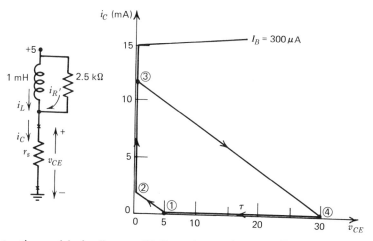

(a) Saturation model of collec-   (b) Operating path on collector characteristics.
tor circuit.   Points 1–4 correspond to times t_1–t_4.

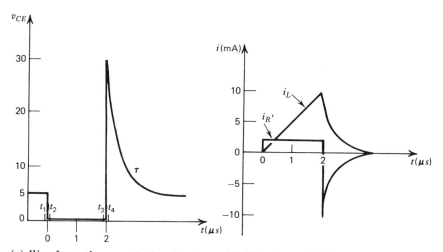

(c) Waveform of v_{CE}, neglecting rise time   (d) Waveforms of inductor current i_L and
limitations.   reflected load current $i_{R'}$.

Figure 6.56 Response of circuit to an input pulse large enough to keep the transistor
saturated for 2 μs. The primary inductance is assumed to be constant at 1 mH.

Gated Blocking Oscillator.

A blocking oscillator is a regenerative tran-
sistor-transformer circuit that produces a single pulse of specified amplitude and duration in response to a trigger input signal. Such a circuit
is particularly desirable when a floating or isolated pulse is needed,
because transformer secondary windings possess the isolation property.

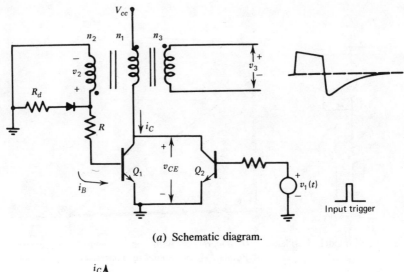

(a) Schematic diagram.

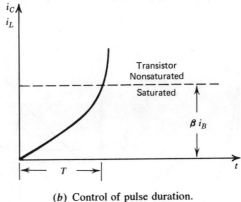

(b) Control of pulse duration.

Figure 6.57 Gated blocking oscillator. The pulse duration T is set by the time required for the inductor-limited collector current to increase to the level $i_C = \beta i_B$.

The basic circuit (Fig. 6.57a) consists of a 3-winding transformer driven by transistor Q_1. The diode and damping resistor R_d are optional; transistor Q_2 is the gate circuit that triggers the pulse. The dot-marked windings n_1 and n_2 are connected for positive feedback, described as follows. Both transistors are initially cut off until an input trigger $v_1(t)$ turns on Q_2, causing v_{CE} to drop toward ground from V_{cc}, which thereby induces a voltage across the transformer primary. Voltage v_2 is positive and turns on Q_1, which further lowers v_{CE} until the positive feedback loop gain is reduced as Q_1 saturates. Transistor Q_1 remains saturated for the duration of the pulse. The level of saturation βi_B is specified by feedback voltage v_2 together with the base-current limiting resistor R.

The saturation level defines the pulse duration T in the following way. The saturation of Q_1 applies V_{cc} across the primary of the transformer, which results in an increase of inductor current according to (6.114). By (6.101), Q_1 remains saturated as long as the $i_C \approx i_L$ is less than the critical value of βi_B. But when $i_C = \beta i_B$, Q_1 comes out of saturation, which means that v_{CE} increases. This reduces the voltage across n_1, which reduces v_2 and therefore reduces i_B. Transistor Q_1 is quickly driven to cutoff by regenerative action, thereby terminating the pulse.

It can be noted from (6.114) that i_L will increase more rapidly as the core begins to saturate and L decreases. The steeper slope means that i_L will cross the critical value βi_B more steeply, therefore should define duration T with greater precision (Fig. 6.57b). Finally, the benefit of core saturation can be achieved by the use of a separate timing inductor driven by the transformer. It is not required that the core of the transformer itself be the saturating element.

6.4.5 Closely Coupled Transformers

A very interesting and useful family of electronic circuits exploits a mode-sensitive property of transformers that are wound in a special way. By careful control of the relative geometry of primary and secondary windings, coupling coefficients of 0.9999 or higher can be achieved routinely. The geometry control consists of making the windings with coaxial or triaxial cable, or possibly with bifilar or trifilar twisted wire in the manner of a balun. So wound, the primary and secondary windings occupy the same region of space and therefore are both linked in a similar manner by the air flux. The air flux, first described in Section 2.2.3, therefore contributes mostly to the mutual inductance and very little to the leakage inductances of the windings. The present principle extends the concept of Section 6.4.1, which imprecisely associated the leakage inductance of a winding with all the leakage flux that links the winding but does not link the transformer core. The broadband transformer of Section 6.4.3 was wound as a balun, therefore might also be included as an example of a closely coupled transformer. However the selected applications described below are a class of circuits that all possess the property of signal selection.

Pulse Isolation Circuit. When using a short pulse to drive a load impedance that is located a meter or more away, it sometimes happens that the signal deteriorates in transmission because of stray inductance of the single drive line and interference on the ground return path. Such circumstances are often improved by using a coaxial drive line, and further improved by taking a few turns of the coaxial line around a ferrite core as suggested in Fig. 6.58. Running the coaxial line through a toroidal core enhances the coupling between center conductor and shield of the coaxial line, thereby increasing the tendency for the currents to be equal and opposite on the two coaxial conductors. In Fig. 6.58c if return current $i_2 = -i_1$, the core will cause no net inductance in the loop from $v_1(t)$ to R_L. The tendency for part of i_1 to return from R_L along the ground loop is suppressed by the inductance of the core, as shown by the analysis that follows. Summing voltages around the upper loop, then around the lower loop of Fig. 6.58c, yields

$$v_1 + v_n = i_1(R_S + R_L) + L_1\frac{di_1}{dt} + M\frac{di_2}{dt} + i_nR_n \qquad (6.115)$$

(a) The problem: to transmit a pulse $v_1(t)$ to a load R_L.

(b) Proposed solution: coaxial line wound around ferrite core.

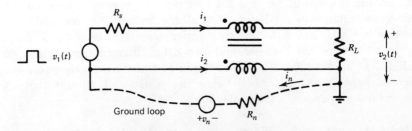

(c) Circuit model of proposed solution.

Figure 6.58 Use of a transformer to reduce ground-loop current and noise.

$$v_n = L_2 \frac{di_2}{dt} + M \frac{di_1}{dt} + i_n R_n, \qquad (6.116)$$

where for clarity the inductances L_1, L_2, and M of the coupled windings are taken separately. Subtracting the two equations gives

$$v_1 = i_1(R_S + R_L) + L_1 \frac{di_1}{dt} - L_2 \frac{di_2}{dt} + M \left(\frac{di_2}{dt} - \frac{di_1}{dt} \right),$$

which is simplified by defining $L_1 = l_1 + M$, $L_2 = l_2 + M$,

$$v_1 = i_1(R_S + R_L) + l_1 \frac{di_1}{dt} - l_2 \frac{di_2}{dt}. \qquad (6.117)$$

Equation 6.116 for the noise voltage can also be rewritten as

$$v_n = l_2 \frac{di_2}{dt} + M \left(\frac{di_1}{dt} + \frac{di_2}{dt} \right) + i_n R_n. \qquad (6.118)$$

In (6.118) $i_n = i_1 + i_2$ is suppressed by the mutual inductance term so that $i_2 \approx -i_1$, which was to be shown. It should be noted that l_1 and l_2 are very small indeed and are normally negligible for a transformer that is wound as described above. Thus in (6.117) $v_1 \approx i_1(R_S + R_L)$, which suggests the result that $v_2 = i_1 R_L$, independent of noise voltage v_n.

Common-Mode Rejection or Enhancement. Our analysis of a single-ended pulse source and a single-ended load can be extended to the analysis of a balanced line driver that drives a load consisting of a differential component of resistance and a common-mode component (Fig. 6.59). A second load resistance R_2, transformer coupled to the circuit with a third winding, is also a component of the common-mode load. It is convenient to define sum and difference input signals, similar to the signals for differential amplifiers, as

$$v_s = \tfrac{1}{2}(v_1 + v_2) \quad \text{and} \quad v_d = \tfrac{1}{2}(v_1 - v_2). \qquad (6.119)$$

It is now shown that R_1 is the load only for difference components and R_2 is the load only for common-mode or sum components.

The circuit diagram is redrawn in Fig. 6.59b, with v_1 and v_2 redefined in terms of sum and difference components

$$v_1 = v_s + v_d, \qquad v_2 = v_s - v_d. \qquad (6.120)$$

We then consider each component separately (Fig. 6.59c, 6.59d). Both components of current in the common-mode circuit enter dot-marked

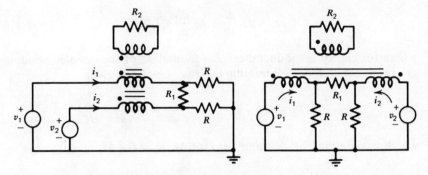

(a) Model of circuit to be analyzed, drawn two ways.

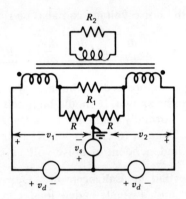

(b) Circuit with sources redefined with sum and difference components.

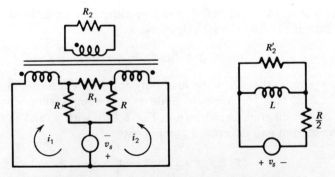

(c) Preliminary and final common-mode circuit models.

Figure 6.59 A transformer-coupled symmetrical circuit.

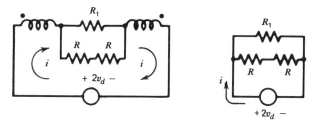

(d) Difference-mode circuit models.

Figure 6.59 (Cont'd).

ends of the transformer, resulting in

$$v_s = i_1 R + L \frac{di_1}{dt} + M \frac{di_2}{dt}$$

$$v_s = i_2 R + L \frac{di_2}{dt} + M \frac{di_1}{dt}$$

(6.121)

where the effect of secondary load R_2 was omitted at this step for simplicity. By symmetry $i_1 = i_2$, also $L = M$, hence each (6.121) becomes

$$v_s = iR + 2L \frac{di}{dt}.$$

It follows that the two halves of the common-mode circuit act in parallel, leading to the final result that $R/2$ is the effective primary resistance and v_s couples to R_2.

In the circuit model for difference-component signals (Fig. 6.59d), we can write

$$2v_d = iR' + 2(L - M) \frac{di}{dt},$$

(6.122)

where $R' = R_1$ paralleled by $2R$. Since $L = M$, the simple result is that $2v_d = v_1 - v_2$ appears entirely across load R'.

The analysis has shown that the circuit routes the outputs to two different ports depending on whether the output is derived from a common-mode input signal or from a difference-mode input.

Grant [21] has used a–c impedance measurements to study the probable effectiveness of cores in suppressing common-mode digital system noise. He found the use of cores to be beneficial in the frequency range where the core impedance is high. In the unreported development of a beam-addressed memory for the Rice University computer nearly two decades ago, Graham used signal-separation memory transformers to isolate large control currents (differential mode) from tiny output signal currents (common mode). The signal current was efficiently coupled to a signal amplifier, whereas only about 10^{-5} of the control current affected the same port.

Hybrid Transformers. A hybrid transformer is a closely coupled, 3-winding transformer that provides a specific pattern of coupling and isolation between ports, under the conditions that certain external impedances are matched. Circuits can be coupled to a common terminal without being coupled to each other. Hybrid coils have been used for many years in telephone systems to accomplish the coupling and isolation required for the bidirectional amplification of voice signals. That is, in a repeater station for a long north–south telephone line, a signal from the south must be coupled to an amplifier that drives the north line but isolated from a similar operation for south-bound signals. When designed for a higher frequency operation, hybrid transformers have been found useful for a variety of other tasks. A recent paper by Gross [22] describes several applications of hybrid transformers that include:

1. Coupling of a single transducer to both transmit and receive circuits, for duplex operation.
2. Coupling of a single driver to two transducers that must remain isolated from each other.
3. Coupling of two isolated signal generators to a common device to measure the intermodulation distortion at the device.
4. A proximity metal detector.

The general hybrid transformer circuit in Fig. 6.60 shows the four ports; normally no more than two of these would be driven simultaneously by external signals. The coupling and isolation can be explained by considering two special cases (Fig. 6.61). In Fig. 6.61a a voltage v_3 applied at port 3 is coupled to ports 1 and 2 with currents i_1 and i_2 as shown. If $R_1 = R_2$, the currents are equal, so that no net ampere·*turns* is induced across the transformer. It follows that

$$v_4 = 0 \qquad \text{and} \qquad v_1 = v_2 = \frac{v_3 R_1}{R_1 + R_3} \qquad (6.123)$$

for the balanced condition. If $R_1 \neq R_2$, (6.123) no longer applies and an output appears at v_4. This configuration can be used for metal detection if R_1 or R_2 is replaced by a sensor.

Figure 6.61b is a little more complicated. Let v_1 be applied at port 1, with some fraction of the voltage taken up across each of the elements of the left-hand loop. That is, av_1 is the voltage across R_1 and bv_1 is the

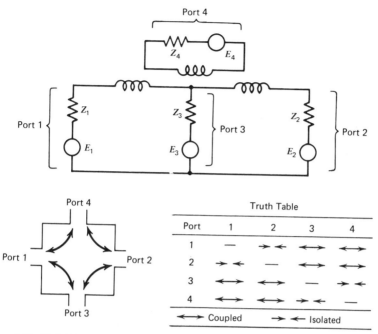

Figure 6.60 Hybrid transformer: a four-port device formed by three windings, two of which are connected series aiding. Truth table shows that each port is coupled to two others but is isolated from a third. (From Gross [22]. Reprinted from *Electronics*, March 3, 1977. Copyright © McGraw-Hill, Inc., 1977.)

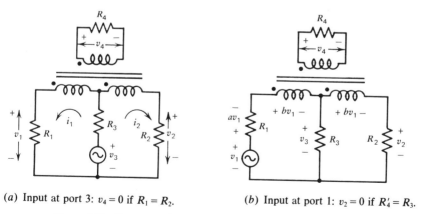

(*a*) Input at port 3: $v_4 = 0$ if $R_1 = R_2$.   (*b*) Input at port 1: $v_2 = 0$ if $R_4' = R_3$.

Figure 6.61 Two examples of how the hybrid transformer works.

voltage developed across R_4' at the transformer. It follows that

$$v_3 = v_1(1 - a - b) \tag{6.124}$$

and

$$v_2 = v_3 - bv_1 = v_1(1 - a - 2b), \tag{6.125}$$

from which the condition for a null at v_2 can be deduced. The null condition is

$$R_3 = R_4' \quad \text{for any } b = \tfrac{1}{2}(1 - a), \tag{6.126}$$

where R_4' is the value of R_4 as it appears in the transformer primary circuit. If $R_1 = R_4' = R_3$, then $a = b = \tfrac{1}{3}$. The magnetizing inductance that parallels R_4' was neglected in the analysis. There are no explicit restrictions on the values of R_1 and R_2 as regards the null condition at v_2. The choice of values may be constrained by bandwidth considerations as in Section 6.4.3, or by impedance matching considerations.

The null conditions, $v_4 = 0$ in (6.123) and $v_2 = 0$ in (6.125), mean that the voltage transfer functions v_4/v_3 and v_2/v_1 are both zero, hence the ports are isolated from one another. The two examples of Fig. 6.61 can be extended to other cases by arguments of symmetry and of superposition.

6.4.6 Isolation Applications

An elementary property of transformers mentioned in Section 6.4.1 is the electrical isolation of each winding from the others. A major advantage of the isolation is the flexibility it affords for the different windings to be connected to different reference potentials. A second advantage is the opportunity for current return paths of different circuits to be isolated from one another. Both concepts are illustrated by Fig. 6.62, in which a transformer secondary voltage v_2 is offset from ground by some reference voltage. The secondary load current for each circuit is $i = v_2/R$, which flows in a closed path, independent of the reference voltage. The current i_r that flows in the reference supply loop is determined by different parameters, namely, by the impedance to ground of the total secondary circuit. If the reference voltage has a time-varying component, as in Fig. 6.62b, the stray capacitances of the secondary may be an important consideration. The figure shows a lumped approximation model that includes C_1, the capacitance between windings of the transformer, and C_2, the capacitance to ground of the entire secondary circuit including the secondary windings. An electrostatic shield interposed between the two sets of windings can almost entirely eliminate C_1 but with a corresponding increase in the C_2 component.

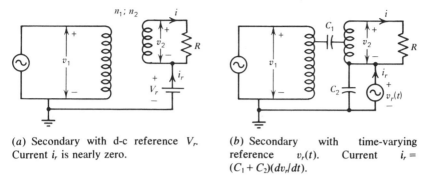

(a) Secondary with d-c reference V_r. Current i_r is nearly zero.

(b) Secondary with time-varying reference $v_r(t)$. Current $i_r = (C_1 + C_2)(dv_r/dt)$.

Figure 6.62 Two examples of secondary windings that have nonzero reference potentials.

Floating d–c Supply. The conventional d–c power supply, represented schematically in Fig. 6.63, produces a d–c output voltage that is isolated from ground. Either output terminal can be connected to ground, which permits the equipment to be used either as a positive or a negative voltage supply. The ratings of some power supplies may permit the output to be referenced to a voltage other than ground, but in most cases the manufacturer's specifications should be consulted before doing this.

SCR Turn-on. A silicon-controlled rectifier (SCR) is a four-layer *PNPN* device widely used for power switching. The operation of an SCR can be compared with an ordinary *PN* rectifier as follows. Both devices are nonconducting for inverse voltages and both are capable of conduction in the forward direction only. However the forward conduction of an SCR is conditional on the forward bias of the gate-cathode junction. When current carriers are injected into the *PNPN* structure by way of the gate terminal, a regenerative current amplification takes place as the device goes into the conducting state. The regeneration can be

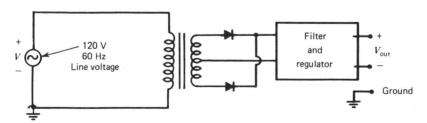

Figure 6.63 A conventional d-c voltage supply with ungrounded output voltage.

visualized as taking place as an interaction between a *PNP* and an *NPN* transistor, connected together to form the *PNPN* configuration.

An SCR can be turned on by applying a positive pulse from gate to cathode, but most SCRs cannot be turned off from the gate. Turnoff is normally accomplished by developing an inverse voltage from anode to cathode. Because of the turnoff problem, the simplest SCR circuitry uses an alternating supply voltage, which automatically terminates the conduction every cycle.

The SCR circuit of Fig. 6.64 is for switching segments of a–c line voltage to a load R. A pulse transformer is used to couple the control voltage pulse $v_1(t)$ to the gate-cathode of the SCR. The waveform conduction angle θ can be varied by changing the time of occurrence of $v_1(t)$. The isolation property of the transformer is critical to this application because v_{GK} is "referenced" to the complicated output voltage waveform, which is zero volts until the SCR fires, then is approximately at line potential.

Implanted Transformers. Perhaps the most dramatic applications of transformer winding isolation are those in which the transformer secondary windings are inserted into living animals and the primary windings are located outside the skin. Figure 6.65 shows two different skin tunnel arrangements, one with the transformer core inside the test animal and the other with the core outside. Serious proposals in other geometries have also been made for devices such as external circuitry

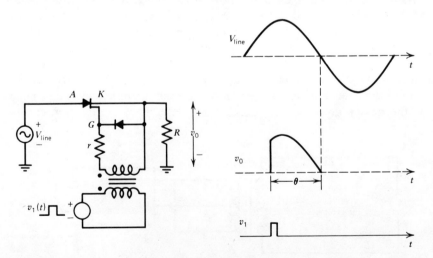

Figure 6.64 Use of a pulse transformer to trigger an SCR. A diode is used to suppress the inductive back-kick of the transformer.

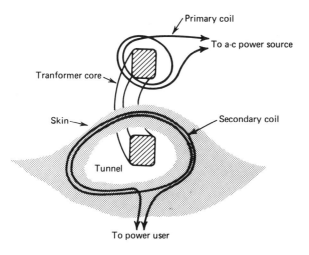

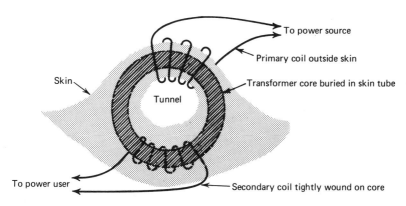

Figure 6.65 Two skin tunnel transformer configurations for coupling tens of watts into an animal. (From Andren et al. [24]. Copyright © by The Institute of Electrical and Electronics Engineers, Inc. Reprinted, with permission, from IEEE Transactions on Biomedical Engineering, Oct. 1968, Vol. BME-15, pp. 278–280.)

for recharging an implanted nickel-cadmium battery that powers a cardiac pacemaker [25].

6.4.7 Nonlinear Magnetics

Nonlinear magnetic circuits are those in which core saturation is intended as part of the normal circuit function. The design principles are laid out for four such circuits.

Morgan Circuit. The Morgan circuit uses a saturable autotransformer to turn off an SCR [26, 27, 37]. As observed in Section 6.4.6, an SCR can be turned on by pulsing the gate but is normally turned off only by an inverse voltage from anode to cathode. When an SCR is used for the control of d–c power, some auxiliary circuitry is required to develop the necessary inverse voltage. One method discharges a capacitor through a second SCR to pick up the load of the first SCR, thereby turning it off. The second SCR turns off automatically when the capacitor is sufficiently discharged. The Morgan circuit, an attractive alternative for many applications, uses a saturable core to accomplish the turnoff function so that a second SCR is not needed. The circuit is like a high current one-shot, yielding an output pulse of fixed duration. The description below shows that the pulse duration, determined by the interaction of a capacitor C with a saturating current transformer, is approximately

$$T \approx 2R_L C \frac{n_2}{n_1} \tag{6.127}$$

The basic Morgan circuit (Fig. 6.66a) consists of a capacitor and a saturable autotransformer in parallel with the SCR that is controlled by the circuit. Thus the anode-cathode voltage is the sum of the capacitor voltage and the voltage across winding n_2

$$v_{ak} = v_c + v_2. \tag{6.128}$$

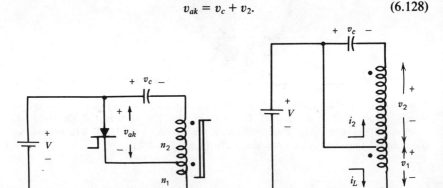

(a) Basic Morgan circuit.

(b) Current transformer model with SCR on.

Figure 6.66 The Morgan circuit: a saturating current transformer for turning off an SCR after a pulse duration T.

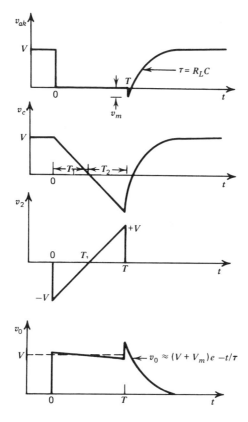

(*c*) Voltage waveforms from analysis.

Figure 6.66 (Cont'd).

The principle of operation can be explained as follows. When the SCR is conducting, $v_{ak} \approx 0$ in (6.128), so that the core voltage v_2 is controlled by the capacitor voltage v_c. The capacitor is discharged at almost a constant rate, in proportion to the load current by the current-transformer action of the core. When the capacitor voltage reaches a sufficient negative value, the core saturates to cause $v_2 = 0$ in (6.128). The result is that v_{ak} is driven to a negative value and the SCR turns off.

The capacitor voltage waveform is shown in Fig. 6.66c as a linear ramp from its initial value, as

$$v_c(t) = V - \frac{1}{C} \int^t i_2 \, dt' \qquad (6.129)$$

where the capacitor current is proportional to load current

$$i_2 = \frac{n_1}{n_2} i_L = \frac{n_1}{n_2} \frac{V - v_{ak} - v_1}{R_L}. \tag{6.130}$$

Neglecting v_{ak} and v_1, v_c reaches zero after a time T_1, which is

$$T_1 = R_L C \frac{n_2}{n_1} \tag{6.131}$$

from (6.129). The total pulse duration is about twice T_1, (6.127), because the capacitor voltage continues to discharge to a value of negative V. It now remains to be explained how the core saturates when v_c reaches $-V$, thereby terminating the pulse.

The voltage across winding n_2 of the core, when $v_{ak} \approx 0$ in (6.128), is shown in Fig. 6.66c as a negative triangle followed by a positive triangle. At the beginning of the pulse $t = 0$, the core is at the initial state of positive saturation. The negative triangular component of v_2 corresponds to a flux change of

$$\Delta \Lambda = \frac{V T_1}{2} < 2\Lambda_s = 2 n_2 B_s S_c, \tag{6.132}$$

which takes the core away from positive saturation, but not to negative saturation if the inequality is obeyed. The positive triangular component of v_2, equal in area, takes the core back to positive saturation, which terminates the pulse.

The output voltage waveform in Fig. 6.66, drawn with the assumption that $n_1/n_2 \ll 1$, reflects the same linear decrease during the pulse as $v_2(t)$. Omitting ohmic drop in the transformer windings, the output voltage is

$$v_0 = i_L R_L = V - v_{ak} - v_1, \tag{6.133}$$

where the last term can be recognized as

$$v_1 = \left(\frac{n_1}{n_2}\right) v_2 = \left(\frac{n_1}{n_2}\right)(v_{ak} - v_c). \tag{6.134}$$

If (6.129) is substituted into (6.134), after some manipulation of (6.133) the result is

$$v_0(t) = (V - v_{ak}) \frac{1 + (n_1/n_2)}{1 + (n_1/n_2)^2 t / R_L C} \tag{6.135}$$

during the pulse.

The final state of the circuit is the transient recovery of the circuit after the SCR has turned off. The recharge of C to the initial voltage $v_c = V$ is predominantly an RC time constant, since the core is already saturated in the same direction as driven by the charging current.

An interesting and useful property of the circuit is that pulse duration T is essentially independent of supply voltage V as long as the inequality of (6.132) is true.

The analysis above is not valid if negative core saturation occurs during T_1. The waveforms for v_c and v_2 would then be trapezoidal rather than triangular. The pulse duration would be shorter and would vary inversely with supply voltage.

Ferroresonant Transformers. The ferroresonant transformer is one of the most interesting magnetic circuits for regulated power supplies. Using only passive components, the circuit provides an a–c output with moderate regulation against line and load variations, and furthermore provides excellent filtering against voltage spikes on the input waveform. These desirable properties are achieved by essentially three design concepts as follows.

1. There is a shunt magnetic path that enhances the leakage flux, thereby causing the transformer to have an inductive output impedance.
2. There is a capacitor that is nearly but not exactly at resonance with the output inductance at the line frequency, therefore tends to drive an output voltage to large excursions while suppressing harmonic distortion.
3. Part of the magnetic circuit is thereby driven between saturation limits each half-cycle. It follows from the half-cycle limits of $\int v\, dt = 2\Lambda_S$ that the average voltage over the half-cycle is defined by the magnetic parameter

$$\langle v \rangle = 4f\Lambda_S. \tag{6.136}$$

This has the effect of maintaining the output voltage constant.

The following description of a ferroresonant transformer, based on a paper by Biega [28], uses the duality method (Section 6.4.1) for developing an electric circuit model of the magnetic circuit. Figure 6.67a shows the total transformer configuration, with the windings described in the legend.

The half-circuit to be analyzed appears in Fig. 6.67b, and the topologically similar magnetic analog for the half-circuit is given in Fig. 6.67c. The next step in the development of an electrical circuit model is made easier by the construction of the topological dual circuit (Fig. 6.68a), which leads to the final result in Fig. 6.68c. The result shows the output voltage consists of two components

$$v_0 = v_A \left(\frac{N_D}{N_A}\right) - v_B' \left(\frac{N_B}{N_A}\right), \tag{6.137}$$

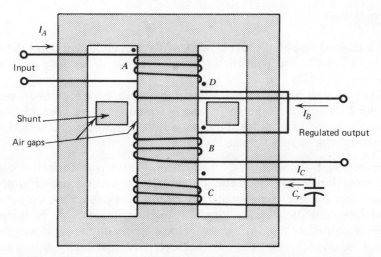

(a) The magnetic circuit includes a shunt leakage path with airgaps. The primary winding A is connected to the unregulated input; secondary winding B supplies a stable a-c voltage to the load. Winding C is resonated with capacitor C_r. Winding D, in series with B but bucking it magnetically, is used in many designs to provide additional compensation.

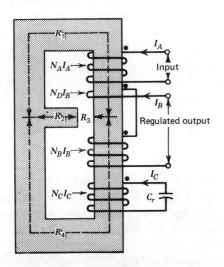

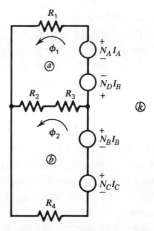

(b) Half the circuit of (a), split down the axis of symmetry. Note the reluctance definitions; R_3 includes both airgaps lumped together. From Biega [28], reprinted with permission.

(c) Analog circuit of (b). Adapted from Biega [28].

Figure 6.67 A ferroresonant voltage-stabilizing transformer. (From Biega [28], reprinted with permission of Sola Electric, Elk Grove Village, Illinois, a unit of General Signal.

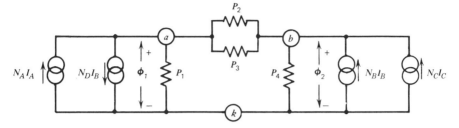

(a) Dual of Fig. 6.67c by construction.

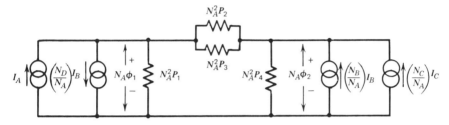

(b) The circuit of (a) scaled to the primary side by multiplying all P's by N_A^2.

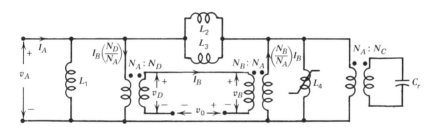

(c) Final electrical model for ferroresonant transformer, referred to input. The three transformers are ideal, but each is parallel to an inductance.

Figure 6.68 Electric circuit model for a ferroresonant transformer, developed by use of duality procedures.

where v_B' is the regulated component and v_A is the unregulated input voltage. It seems that N_D/N_A provides additional compensation for line voltage changes.

Finally, we can look at a simpler circuit to get a better idea how the circuit is nearly resonant. In Fig. 6.69 leakage inductance l represents the parallel combination of L_2 and L_3, $L = L_4$, $C = C_r(N_C/N_A)^2$, and R is the load. The inductance L_1 is omitted, since it has no effect on the

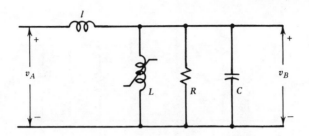

Figure 6.69 A simplified version of Fig. 6.68c.

transfer function. The transfer function in the frequency domain is easily found to be

$$\frac{V_B}{V_A} = \frac{L/(l+L)}{s^2 L'C + sL'/R + 1},$$ (6.138)

where $L' = lL/(l+L)$ is dominated by l, which is much smaller than L and is also not subject to saturation. We may conjecture that the transfer function has high enough Q (a) to cause V_B to have a large value near resonance, thereby driving inductance L to saturation, and (b) to be frequency selective, so that distortion harmonics are suppressed somewhat and spikes on the input waveform are very greatly suppressed. Both these effects are desirable. For more detailed models, analysis, and applications of ferroresonant transformers, the literature may be consulted [29, 30, 31].

Magnetic Modulator. The second-harmonic magnetic modulator, sometimes called a flux-gate circuit, generates an a–c output signal in proportion to a d–c or slowly varying input signal. Circuits of this type have been useful for applications that require amplification of signals at extremely low power levels because transformerlike circuits have an impedance-matching property. Commercial instruments for measuring d–c current in a wire have also been developed around the flux-gate circuit. The flux-gate concept has also been used for the detection and measurement of low H-fields, usually using open cores rather than toroidal. Reference 32 gives an extensive review and bibliography.

The two-core circuit in Fig. 6.70 is used to describe the principle of operation. Single-core circuits, probably more widely used, are explained in the references [32–34]. The circuit consists of two matched cores a, b wound with three sets of windings: N_i, N_s, N_0. The signal windings are connected series aiding, whereas the input and output windings are connected in opposition. It is assumed that the power

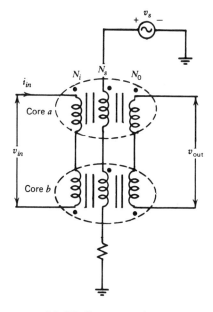

(a) Winding connections.

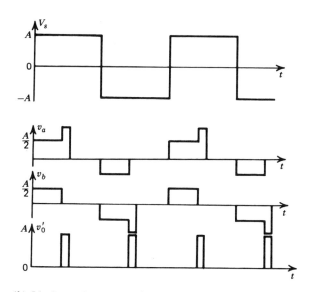

(b) Ideal waveforms assuming square-wave v_s, for negative i_{in}.

Figure 6.70 A second-harmonic magnetic modulator using two matched square-loop cores.

signal input will cause core saturation each half-cycle. In the absence of input current, both cores fire at the same time, so the output voltage

$$v_0 = (v_a - v_b)\frac{N_0}{N_s} \tag{6.139}$$

is zero. However an input current will advance the saturation of one core and retard the saturation of the other, yielding an output pulse when the two voltages are subtracted. Figure 6.70b shows, for a square-wave power signal V_s, that the output is a series of positive (or negative) pulses at twice the frequency of V_s. It is well known that the Fourier series expansion of a symmetrical square wave contains only odd harmonics. It is easily shown that a slight disturbance of the symmetry gives the waveform a second-harmonic component that is proportional to the asymmetry.

Some applications of the flux-gate circuit use another core winding N_f as a feedback element. The amount of feedback current required to maintain a null condition is a measure of the input current or field.

Magnetic Amplifier. A magnetic amplifier (called a transductor in Europe) is a controlled magnetic impedance located in series with an alternating supply voltage and its load. Current to the load either flows or does not, depending on whether the magnetic amplifier core is saturated. Control of the device consists of varying the time at which its core saturates during a half-cycle of the supply voltage waveform. A magnetic amplifier thus establishes an off-on switch type of load control, similar to the thyratron and similar to the SCR. Historically, the magnetic amplifier replaced the thyratron for many applications and was in turn replaced by the SCR in many cases. Each device still survives with its own unique applications, but since the early 1960s the design of magnetic amplifier circuits has become a rather special topic rather than one of universal interest. Accordingly, we limit this discussion to a description of the simplest magnetic amplifier (Fig. 6.71), which has two windings on a single tape-wound, square-loop core. The reader may consult the references [35, 36, 38] for descriptions in greater depth or for circuits of greater utility.

In describing the circuit of Fig. 6.71, it is convenient to assume that the supply voltage v_s is a square wave of $\pm V_s$. The output voltage is taken across load resistor R; the series diode reveals that only half-wave output voltages are possible. The input voltage v_{in} with a series resistance r is coupled to the core with control windings N_C. The core is assumed to be a square-loop toroid; the gate winding and the control winding have turns ratio $N_C/N_G = 1/N$. The circuit can be modeled,

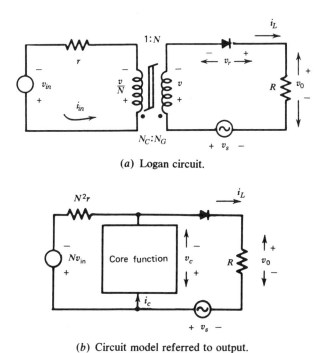

(a) Logan circuit.

(b) Circuit model referred to output.

Figure 6.71   A single-core magnetic amplifier and its circuit model.

referred to the output side as in Fig. 6.71b. The number of gate turns is usually chosen so that $2\Lambda_s$ just exceeds the supply voltage maximum half-cycle area $V_s/2f$. This gives the core the capability of absorbing V_s over an entire half-cycle, for minimum output voltage.

The circuit operation consists of two half-cycles because of the series diode. When v_s is positive, the diode can conduct and the core has the possibility of saturating. This is called the "gate" or "output" half-cycle. When v_s is negative, the reverse-biased diode is an open circuit that disconnects v_s from the core. The negative half-cycle is called the "reset" or "control" half-cycle. During the reset half-cycle the input voltage sets up the control of the next gate half-cycle. In other words, the input voltage during the nth half-cycle, $\langle v_{\text{in}}(n) \rangle$, controls the output at the next half-cycle $\langle v_0(n + 1) \rangle$, where the symbol $\langle\rangle$ means half-cycle average.

Circuit models for the two half-cycles are given in Fig. 6.72. During the gate half-cycle the core may be saturated or not. If the core is not saturated, the input and output circuits are transformer coupled to each other, which gives a somewhat messy but straightforward circuit analy-

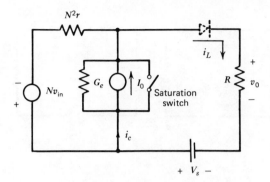

(a) During "gate" half-cycle.

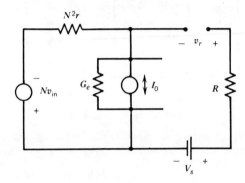

(b) During "reset" half-cycle.

Figure 6.72 Circuit models during each half-cycle of the square-wave signal.

sis problem. After saturation, the core function is a short circuit, so that $v_0 = v_s$.

The circuit operation can also be explained by reference to the hysteresis characteristic for the core (Fig. 6.73a). During the gate half-cycle the core is driven toward positive saturation, starting from the point to which the core was reset on the prior half-cycle. During the reset half-cycle, the core is driven negatively from $+\Lambda_s$, down the left side of the hysteresis curve. The reset flux linkages cause the same delay of core saturation during the following gate half-cycle. Using the voltage polarity notation in the figures, only negative input signals can reset the core. Furthermore, the minimum signal must be more than enough to supply the magnetizing current I_0. Various performance criteria can be worked out analytically for the circuit, such as the gain characteristic in Fig. 6.73c. There can also be defined a voltage gain as a change of half-cycle average output voltage due to a change of average input voltage. Since voltage averages are the parameters of interest, whether v_s is a square wave or a sine wave is of little importance. The major analytical tools for magnetic amplifier analysis are difference equations using piecewise-linear models for the core.

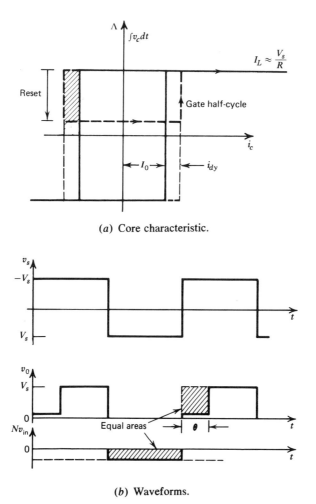

(a) Core characteristic.

(b) Waveforms.

Figure 6.73 Principles of operation of a magnetic amplifier. (Adapted from Bourne [35].)

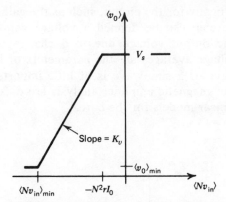

(c) Idealized gain characteristic for half-cycle-
average voltage values.

Figure 6.73 (Cont'd).

6.4.8 Selection of Core Size

The practical implementation of a design raises the question of selecting
a core of the proper size to do the job. Experience is often the best
guide because of the omission here of such vital parameters such as core
losses, heat dissipation, allowable operating temperature, and cost. Some
of the core manufacturers publish design manuals that can be very
helpful. Alternatively, there follows a derivation of transformer power
rating as proportional to WS_c for the core, the product of window area
and the cross-sectional area of the core. It follows that $WS_c \propto l^4$, where l
is some linear dimension of a core, if the size is scaled while the aspect
ratio is kept constant. Thus the core size is not very sensitive to the
power rating; a doubling of power would increase l by $2^{1/4} = 1.19$, only
19% increase.

The maximum square wave of primary voltage that can be applied to a
core to just cause its saturation is

$$V_1 = 4\Lambda_s f = 4B_s n_1 S_c f. \qquad (6.140)$$

The window area of a core required to have the space for primary and
secondary windings is

$$W = \frac{n_1 a_1 + n_2 a_2}{k} = \frac{2n_1 i_1}{Jk}, \qquad (6.141)$$

where a_1 is the wire area of the primary, J is current density, and k is a geometrical fill factor. The fill factor depends on the winding method, but 0.4 is said to be a reasonable value for a toroid. For the right-hand term of (6.141) it was assumed that $n_1i_1 = n_2i_2$. Solving for i_1 gives

$$i_1 = \frac{JWk}{2n_1},$$

and multiplying by V_1 from (6.140) gives the input power

$$V_1i_1 = 2k(JB_s)f(WS_c), \tag{6.142}$$

which is the result of interest. For a given required value of input power, the left-hand side is constant. The possible effect on core size of changes of frequency, current density, saturation induction, and coil-winding strategy can be assessed according to (6.142). The upper limits of those various parameters are set by other considerations, such as allowable power dissipation and the thermal design.

PROBLEMS

1 (Section 6.2).   Specifications for a ferrite memory core of dimensions O.D./I.D./ht = 0.46/0.28/0.13 mm, all ±0.03, are taken from a data sheet as follows. The test conditions are: full drive current = 850 mA, partial drive current = 510 mA, pulse rise time = 50 ns, pulse duration = 400 ns. The performance characteristics are: min $uV_1 = 30$ mV, max = 45 mV; min $dV_z = 8$ mV, max = 10 mV; $T_p = 85 \pm 10$ ns, $T_s = 155 \pm 10$ ns.

   a. Deduce probable values for H_0 and for B_s for the core material.

   b. If the core is reversed twice (cycled through a $B-H$ loop once) every 800 ns, find the average power dissipated in the core. Note that the total width $2I$ includes a dynamic width term. Compare your result, in mW/cc, with power loss data for linear ferrites, Section 5.3.2.

   c. Consider the geometry of threading 3 wires through the core center, and estimate a maximum wire size. Determine current density J required for coincident-current operation. How does the value of current density compare with the guidelines of Section 3.1.3?

2 (Section 6.2.2)

   a. Draw the ideal signal waveforms, as in Fig. 6.8, that are appropriate for a $2\frac{1}{2}$-D, 3-wire core memory.

   b. Examine the 3-D, 3-wire core plane layout (Fig. 6.9) in enough detail to explain in detail the operation of the inhibit. Your explanation should be valid for any core [e.g., $(x1, y0)$ or $(x2, y0)$].

3 **(Section 6.2.2)**

   a. Suppose core 10 of Fig. 6.7 is being read. Trace along the sense wire to tabulate the number and polarity of the half-select delta voltages.

   b. How would your tabulation be affected if the core plane contained a "worst-case" data pattern?

4 **(Section 6.3.1).** The text describes in words the inductance of a shielding bead as a function of d–c current, assuming an ideal piecewise-linear material as in Fig. 2.11 and further assuming a partial saturation effect as in Fig. 2.13. Carry out the analysis in detail, make a graph of ideal inductance versus I.

   Hint. Consider (2.28) and plot $d\Phi_d/dI$ versus R as an intermediate step.

5 **(Section 6.3.2)**

   a. Design a ballast for a 20-W fluorescent lamp, modeled as $v_t = 70$ sgn (i), which is to be driven by a square-wave supply voltage of ±105 V, 500 Hz. "Design" means to specify the values of L, Λ_{max}, and I_{max} for this application.

   b. Give T_1 and T_2 for this case, then derive (6.15) for their ratio.

6 **(Section 6.3.3)**

   a. Specify the value of L and C for a resonant circuit to meet the following requirements. In a circuit like Fig. 6.18, the peak value of the transfer function should occur at $f = 10^4$ Hz, with selectivity such that any signals farther than ±50 Hz from the center frequency are to be attenuated 3 dB or more. The lossy effect of G_1 and G_2 is to be $R = 1/(G_1 + G_2) = 10^6 \, \Omega$.

   b. Consider the Q of the inductor alone, which is given as twice (2×) the Q of the circuit as specified in (a). Find the resistance of the windings and find the loss tangent of the core, assuming that these two components of inductor loss are equal.

7 **(Section 6.3.4).** A choke-input filter is used following the full-wave rectifier in a d–c power supply.

   a. Specify the peak value A of the rectified a–c voltage to yield 12.5 V d–c output, at 1 A load.

   b. Specify the LC product of the filter to ensure that the output ripple voltage will not exceed 10 mV peak, approximately.

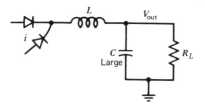

Given:

1. Frequency before rectification is 60 Hz.

2. Fourier series of rectified signal is $v(t) = \dfrac{2A}{\pi}(1 + \tfrac{2}{3}\cos 2\omega t - \tfrac{2}{15}\cos 4\omega t + \cdots)$.

8 (Section 6.3.4). Design a simple choke-input filter for a d–c power supply to supply 30 V d–c at a maximum current of 25 A, assuming a full-wave rectified source and a power line frequency of 60 Hz.

  a. Specify the LC product so that the peak ripple of the output voltage is less than 2% of the d–c output.

  b. Suppose we have a special need for a nonresonant filter. Deduce the value of R, then choose L, C to obtain a response that is approximately "critically damped."

  c. Assume that L is invariant for low currents (does not swing); define the minimum value of d–c current for proper filter operation.

  d. Take into account the required operating point (Λ vs. I) for your inductor, and specify whatever you can as regards B_s, n, and core area. Choose transformer iron as the core material, then make a first estimate of a preliminary design for the core.

9 (Section 6.3.5)

  a. Find t_1 and t_2 for the switching regulator of Fig. 6.32 given $V_1 = 25$ V, $V_3 = 5$ V, $f = 20$ kHz, and $i_R = 4$ A d–c.

  b. Draw the waveforms $v_L(t)$ and $i_L(t)$ under the design constraint that i_L may fluctuate ± 0.5 A maximum about the 4-A average value.

  c. Choose the value L and Λ_{sat} for the inductor.

  d. Choose C to permit 0.1-V peak-to-peak ripple.

10 (Section 6.4.1). Devise two different experimental methods for determining the dot-mark convention for a small transformer, one for minimum equipment and a second for a laboratory environment. Briefly explain each idea.

11 **(Section 6.4.1).** We want to use a transformer to couple a signal generator to a load resistor, to supply maximum power to the load. The signal generator has an open-circuit voltage of 100 V a–c, rms, and an output resistance of 100 Ω; the load resistor is 8 Ω. Define the best ratio n_1/n_2 and find the output power. Also find v_1, i_1, v_2 and i_2 and compare what they would be if the load were connected directly to the generator, without the transformer.

12 **(Section 6.4.1).** This problem identifies the source of a component of leakage flux for transformers, even if the "air flux" (Section 2.2.3) for each winding were zero, and even if the core were ideal so that the first term on the right-hand side of (6.61) is zero.

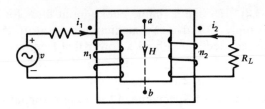

a. Given that $n_1 i_1 + n_2 i_2 = 0$ and $n_1 i_1 \neq 0$, evaluate $\int_a^b \bar{H} \cdot d\bar{l}$.

b. Let $R_L = 0$ and let v be very small so that i_2 is at the rated value for the transformer. How can the leakage reactance of the transformer be determined experimentally? In other words, what effect shall we seek to measure?

13 **(Section 6.4.1).** Consider the footnote near (6.62), which explains induced voltage per turn as the line integral of the electric field around the periphery of a core. In practice, the geometry of a turn may be unclear, and furthermore the turn may be of a good conductor that permits no E-field along it. The accompanying figure shows the cross section of a toroidal core that is excited by an rms $d\phi/dt$ of 1 V/t.

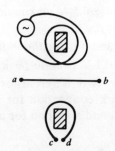

a. What voltage is developed between points a and b? Does the measured voltage depend on how you connect the voltmeter?

b. Given that $|v_{cd}| = 1$ V$_{rms}$ and given that the turn from c through the core and back to d is a heavy conductor, explain how the voltage can be developed.

14 (Section 6.4.1). A 3-winding transformer as in Fig. 6.33 has negligible leakage and a turns ratio $n_1 : n_2 : n_3 = 10:1:2$. Given $R_1 = 10\ \Omega$, $R_2 = R_3 =$ open circuit, and inductance L_{11} is 0.5 H, find the Thévenin output resistance and inductance at windings 2 and 3.

15 (Section 6.4.1). A transformer core has three legs of reluctance R_1, R_2, R_3, with n turns on leg 1. Find the inductance of the winding using two methods, then show their equivalence.

a. Use the direct method with $L = n\phi/i$ expressed in terms of reluctances.

b. Use the dual method with L expressed as a function of permeances.

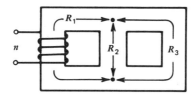

16 (Section 6.4.2). Figure 6.41 shows a 120–150 V autotransformer connection using a 120–30 V standard transformer, which is rated at 120 V·A.

a. Show how to connect the transformer for 150-to-30 V transformation. Show the distribution of rated currents and find the resulting volt·ampere rating.

b. Repeat for 120–90 and for 90–30 V connections.

17 (Section 6.4.2). If the variable autotransformer of Fig. 6.42 is connected to the power line with the input terminals interchanged (i.e., if the transformer "common" is connected to the "hot" side of the line), find the voltage to ground of each output terminal of the autotransformer.

18 (Section 6.4.3). Find the allowed frequency range of operation for the following transformer circuit. The transformer has a primary inductance of 10 mH, turns of 72-to-3, and coupling coefficient of $k = .98$. It is used as a step-down transformer to drive a load of 10 Ω from the output of a broad-bandwidth operational amplifier. The operational amplifier has essentially zero output resistance but its maximum voltage and current ratings are 12 V and 10 mA, respectively. Find the low- and high-frequency limits of the circuit. Briefly state the limiting mechanisms, and your assumptions.

19 (Section 6.4.3). Two distinct mechanisms have been suggested to limit the low-frequency response of a transformer: core saturation as explained in Section 2.3.2, and a time-constant effect involving the magnetizing inductance as shown in Fig. 6.46*b*. What symptoms would you look for to determine which mechanism is dominant in a particular case? What simple tests could you make to test your conjecture?

20 (Section 6.4.3). Consider the operation and the low-frequency limitations of the transformer circuit below.

    a. Assuming that the transformer does not saturate, find the amplitude of v_2 in the midfrequency range of operation.

    b. Noting the characteristics of the transformer core as given, do you expect the transformer to function acceptably or do you expect the core to saturate because of the high load current? Explain your answer.

    c. For this circuit, find the low-frequency limit and explain which physical process imposes the limit.

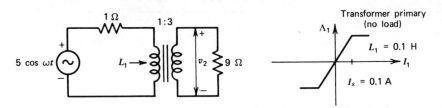

21 (Section 6.4.3). Three distinct mechanisms have been suggested that can limit the high-frequency response of a transformer: a leakage-inductance effect as in Fig. 6.46*c*, effects of winding capacitance, and limitations of the core due either to excessive losses or to bandwidth limitations (Snoek's limit). For a particular case, what symptoms would you look for to determine which mechanism is dominant? What simple tests could you make to test your conjecture?

22 (Section 6.4.3). For radiofrequency transformers, an important practical class of core materials consists of powdered irons, including the carbonyls, which are said to be superior to ferrites for many applications. As a project, find and compare data for powdered iron with data, such as Fig. 5.15, for ferrites.

23 **(Section 6.4.3).** Complete the design of a broadband balun transformer, intended to provide impedance matching of a 200-Ω load to a 50-Ω signal generator over the frequency range 0.1–100 MHz. You may use the finding [11] that a tightly twisted pair of AWG 30 wires (vinyl coated, 0.05-cm O.D.) has a characteristic impedance z_0 of about 100 Ω and a phase velocity of $v = 1.16 \times 10^8$ m/s. The suggested ferrite toroidal core is Ferroxcube® 266T125 with O.D./I.D./ht = 0.375/0.187/0.125 in. in type 3B7 material, which gives the core a permeance $P = 1.1 \ \mu H/t^2$ ±20%, which remains reasonably constant over a temperature range 0–60°C. Choose the remaining design parameters to meet or exceed the frequency specifications.

Check. Will the required number of turns fit through the window area of the core? Is the transmission line long enough to wind the required number of turns?

24 **(Section 6.4.4).** Use the principles of a magnetically coupled multivibrator to design an inverter that produces a square wave of about 105 V peak (210 V peak to peak) from 12 V d–c. (We want to drive a 20-W fluorescent lamp from an automobile battery; the ballast is a separate problem addressed elsewhere.)

Specify a square-loop core and specify the turns and wire sizes of the windings to meet the requirements above. It is suggested that primary and secondary currents can be determined from the wattage of the load and from the estimated efficiency of the inverter, about 0.8. Use Table 6.1, to select the core. You may assume transistors with $V_{BE}(ON) = 0.7$ V, $h_{FE} = \beta = 50$ at the required current. Choose any multivibrator frequency that is consistent with the core rating.

25 **(Section 6.4.4).** Wind a small transformer using a linear ferrite core, and drive it with a transistor as in Fig. 6.54. Carefully observe voltage and current waveforms as you vary the amplitude and the duration of the input pulse. Demonstrate the use of a diode to suppress the inductive back-kick. Set up the following conditions:

a. Transistor not saturated and core not saturated.

b. Transistor is saturated for the entire pulse duration but the core does not saturate.

c. Transistor is saturated for the initial portion of the pulse duration only.

d. Transistor and core are saturated, each during portions of the pulse.

Summarize your observations as a critique for Figs. 6.55 and 6.56.

26 (Section 6.4.4)

a. Design and build a gated blocking oscillator using the concept of Fig. 6.57, and demonstrate its operation.

b. How could you modify the design, to eliminate the need for an external trigger?

27 (Section 6.4.5). Digital signals are often transmitted to and from remote terminals using twisted pairs of wires in a difference mode of operation. In some environments common-mode signals due to nearby lightning have caused the destruction of the differential receiver circuits. Devise a common-mode rejection transformer circuit to alleviate this problem. As a point of departure, you may assume the common-mode signal waveform is triangular, of 50 V peak amplitude, and of 50 μs duration.

28 (Section 6.4.5)

a. Analyze the hybrid transformer circuit of Fig. 6.61 for the case $R_1 \neq R_2$, to determine an expression for v_4.

b. How does the hybrid transformer concept (Fig. 6.60) compare with the symmetrical circuit of Fig. 6.59?

29 (Section 6.4.7). Do a preliminary paper design of a Morgan circuit to yield a 25-V, 10-A pulse of 2 ms duration. Your design should specify C, the core, n_1, n_2, and wire sizes. State your assumptions.

30 (Section 6.4.7). What would the Morgan circuit waveforms look like if core saturation were to occur during time period T_1? What design conditions would you choose to make this happen?

31 (Section 6.4.7). Derive (6.135) for the output pulse waveform for the Morgan circuit.

32 (Section 6.4.7). The circuit below uses shunt reluctances $R_2 + R_3$ to increase leakage flux, hoping to increase the output inductance of the transformer as suggested by Figs. 6.40 and 6.67. Develop an

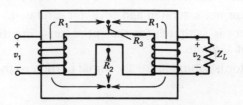

electric circuit model for the circuit using the duality method, then find an expression for output inductance. Reluctances are noted in the figure.

33 (Section 6.4.7). Suppose the magnetic modulator of Fig. 6.70 consisted of only one core with 3 windings. What would be the effect of the input current on the output voltage waveform?

REFERENCES

6.2 Ferrite Core Memory

1. Aaron P. Greifer, "Ferrite Memory Materials," *IEEE Trans. Magn.*, MAG-5, 774–811 (December 1969). A comprehensive review paper that treats the history of ferrites, the physical theory of loop squareness, the mechanism of flux switching, and the technology of core manufacture.

2. T. J. Gilligan, "$2\frac{1}{2}$-D High Speed Memory Systems—Past, Present and Future," *IEEE Trans. Electronic Computers*, EC-15, 475–485 (August 1966). Concerns the organization of memory systems, especially $2\frac{1}{2}$ D.

3. J. Reese Brown, Jr., "First- and Second-Order Ferrite Memory Core Characteristics and Their Relationship to System Performance," *IEEE Trans. Electronic Computers* EC-15, 485–501 (August 1966). Addresses the causes of noise due to half-select currents.

4. R. H. Tancrell and R. E. McMahon, "Partial Switching of Ferrite Cores," *J. Appl. Phys.*, 31, 762–777 (May 1960). Identifies domain wall motion as the dominant mechanism for ferrite memory core reversal.

5. R. S. Weiss, "Square-loop Ferrites," in *Magnetic Properties of Materials*, Jan Smit, Editor, McGraw-Hill, New York, 1971, Ch. 6, pp. 205–237. A broad review with emphasis on material properties.

6. D. E. Elder and R. H. Norman, "A Fresh Look at Coincident Current Core Memories," *Comput. Des.*, 42–44, November 1967. Describes a 3-D, 3-wire system in tradeoff comparison to $2\frac{1}{2}$ D.

6.3 Inductance

7. *Linear Ferrite Materials and Components*, Ferroxcube catalog, Ferroxcube Division of Amperex Corp., Saugerties, N.Y.

8. Truman S. Gray, *Applied Electronics*, Wiley, New York, 1954. For historical interest, pages 337–348 describe a full-wave rectifier with inductor-input filter with references to the original 1932 papers.

6.4 Transformers

9. MIT Staff, *Magnetic Circuits and Transformers*, Wiley, New York, 1952. Although dated, there is a great deal of information here, with emphasis on power transformers.

See Ch. XIII, Leakage Inductances; Ch. XVII, Self- and Mutual inductances; Ch. XV, Autotransformers; Ch. XX, Hybrid Transformers in Telephone Applications.

10. E. Colin Cherry, "The Duality Between Electric and Magnetic Circuits and the Formation of Transformer Equivalent Circuits," *Proc. Phys. Soc.*, **62B**, 101–111 (February 1949). A pioneering reference on the use of duality in magnetic modeling.

11. H. L. Krauss and C. W. Allen, "Designing Toroidal Transformers to Optimize Wideband Performance," *Electronics*, **46**, 113–116 (August 16, 1973).

12. Jerry Sevick, "Broadband Matching Transformers Can Handle Many Kilowatts," *Electronics*, **49**, 123–128 (November 25, 1976).

13. R. H. Turrin, "Application of Broad-band Balun Transformers," *QST*, 42–43 (April 1969).

14. C. L. Ruthroff, "Some Broadband Transformers," *Proc. IRE*, **47**, 1337–1342 (August, 1959).

15. W. Hilberg, "High-Frequency Transformers with Separate Windings and Very Broad Transmission Bandwidth," *IEEE Trans. Magn.*, **MAG-6**, No. 3, 667 (September 1970). (Abstract only—seems to be a new design idea.)

16. "Conventional Converter and Inverter Design," Design manual featuring tape wound cores, pp. 19–22, TWC-300R, Magnetics, Inc., Butler, Pa.

17. Del Johnson, "Help yourself to a Good Dc-to-dc Converter Design," *Electronics*, **43**, No. 21, 102–105 (October 12, 1970). The design procedure for d–c to d–c converters in Section 6.4.4 was adapted from this paper.

18. Fred C. Y. Lee and Thomas G. Wilson, "Analysis and Modeling of a Family of Two-Transistor Parallel Inverters," *IEEE Trans. Magn.* **MAG-9**, No. 3, 414–418 (September 1973). Shows several variations of d–c to d–c converters. See also references to the original paper by Royer.

19. L. T. Rees, "Charging Energy-Storage Capacitors from Low-Voltage Sources," *Electron. Eng.*, January 1969. Reprint courtesy Ferroxcube Corp., Saugerties, N.Y. Innovative circuitry for a d–c to d–c converter. Uses inductive back-kick to charge a capacitor.

20. "Search for a Better Transformer," *Gen. Radio Exp.*, November–December 1969. Briefly describes low-leakage transformer design strategies.

21. Peter W. Grant, "The use and misuse of Cores to Suppress Digital System Noise," *Electronics*, **44**, 77–80 (January 18, 1971).

22. T. A. O. Gross, "Hybrid Transformers Prove Versatile in High Frequency Applications," *Electronics*, **50**, No. 5, 113–115 (March 3, 1977).

23. R. S. Segsworth and S. B. Dewan, "A Hybrid Magnetic Solid-State Control," *IEEE Trans. Magn.*, **MAG-6**, No. 3, p. 668 (September 1970). (Abstract) Uses a 3-legged transformer with supply, control, and load isolated from one another.

24. C. F. Andren et al., "The Skin Tunnel Transformer: A New System that Permits Both High Efficiency Transfer of Power and Telemetry of Data Through the Intact Skin," *IEEE Trans. Biomed. Eng.*, **BME-15**, No. 4, 278–280 (October 1968).

25. P. W. Barnhart et al., "A Fixed-Rate Rechargeable Cardiac Pacemaker," *APL Tech. Dig.*, **9**, No. 3, 2–9, (January–February 1970).

26. General Electric Co., *Controlled Rectifier Manual*, Schenectady, N.Y., (1967).

27. R. E. Morgan, "A New Power Amplifier Using a Single Controlled Rectifier and a Saturable Transformer," AIEE Conference Paper 60-410, presented at AIEE winter meeting, 1960.

28. B. C. Biega, "Practical Equivalent Circuits for Electromagnetic Devices," *Electron. Eng.*, 52–56 (June 1967). The analysis of a ferroresonant transformer in Section 6.4.7 was inspired by this paper.

29. Robert J. Kakalec, "A Feedback-Controlled Ferroresonant Voltage Regulator," *IEEE Trans. Magn.*, **MAG-6**, No. 1, 4–8 (March 1970). Gives a nice introductory description of ferroresonant voltage regulators, then describes a circuit to overcome the sensitivity to frequency variation.

30. H. P. Hart and R. J. Kakalec, "The Derivation and Application of Design Equations for Ferroresonant Voltage Regulators and Regulated Rectifiers," *IEEE Trans. Magn.*, **MAG-6**, No. 3, 668 (September 1970). (Abstract only.)

31. H. W. Lord, "Analog Equivalent Circuit Aided Design of Ferroresonant Transformers and Circuits," *IEEE Trans. Magn.*, **MAG-13**, No. 5, 1293–1298, (September 1977).

32. D. I. Gordon and R. E. Brown, "Recent Advances in Fluxgate Magnetometry," *IEEE Trans. Magn.*, **MAG-8**, No. 1, 76–82 (March 1972). Also see companion papers on magnetic field measurement.

33. R. C. Barker, "On the Analysis of Second-Harmonic Modulators," *IEEE Trans. Magn.*, **MAG-3**, No. 3, 337–341 (December 1965).

34. S. V. Marshall, "An Analytic Model for the Fluxgate Magnetometer," *IEEE Trans. Magn.*, **MAG-3**, No. 3, 459–463 (September 1967).

35. Henry C. Bourne, Jr., *Magnetic Circuits*, California Book Co., Berkeley, 1961.

36. H. F. Storm, *Magnetic Amplifiers*, Wiley, New York, 1955.

37. B. D. Bedford and R. G. Hoft, Editors, *Principles of Inverter Circuits*, Wiley, New York, 1964.

38. F. J. Friedlaender, "Magnetic Amplifiers and Other Magnetic Devices," in *Methods of Experimental Physics*, Vol. 2, *Electronic Methods*, 2nd ed., Academic Press, New York, 1975, Ch. 11.3, pp. 359–373.

7.
Magnetic Recording and Reproduction

7.1 INTRODUCTION

Although information can be recorded in either metal or oxide magnetic media, our emphasis is exclusively on oxides as used in flexible disks or magnetic tape.

The central idea of magnetic tape recording and playback can be described simply as follows. Magnetic tape is essentially a long, flexible permanent magnet that can be locally magnetized. A signal is recorded on tape by creating a specific pattern of magnetization along the tape. This is done by passing the tape across a recording head, which has a region of time-varying H-field, intense enough to leave the tape magnetized with the desired pattern. In principle the recording head is merely a core with an airgap (Fig. 7.1). When the head is driven by a time-varying current, a proportional time-varying fringing field is produced at the gap to magnetize the tape as it is passed across the gap

$$H(t) \propto Ni(t). \tag{7.1}$$

After a signal is recorded on tape, it can be recovered by once more passing the tape across the head. The magnetic pattern on tape induces flux changes in the head that result in a time-varying voltage across the head windings. The voltage is proportional to the rate of flux change

$$e = N \frac{d\phi}{dt} \propto N \frac{dB}{dx} \frac{dx}{dt} \quad \text{V.} \tag{7.2}$$

In (7.2), N is the turns on the head, dB/dx is the spatial variation of magnetization along the tape, and dx/dt is tape velocity.

On comparing (7.1) with (7.2) it can be deduced that the induction

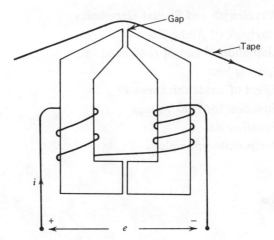

Figure 7.1 Schematic view of a head used both for recording and for reproduction. In recording the head windings are driven by a current i to produce a proportional field H at the gap of the head. The tape is magnetized as it passes through the fringing field. On playback, the magnetized tape again moves past the gap to induce a voltage e across the head windings.

along the tape $B(x)$ is recorded in proportion to the record current i. However on playback the induced voltage e is proportional to the spatial derivative dB/dx. This means the electrical waveforms for record current and playback voltage will differ from one another in the predictable manner of the derivative operation. This property identifies a phenomenon of the physics of recording that requires attention in the system design. For instance, an audio system requires an equalization network, which is usually in the playback amplifier.

Central features of four types of magnetic tape recording are described below:*

1. Digital recording of pulses that represent data.
2. Instrumentation systems that use FM modulation.
3. Audio recording and playback, using an a–c bias.
4. Television systems, which use rotating heads.

The basic elements, shown schematically in Fig. 7.2. are now described briefly.

*The technology of magnetic recording is rapidly developing, and our purpose here is only to introduce the topic. National and international standards now exist for all four areas of magnetic recording and should be consulted for the latest engineering information. The reference by Sallet [3] cites 79 standards.

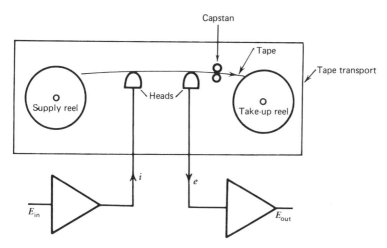

Figure 7.2 Elementary block diagram of a magnetic tape recorder/reproducer.

A magnetic tape system consists of four basic components: magnetic tape, recording and playback heads, tape transport, and record/playback electronics. The tape is made by coating one surface of a plastic substrate with a thin magnetic layer that consists of tiny elongated particles of magnetic oxide held together by a nonmagnetic binder. Each oxide particle exists as a single magnetic domain that can be magnetized to either polarity, along with its neighbors. Each particle is a microscopic permanent magnet, and the tape is an aggregation of such particles, described in more detail in Section 7.2. The functional purpose of the heads was outlined above. More detailed models are given in Section 7.3.

Tape transports are so varied in their design that only a few general comments on Fig. 7.2 can be made here. The major task of a transport is to move the tape with precision past the heads at constant velocity. The tape velocity at the heads must be controlled with great accuracy, which mandates the use of a separate constant-speed capstan to drive the tape. A simple reel-to-reel guide is not adequate because the rotation of the supply reel and the take-up reel must vary. For constant circumferential velocity, the reel rpm varies inversely as the diameter of the outer layer of tape wound on the hub. The effective radius of the reel depends on the amount of tape wound on it. Transport design is further complicated by requirements for fast start/stop times inasmuch as the inertial dynamics of the reels also vary with the quantity of tape. Several innovative solutions to these electromechanical design problems are described by Lowman [1].

7.1.1 Digital Recording

Magnetic recording is widely used in digital applications that require nonvolatile memory in an inexpensive medium. This includes virtually all computer systems, but especially those with a volatile main memory. The advent of smaller computers has stimulated the development of a great variety of magnetic digital recorders. They include not only disk units that store onto plated metal surfaces, but also equipment that stores on oxide surfaces: digital tapes, cartridges, magnetic cards, cassettes, the floppy disk, and the minifloppy. All these obey the same general principles of magnetic recording and reproduction; they differ mainly in the transport mechanics of bringing together the head and the storage medium. They also differ in that conventional magnetic tape systems possess several channels or tracks of data that are written or read in parallel, whereas a disk handles only one channel of data in a serial format.

Noncomputer applications of digital recording include memory for office equipment such as editing typewriters, and magnetic strips on the backs of credit cards as used in 24-hour bank machines.

Digital Tape.   Consider a conventional digital system that uses $\frac{1}{2}$-in.-wide tape with nine tracks. As a matter of interest, a few selected standard specifications are listed* as follows.

The tape itself consists of a base material of polyester film having a nominal thickness of 1.42 mils (36 μm), coated on one side with a magnetic oxide coating of 0.6-mil maximum (15-μm) thickness for a total of 1.9 ± 0.3 mils ($48.3 \pm 7.6\ \mu$m). Tape width is 0.498 ± 0.002 in. (1.265 ± 0.005 cm), which indicates the required accuracy of the slitting operation during tape manufacture. The maximum tape length is 2500 ft (762 m) per reel.

The nine tracks across the tape are located on nominal 0.055-in. centers (0.14 cm) with track 1 centered 0.029 in. (0.074 cm) from the tape reference edge (Fig. 7.3). The minimum track width is 0.043 in. (0.109 cm). Half-inch tape formerly had only seven tracks. Having nine tracks makes it possible to accommodate an 8-bit character plus parity (odd) recorded in parallel across the tape. The standard track assignments of the bits in the character were selected for maximum reliability (Fig. 7.3). The criteria for the assignment are that a "1" bit is more likely to fail than a "0," errors are more likely near the edges of the tape, and some 8-bit codes are used more frequently than others.

*American National Standards Institute, Inc. (ANSI) No. X3.22-1967, Recorded Magnetic Tape for Information Interchange (800 CPI, NRZI).

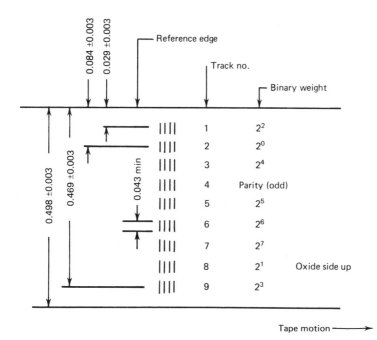

Figure 7.3 Recording format for 800-cpi magnetic tape; dimensions in inches.

It is necessary for the 9-channel head to be well aligned in the transport in order that the nine simultaneously recorded bits of a character will be located in the correct geometry across the tape. Minimum skew is particularly important if data are recorded on one transport and played back on a second. The main criterion is that the time between the first detected bit and the last detected bit of a character must be substantially less than the time between successive characters. Most digital data is recorded at 1600 characters per inch (cpi) longitudinally along the tape (630 c/cm), which corresponds to 0.625 mil (15.9 μm) between successive characters. ANSI standards also exist for the data density of 6250 cpi (2460 c/cm).

From a data management view, the bits that comprise a character are recorded in parallel and successive characters are recorded serially, one after the other on tape. The data transfer rate is given by the product of data density times tape velocity. The number of characters recorded in one sequence is called the block length. One of the design decisions for a system is whether the block shall be of fixed or variable length. The ANSI standards for 800 cpi suggests a minimum block length of 18 characters and a maximum of 2048 characters, followed by a cyclic redundancy check (CRC) character and a longitudinal redundancy check (LRC) character. Blocks are separated by unrecorded (saturated) gaps of nominal length 0.6 in. (1.5 cm).

A widely used recording method for digital tapes is the NRZI (non-return-to-zero invert, Fig. 7.4a), in which a flux change occurs for each "1" to be written. Except at transitions, the tape oxide is at magnetic saturation. The NRZI pattern can be written by a center-tapped head driven by a flip-flop (FF) so that either polarity of flux can be recorded (Fig. 7.4b). With such an arrangement, complementing the FF at each "1" will cause the required flux transitions. The playback or read signal of Fig. 7.4 resembles the flux derivative as suggested by (7.2). Often the same head is used both for reading and writing digital data.

Another recording method of interest is phase modulation, also called the Manchester method (Fig. 7.5). A flux transition now occurs for every bit, with a different polarity transition for "1"s and "0"s. A somewhat more complicated pulse sequence is now required to control the write FF (Fig. 7.4b). At every time of writing, the FF is merely complemented by a clock pulse. But for the polarity of transition to be correct, the FF must be preset a half-period earlier to the same "1" or "0" state as the input data bit. Phase encoding is widely used at high density. Compared

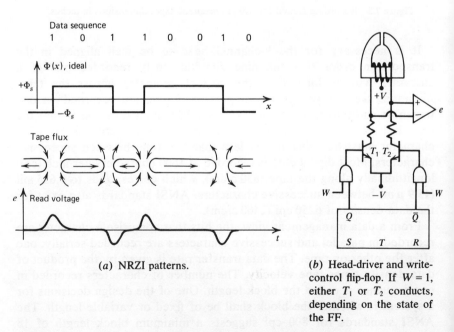

(a) NRZI patterns.

(b) Head-driver and write-control flip-flop. If $W = 1$, either T_1 or T_2 conducts, depending on the state of the FF.

Figure 7.4 Flux patterns and circuit for digital recording.

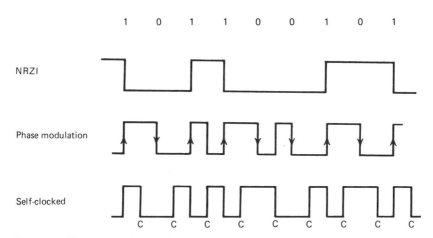

Figure 7.5 Three methods of digital recording, as they appear at the recording medium. The binary pattern represents a serial sequence of bits at a single head. The flux transitions are between positive and negative saturation values.

with the NRZ codes, its disadvantage is the higher frequency requirement. Its advantage is the lower total bandwidth, since all transitions are separated by either period T or $T/2$. NRZ signals are more sensitive to the pattern of data, especially for a long string of zeros.

Many other recording methods and codes have been devised* that cannot be compared here, except for one with a self-clocking feature that is applicable to disks.

Floppy Disk. This inexpensive form of storage was developed in the early 1970s to provide bulk storage for small computers [4]. The storage medium is an oxide-coated disk of Mylar or polyester, similar to tape in flexibility. The diskette operates inside a sealed protective paper jacket, with a round access hole for the diskette drive hub and a long access aperture for the read/write head. A single head, used both for writing and reading, is moved by a positioning mechanism to different radii to access different tracks. A common technology at the time of writing has 77 tracks at 48 tracks per inch (1.89/mm) and a maximum data density of 3200 bits per inch (1260/cm), varying with track radius. Up to 3 million bits of data can be recorded on a single diskette in an $8 \times 8 \times 0.06$ in. jacket ($20 \times 20 \times 0.15$ cm).

Timing phase information is absolutely necessary for the correct reconstruction of data from playback waveforms. The clock and data

*Sallet [3] briefly compares fourteen digital codes.

are usually mixed together in some manner when recording serial data on the floppy disk. The self-clocked example in Fig. 7.5 shows two types of flux transition. The periodic transition at every bit position is due to the system clock. Halfway between the clock transition is an NRZI type of data transition. This code can be generated by the logical OR of two strings of pulses, such that the leading edge of any pulse will complement the write FF described earlier. The decoding of the read signals can be done with a phase-locked loop.

7.1.2   Instrumentation Recording with FM

When tape recording a slowly varying signal, at low frequency it becomes increasingly necessary to use modulation to achieve a significant time variation of flux. Frequency modulation (FM) provides a way of recording to d–c, as well as immunity to the inherent amplitude nonlinearity of the magnetic recording media. The tape speed must be controlled with great accuracy and stability because signal frequency is directly proportional to tape velocity. Speed control is usually accomplished by servo control of the capstan drive motor, controlled so that a tachometer signal is locked to the same frequency as a reference signal recorded on tape. Standards of the Inter-Range Instrumentation Group (IRIG) have been established for the FM carrier of the data, and for reference frequencies, for all standard tape speeds.

7.1.3   Audio Recording

In audio recording, a–c bias is added to the audio signal to achieve amplitude linearity. Linearity of the recording process is necessary for faithful reproduction. The bias frequency is usually about 100 kHz, high enough that any intermodulation harmonics* generated by magnetic nonlinearity will lie outside the audio range. The waveform of the bias signal should be symmetrical, free of second-harmonic distortion, which has the effect of a d–c recorded signal and also increases tape noise. The amplitude of the bias signal involves a tradeoff between less signal distortion for high bias or better high-frequency response for low bias. The bias amplitude is larger for tapes with high-coercivity oxide. The optimum bias current is probably in the range of 3–6 times the signal current, for ferric oxide tape. The sections that follow describe how a–c bias improves the linearity of the tape.

---

*In case of recording from an FM multiplex tuner, both 19- and 38-kHz signals are present in addition to the audio signal.

Demagnetizing with a–c. An effective way to demagnetize any object is to place it in a high a–c field, then gradually reduce the field amplitude to zero. Withdrawing the object from the field has the same effect. This general procedure is widely used in all sorts of applications. The initial field should be large enough to drive the object around the major magnetization loop (Fig. 7.6). Gradually decreasing the drive field to zero results in tracing ever smaller minor hysteresis loops as shown.

Audio recorders usually have an erase head located just in front of the record head. The erase head provides a region of high a–c field through which the tape is passed before going to the record head.

The Anhysteretic Recording Process. "Anhysteretic" means without hysteresis, the result of adding high-frequency a–c bias to the signal to achieve better linearity. This remarkable phenomenon, discovered experimentally, was applied to tape recording some 20 years before a more or less satisfactory explanation emerged. Evidently the a–c bias field provides the energy required to reverse the magnetization of the ferric oxide particles during recording. Their residual state of magnetization then depends on the interplay of signal field and the field from neighboring particles. This interaction has been described successfully by a Preisach model. Schwantke [8] has worked through the Preisach formulation, which is too detailed to include here.

An early push-pull interpretation of recording with a–c bias was based

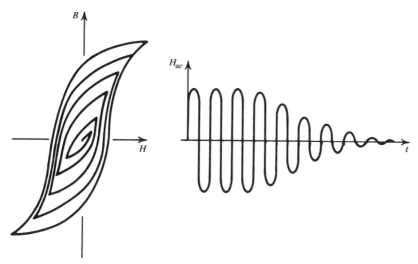

Figure 7.6 Demagnetizing an object or erasing a tape by gradually decreasing the amplitude of the a-c H-field.

on the idea of a transfer characteristic graph. The addition of a bias field to the signal field was visualized as boosting the signal so it would project onto the ± linear regions of the magnetization curve, to yield a net result of M. However anhysteretic recording is subtly different, as was revealed by the following uniform field experiments described by Westmijze [13]. The key concept is that of *remanence*, the residually magnetized state left by a recording process.

A length of demagnetized tape is put into a solenoidal coil through which a known current can be supplied. After the direct current is turned off, the residual magnetization of the tape is measured. The result of a set of such measurements, made for monotonically increasing values of current, is shown as the initial remanence curve (Fig. 7.7b). This curve is not the same as the locus of the tips of the set of minor hysteresis loops, but corresponds to the set of values (B_r, H_{max}) plotted for each loop.

Now suppose the experiment is repeated, but to each value of direct current we add an alternating current (which is reduced to zero before the d–c is removed). The results (Fig. 7.7a), show that the great nonlinearity near the origin of the initial remanence curve is partly removed by a small a–c field and entirely disappears for larger values. Still higher values of a–c give no further improvement after the anhysteretic remanence curve is reached. The maximum slope of the latter is called the anhysteretic susceptibility; typical values can be as high as 10 to 40.

The field sequence of the experiments above differs from tape recording with a conventional head, which excites the tape with both the signal and bias fields together. A third solenoid experiment was done in which the d–c field and the a–c field were decreased simultaneously by pulling the tape out of the solenoidal coil (Fig. 7.7b). For moderate values of a–c field the results were similar to the second experiment. But as the amplitude of bias field was further increased, the remanent magnetization was found to decrease once again. There exists an optimum value of a–c bias field, beyond which the recording sensitivity is degraded.

The experiments just described are very relevant to tape recording: the d–c represents the audio tape signal, which varies only slowly over several cycles of a–c bias. Indeed an optimum value of bias current is found when the third experiment is repeated on an actual tape recorder, but with one complication. The optimum bias current varies with the frequency of the audio signal. The maximum output at 16 kHz occurs at only about half the bias as is optimum for an audio signal of 100 Hz. Thus small bias gives a better frequency response but permits more distortion of low-frequency signals.

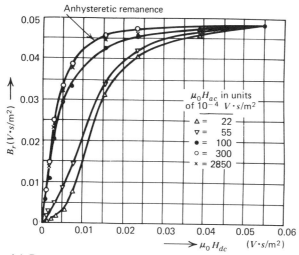

(a) Remanent magnetization versus direct field for various values of collapsing a-c field.

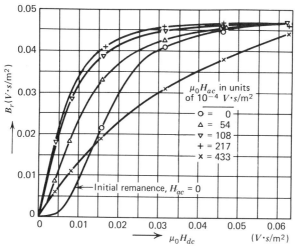

(b) Remanent magnetization versus initial direct field for the case of the d-c and a-c fields decreasing together.

Figure 7.7 Two experiments that demonstrate anhysteretic recording. (Adapted from Westmijze [13] with permission of Philips Research Reports.)

Audio Machines.   A very broad range of audio tape machines is in use. They can be divided into two general categories of applications: professional and consumer. Each class has its own spectrum of tapes and its own record/playback systems. Development of professional equipment has brought the master tapes from which records and prerecorded tapes are made. The transports are reel-to-reel type. Some systems have as many as 24 channels on 2-in. (5.08-cm) wide tape. Master tape has an unusually thick oxide (0.55 mil = 14 μm) to provide a very wide dynamic range (better than 63 dB), very high signal-to-noise ratio (60–65 dB), and low distortion over a bandwidth from 20 Hz to 20 kHz. Master tapes are usually run at 30 or 15 ips (in./s: 76 or 38 cm/s). A growing practice is to record musicians individually for subsequent blending in the taping studio. Other professional use, as radio broadcasting, is somewhat less demanding with tape speeds of 15 or $7\frac{1}{2}$ ips.

Consumer systems are by far the largest market using tape speeds of $7\frac{1}{2}$, $3\frac{3}{4}$, or $1\frac{7}{8}$ ips (19, 9.5, 4.76 cm/s). Consumer reel-to-reel systems use $\frac{1}{4}$-in. tape in the stereo recording format of Fig. 7.8a. Audio cassettes

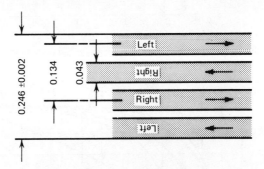

(a) Reel-to-reel four-track stereo.

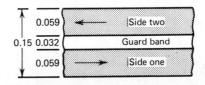

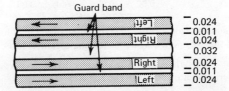

(b) Cassette monophonic (top) and stereo (bottom) tapes.

Figure 7.8 Recording formats for consumer tapes. Dimensions are in inches, multiply by 2.54 for centimeters.

were developed in the mid-1960s by the Philips Company, the Netherlands, using the recording format of Fig. 7.8b. The side-by-side, left-right format for stereo cassette tapes permits stereo recordings to be played back by a monaural reproducer. The cassette itself is the tape-handling portion of the system. It consists of two small reels, tape, and tape guides, all separated by lubricated spacers from a plastic housing. The $100 \times 64 \times 12.5$ mm housing has access holes for the erase head, the record/playback head, and the capstan and associated pinch roller, as well as for the drive mechanisms for the reel hubs. The tape speed is $1\frac{7}{8}$ ips, which restricts the signal-to-noise ratio and the bandwidth. These restrictions have stimulated the development of better tapes and noise reduction circuits.

7.1.4 Video Recording

The high bandwidth requirements of standard television signals (4.2 MHz in the United States) has led to the development of moving-head recorders. High-frequency recording requires high head-to-tape velocity, a requirement that has been met by the rotating-head principle.

Machines for television broadcasting use a quadruplex head arrangement for the video recording. Four heads are mounted 90° apart on a 2-in. diameter drum that rotates at 240 rps (in the United States). The heads are swept almost transversely across 2 in. wide tape that moves at 15 or $7\frac{1}{2}$ ips, to achieve more than 1500 ips (38 m/s) head-to-tape velocity. The geometry is such that two heads are on the tape at the same time for part of the rotation, the redundancy providing synchronization from one track to the next. Audio signals and timing control signals are recorded on separate tracks that run longitudinally along either side of the tape.

Several designs of video recorders have been developed for less stringent nonbroadcast applications using $\frac{1}{2}$, $\frac{3}{4}$, 1- and 2-in. tapes. The helical-scan recorder uses two video heads (sometimes only one) mounted on a rotating drum. The tape moves at $7\frac{1}{2}$ ips. It is guided around the drum along a helical path for slightly more than a half-turn to establish redundancy between the two heads. The heads are swept on a path that is almost longitudinal along the tape (the angle is less than 10°) at a head-to-tape velocity of the order of 700 ips (18 m/s). The audio signals and time control signals are on separate tracks along the tape edge.

The slow motion "instant replay" video recorder uses plated metal disks, rather than oxide tape, to continuously store the previous 30 s of video information. The information can be played back for display at any video frame rate.

7.2 MAGNETIC TAPE OXIDE

The magnetic coating of tapes and disks consists of small oxide particles held in a flexible nonmagnetic binder. The particles are small to be able to record short-wavelength signals and to achieve a low noise level. The most commonly used particle at this time, γ-Fe$_2$O$_3$, is carefully made in an acicular or needlelike shape with dimensions in the range 0.1 × 0.5 μm. Since the size is too small to sustain a domain wall, the particle exists as a single domain, magnetized to saturation along its major axis. The saturation induction of commercial γ-Fe$_2$O$_3$ powder is about 0.48 T,* but the particles comprise something less than half the volume of the magnetic coating. The packing fraction is usually given as about 40% and the remanence ratio J_r/J_s as about 0.7. Using those values give calculated values $J_s \approx 0.19$ T and $J_r \approx 0.13$ T; however experimental values cited in the literature are in the range $J_s \approx 0.13$ T and $J_r \approx 0.1$ T. The measured coercivity for such tapes is 250–350 Oe (20–28 kA/m).

There is strong and continuing interest in improving γ-Fe$_2$O$_3$ and in developing alternative oxides. In 1972 there was reported [5] an improved γ-Fe$_2$O$_3$ particle of average length 0.9 μm, average width 0.15 μm, and improved particle morphology that permits higher packing fractions and better orientation. When made up into a mastering tape with coating thickness 0.54 mil (13.7 μm), $J_r/J_s = 0.15T/0.1725$ T was achieved, which resulted in an improved signal-to-noise ratio when compared with commercial tape. The anhysteretic susceptibility was reported to be 3.9 for the new material as compared with 1.85 for the commercial tape.

Several alternatives to γ-Fe$_2$O$_3$ have been reported in the research literature and some of them have enjoyed some commercial success. Chromium dioxide, reported in 1961, is a ferromagnetic oxide with $J_s \approx 0.62$ T, particle length in the range 0.2–1.5 μm, and a highly acicular aspect ratio, as much as 20:1. The coercivity has been given as $H_c \approx$ 450–550 Oe (36–44 kA/m). The smaller particles are single crystals with the magnetocrystalline anisotropy favorably aligned with the particle axis. The crystallinity evidently gives the particles a smooth surface that results in high remanence because of superior orientation. For a video test tape with coating thickness of 5 μm, $J_r/J_s = 0.13T/0.17$ T was reported, but there was increased wear of the head due to abrasion. Other new particle chemistries include cobalt-doped γ-Fe$_2$O$_3$ and γ-Fe$_2$O$_3$ with cobalt adsorbed on the particle surfaces [6]. Some of these have better temperature properties than Chromium dioxide, which has a Curie

---

*Speliotis [17] gives $\sigma_s = 74$ emu/g and density = 5.26 g/cc; hence $M_s = 390$ emu/cc or $J_s = 0.49$ T. Mallinson [2] gives $M_s = 370$ emu/cc and $J_s = 0.47$ T.

temperature of only 126°C.

Magnetic alignment of the particles is part of the tape manufacturing process; the alignment is longitudinal (except in tape that is made for broadcast video machines and some instrumentation tapes that also use transverse-scan rotating heads).

The particles should be well shaped, well oriented, and uniformly dispersed at a high fraction of the coating volume. The oxide thickness should also be uniform, generally in the range ·2–15 μm, depending on the application. The recording surface should be very smooth. Many methods have been used to plane, buff, polish, or even iron the surface flat to an optical finish. It has been observed that the quality control of all these parameters is an extremely demanding task. Significant improvements have been made in all these aspects of γ-Fe$_2$O$_3$ particles and surfaces.

It has been stated that variations in the factors just named can easily account for greater performance differences than are attributable to the magnetic material used.

There exist certain fundamental limits on the practical size of particles. On the high side, the particles must be smaller than the critical size for existence as a single domain. On the small side, the particles must be large enough to ensure that the energy required to switch magnetic states is well above thermal energy kT. In standard tape, the smallest in the distribution of particles sizes are susceptible to "print-through," in which the fields from a neighboring wrap of tape are recorded weakly. The need to avoid print-through also limits how thin the tape substrate can be.

The theory of reversal processes in systems of interacting particles has been qualitatively successful. Apparently individual particles reverse by some nonideal form of rotation such as "fanning"; domains do not exist. The coercivity is attributed to a combination of magnetocrystalline and particle shape anisotropies, where the influence of the latter component decreases as the packing fraction increases. Calculated and measured values of coercivity are in rough agreement. The Preisach function has been used successfully to model the curve for anhysteretic susceptibility, relevant to audio recording with a–c bias. These topics, omitted for the sake of brevity, have recently been reviewed [2].

7.3 RECORDING ON TAPE

The recording process is achieved by passing the tape through an intense, localized time-varying field that fringes from the gap of a recording head.

7.3.1 The Recording Head

Recording and playback heads nearly always have two gaps (Fig. 7.1) in a sacrifice of head efficiency that achieves greater ease of manufacture. It is easier to maintain the required close tolerance for the front gap if the head is made in two parts. Head materials include permalloy in very thin laminations for low eddy currents, and high-density ferrites.

Using a reluctance model of a write head (Fig. 7.9) gives the magnetic potential at the front gap as a fraction of the applied ampere·turns

$$F_g = Ni\left(\frac{R_g}{R_1 + R_g + R_2 + R_r}\right) \quad \text{A·t,} \qquad (7.3)$$

The term in parentheses is a head efficiency factor η for writing. The pole surfaces of the rear gap are usually larger than for the front gap for better efficiency.

Field Models. A quick impression of the fringing field at the gap of a recording head can be gained from a graphical construction of curvilinear squares (Fig. 7.10). The method [19] assumes that the pole pieces are large relative to the gap and that each pole piece is an equipotential. The latter assumption implies high permeability and low reluctance of the magnetic components of the circuit.

The curvilinear squares construction uses the head symmetry to define approximate equipotential contours F. The F-lines then are used to deduce plausible ϕ-lines, drawn normal to the F-lines, and spaced apart so as to retain a similar ("square") aspect ratio. The ϕ-lines are the result of interest, since they define the local direction of H as well as its relative value. The reason for this lies in the definition of H as the

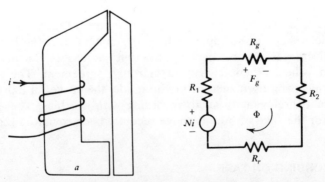

Figure 7.9 Reluctance model of a recording head, including front and rear gap reluctances R_g, R_r, and lumped reluctances R_1, R_2 for the magnetic circuit. Some head designs consist of two pole pieces like a, with coils connected series-aiding.

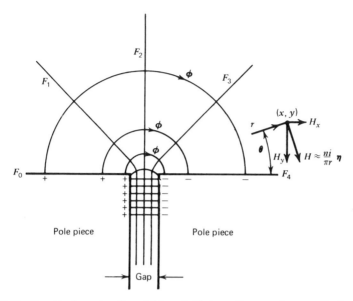

Figure 7.10 Graphical construction of fringe field above the gap of a recording head using the method of curvilinear squares. Each pole piece is assumed to be an equipotential, as are fictitious lines F_1, F_2, F_3. Equal quantities of flux lie between each ϕ-line. The field strength H is inversely proportional to the length of the ϕ-line.

negative gradient of potential F, therefore normal to the equipotentials for F.

Analytical expressions for $H(x, y)$ have been worked out for various idealized head geometries. Typical approximations are that the dimensions are very large relative to the gap, the permeability is infinite, and excitation is by sheets of surface magnetic poles on either side of the gap. Mallinson [11] has found that

$$H_x(x, y) = \frac{H_g}{\pi} \tan^{-1} \frac{2yg}{x^2 + y^2 - g^2} \qquad (7.4)$$

is a reasonable approximation to the x-component of the field in the region near the gap. Figure 7.11 defines the coordinates for the equation, then illustrates the variation* of H_x along each of two directions. The field profile (Fig. 7.11b) along the x-axis, which is the path taken by the

---

*Using (7.4) with a pocket calculator has a couple of potential pitfalls. Keep in mind first of all that $\tan^{-1}$ must be in radians. Furthermore, π should be added to negative values of $\tan^{-1}$ to find angles between $\pi/2$ and π. To understand why, sketch the periodic function $\tan \theta$ versus θ.

tape, shows a prominent peak at the center of the gap. The peak amplitude, at $x = 0$, is very sensitive to height above the head along the y-axis (Fig. 7-11c). The value drops to only 0.3 of the gap field H_g at a height of one gap length, $y = 2g$.

Equation 7.4 can also be manipulated to show contours of constant H_x, as

$$x^2 + (y - ag)^2 = g^2(1 + a^2)$$
$$\frac{1}{a} = \tan \frac{\pi H_x}{H_g}. \tag{7.5}$$

Equation 7.5 is an equation for a family of circles of radius $r = g\sqrt{1 + a^2}$, centered at $(x, y) = (0, ag)$ (Fig. 7.12).

Figure 7.12 shows the field contours of interest in recording on tape. The tape is recorded as its oxide coating passes through a high-field contour. The contour value of field is proportional to head current and possesses the same time dependence.

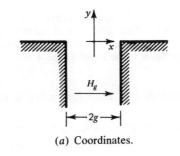

(a) Coordinates.

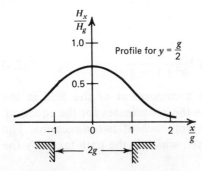

(b) Field at constant height above head.

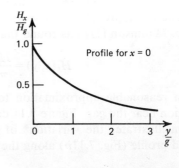

(c) Variation with height above gap.

Figure 7.11 Illustration of (7.4) for the x-component of H, normalized to the deep gap field H_g.

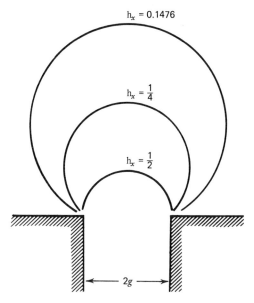

Figure 7.12   Lines of constant $h_x = H_x/H_g$ of (7.5).

7.3.2 Recording Processes

We are now in a position to expand further upon (7.2), which gave the output voltage of the read head as proportional to $d\phi/dx$, the derivative of flux along the tape. The recording process must generate the flux changes that ultimately will be detected. From the chain rule

$$\frac{d\phi}{dx} \propto \frac{dB}{dH} \cdot \frac{dH}{dx}, \tag{7.6}$$

it appears that dB/dH, an oxide property, is multiplied by dH/dx, the field gradient of the recording head. Audio recording with a–c bias probably takes place not in the center of a high-field contour, but at the high-gradient region as the tape leaves the contour.

Saturation Recording.   In digital recording the storage medium is driven between ± flux saturation limits.* At the recording head, this means the field contour for H_{sat} must extend deeper in the y-direction than the depth of the tape oxide layer [9], where $H_{sat} > H_c$ as in Fig. 7.13. The definition of H_{sat} for this application is a little tricky: H_{sat} must be large

---

*Apparently in practice it is found that the read signal is larger if the tape is recorded at slightly less than saturation. See Potter [10].

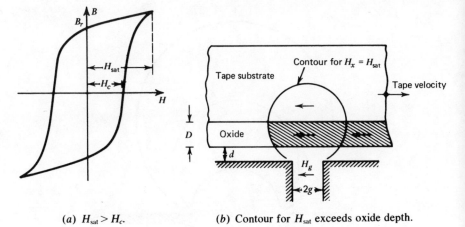

(a) $H_{sat} > H_c$.   (b) Contour for H_{sat} exceeds oxide depth.

Figure 7.13   Field requirements for saturation recording.

enough to include not only the intrinsic property of the recording material, but also some additional field required to overcome the demagnetizing field of the magnetized region on tape.

Field Amplitude for Anhysteretic Recording.   To avoid tape saturation, audio recording with a–c bias is done at a smaller field than digital recording. The literature suggests that the optimum a–c bias field is probably near the value such that the field contour just penetrates the oxide for $H \approx H_c$ (Fig. 7.14). In that case the recording should take place

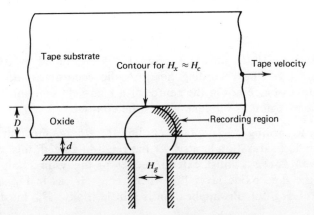

Figure 7.14   Probable field requirements for recording with a-c bias. The contour is for the a-c bias field. Region where the recording takes place is cross-hatched.

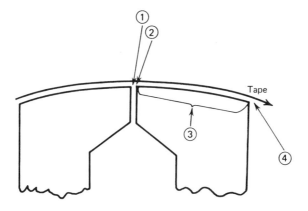

1. High field or "erase" region.
2. High gradient or "record" region.
3. Keeper region.
4. Demagnetization region.

Figure 7.15 Four magnetic regions along the top surface of a recording head. The radius of the surface is contoured for minimum air-bearing effects.

near the trailing edge of the field contour. The audio signal is considerably smaller than the bias field, perhaps about 25%. The signal recorded near the tape surface is more effective during playback than the signal deep in the oxide.

As the newly recorded tape moves past the gap and along the pole pieces of the head, the magnetized tape is not yet in its final environment. The head has a "keeper" effect on the tape pattern (as for a permanent magnet) because of its close proximity and high permeability. The tape may demagnetize slightly as it leaves the vicinity of the head (Fig. 7.15).

7.3.3 Design Example for Digital Recording

I believe that successful design is often a process of successive approximations. In that spirit there follows a simplistic paper design to illustrate the first principles of digital recording discussed earlier. The design has not been confirmed experimentally.

Problem Statement and Assumed Specifications. Define the parameters for a digital recording head capable of saturation recording with 100 mA of head current on conventional tape at 800 cpi, 45 ips.

ASSUMPTIONS

track width = 1 mm;
separation of tape above head, guess $d \approx 3\,\mu$m (see Fig. 7.13b)
$H_c \approx 300$ Oe
oxide thickness $D = 8\,\mu$m.

ESTIMATES AND JUDGMENTS.   Guess $H_{\text{sat}} \approx 2H_c = 600$ Oe (48 kA·t/m)
on a contour at least $(d + D) = 11\,\mu$m above head. Choose center of field
contour circle at assumed center of oxide, thus from (7.5) $ag = 7\,\mu$m =
$d + D/2$. Ignoring the possibility of an optimum tradeoff between a and
g, choose gap = $2g = 10\,\mu$m; hence $a = 1.4$ and radius $r = 8.6\,\mu$m. Thus
the field contour for 48 kA·t/m will extend to 15.6 μm. Since it follows
that $H_x/H_g = 0.1974$, the required deep-gap field is $H_g = 2.4 \times 10^5$ A·t/m.
The gap potential $H_g 2g$ is 2.4 A·t. If the writing efficiency (7.3) is
$\eta = 0.5$, then 48 turns will meet the current requirement. Presumably the
48 turns is one-half of a center-tapped total winding.

HEAD INDUCTANCE.   If the head is 1 mm wide, assume that 0.5 mm is
the pole-piece depth at the front gap, the gap reluctance is $R_g = l/\mu_0 S =$
$10^{-5}/4\pi 10^{-7}\cdot 0.5 \times 10^{-6} = 10^8/2\pi$, which is half the total circuit reluctance,
by assumption of $\eta = 0.5$. The permeance is then $P = \pi 10^{-2}\,\mu$H/t^2, and
the inductance $L = n^2 P = 72.4\,\mu$H. This concludes the required calculations except for checking. Would the head saturate? $B = \mu_0 H_g =$
$4\pi 10^{-7} \times 2.4 \times 10^5 = 0.3$ T—a little large, but not excessive unless the
head is ferrite. Gap potential $F_g = \Phi R_g = 0.3 \times .5 \times 10^{-6} \times 10^8/2\pi =$
2.4 A·t, which checks.

Magnetized Pattern on Tape.   In principle we would like to know the
patterns of magnetization along the tape, for subsequent use in estimating the output voltage during playback. An accurate definition of magnetization versus distance is a formidable magnetostatic problem, too
detailed for serious consideration here. However it is a trivial matter to
define the ideal geometry from which the actual distribution of $M(x)$ is
derived.

The ideal bit geometry of 31.75 μm long ×8 μm thick × 1000 μm wide
is defined by the packing density of 800 cpi (315 characters/cm), the
oxide thickness and the track width, assuming NRZI recording of a
continuous string of all "1"s. The specification of tape velocity as 45 ips
(1.14 m/s) implies a data rate of $800 \times 45 = 36 \times 10^3$ bits/s, or about
27.8 μs between flux reversals.

However for presently used tapes abrupt reversals of M are essentially impossible because the demagnetizing fields near the flux transition
would exceed the tape coercivity. The flux transition must occur more

gradually, thereby reducing the pole strength. A transition region of 1 to 2 times the thickness of the oxide coating seems plausible. On that basis the 32-μm bit length would consist of about 20 μm at saturation and about 12 μm of transition region. These values are used in the following commentary on reading digital tape.

7.4 SIGNAL REPRODUCTION FROM RECORDED TAPE

The first step of signal reproduction is the detection of the flux patterns on tape. Our present interest is restricted to inductive-type playback heads and their use for sensing flux changes, described in principle by (7.2). More explicit formulas for playback voltage have been worked out to explain experimental observations. But let us first examine a simpler case, reading back the recorded digital waveform in the example of Section 7.3.3.

7.4.1 Reading Digital Tape

A recorded digital tape consists of a series of regions on tape that are magnetized to saturation, separated by transition regions of finite length. The stray field that surrounds the magnetized regions evidently changes shape as the tape approaches the playback head (Fig. 7.16). The stray field is symmetrical when the tape is remote from the head, but is almost entirely attracted to a nearby high-permeability head.* Part of the flux that links the head will also link the windings to induce an output voltage when the flux changes. Simple analysis shows that the read efficiency of the head is the same reluctance ratio as the write efficiency (7.3).

Numerical Example. Using the numerical values and the model from Section 7.3.3, the tape flux in the center of a saturated region is $B_s S = 0.1(8 \times 10^{-6}\,\text{m}) \cdot (1000 \times 10^{-6}\,\text{m}) = 0.8\,\text{nT}$, which must equal the total leakage flux about a one-bit pattern. The total flux emanating from a transition region is twice that value, hence the average $d\phi/dx = (1.6 \times 10^{-9})/(12 \times 10^{-6}) \approx 1.3 \times 10^{-4}\,\text{T/m}$. Now multiplying by tape velocity (1.14 m/s), head efficiency (0.5), and turns (96) gives an average induced output voltage $\langle E \rangle \approx 7.3\,\text{mV}$, where the average is over the transition time (10.5 μs). The assumptions that underlie the calculation were contrived to permit easy calculation of the output voltage. In practice, one is more likely to work backward from voltage measurements to try to deduce experimental values of tape magnetization. In doing this, the

---

*The fraction has been given as $\mu_r/(\mu_r + 1)$.

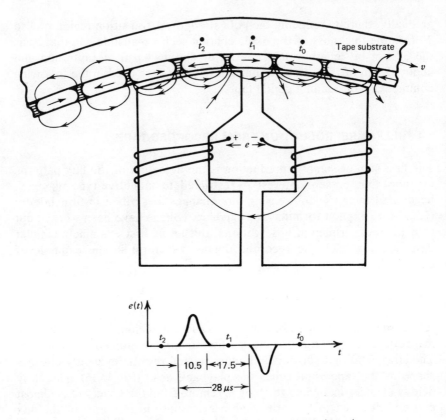

At times t_0, t_1, t_2 the tape positions shown are centered over the read gap.

Figure 7.16 Idealized magnetic picture of a digital tape, recorded NRZI with all "1's", being read by an inductive head. Part of the flux from the magnetized oxide regions of the tape links the windings on the head, to induce an output voltage when the flux changes. Note the change of the tape stray fields as the tape moves along the head.

effect should be noted of the inductance of the full head; $L \approx 290 \, \mu$H is calculated for this example.

7.4.2 Wavelength and Spatial Harmonics

The wavelength along the tape of a recorded signal, a basic parameter of the engineering design, is related to head-to-tape velocity v and frequency f through the equation

$$v = f\lambda \qquad \text{m/s} = (\text{cycles/s})\cdot(\text{m/cycle}). \qquad (7.7)$$

The practical upper limit for wavelength is determined by the overall tape contact length of the read head. The practical lowest value for wavelength is limited by the gap of the read head; thus high-frequency recording requires high tape velocity, to meet the need for a recorded wavelength that is long enough to be detectable. In the case of video recording, the required high velocity is achieved by rapidly rotating the heads while moving the tape at a moderate speed. The purpose of recording high-fidelity audio at $7\frac{1}{2}$ ips (19 cm/s), rather than $1\frac{7}{8}$ ips (4.75 cm/s), is to maintain longer recorded wavelengths on tape for better high-frequency reproduction with less noise.

Consider a sinusoidal variation of intrinsic induction with distance x along the tape

$$B_i(x) = B_m \sin \frac{2\pi x}{\lambda} \qquad \text{T.} \tag{7.8}$$

The sinusoid is sometimes written as $\sin kx$, where $k = 2\pi/\lambda$ is the spatial harmonic with dimension (rads/m). Using that notation, the spatial derivative of (7.8) is

$$\frac{dB_i}{dx} = kB_m \cos kx \qquad \text{T/m,} \tag{7.9}$$

so the time derivation of induction on a moving tape is

$$\frac{dB_i}{dt} = \frac{dB_i}{dx} \cdot v = \omega B_m \cos \omega t \qquad \text{T/s,} \tag{7.10}$$

where $\omega = 2\pi f = kv$.

7.4.3 Playback of Audio Tape

The value of B_m in (7.8) should be fairly carefully defined for audio recording. Linearity of response requires that $B_m < B_{sat}$ for any wavelength signal. In practice it is considered desirable to record at a high level such that B_m is just less than B_{sat} for the input signal of maximum amplitude. If so, it is desirable that B_m for the input signal of lowest amplitude still be well above the tape noise level. The objective is to match the dynamic range of input signal amplitude to the amplitude range of the tape, which is limited by tape saturation at one extreme and by tape noise at the other.

The wavelength parameter of (7.8) is particularly relevant to audio recording. The full range of audible frequency, from 20 Hz to 20 kHz, corresponds to a wide range of 1000 to 1 of recorded wavelengths. The output signal from a reproduce head is affected by signal wavelength in several ways that are now considered.

Limitation of Gap of Read Head. Equation 7.10 gives the flavor of the response of an ideal read head, assuming that the head can somehow respond to the derivative of induction from a moving tape. As the next step of the modeling process we show that the recorded wavelength must be longer than the read gap.

The sinusoidal induction along the tape, (7.8), is in a frame of reference x that moves with velocity v relative to the read head. A general point on tape is therefore located at a distance

$$x' = x + vt \tag{7.11}$$

from the origin at the center of the read head gap. Solving for x and substituting into (7.8) gives

$$B_i(x', t) = B_m \sin k(x' - vt), \tag{7.12}$$

which is shown in Fig. 7.17 at the instant $t = 0$ when $x = x'$. The increment of induction developed across the gap $2g$ can be worked out by subtracting the values at $x' = \pm g$,

$$\Delta B = B_m[\sin k(g - vt) - \sin k(-g - vt)]. \tag{7.13}$$

After some manipulation of trigonometric identities, the result is

$$\Delta B = 2B_m \sin kg \cos \omega t. \tag{7.14}$$

The simple function $\sin kg$ shows wavelength sensitivity, with zeros for integer values of $2g/\lambda$. The magnitude of $\sin kg$ is plotted log–log in Fig.

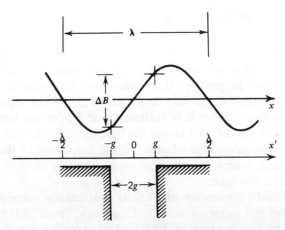

Figure 7.17 Waveform of $B_i = B_m \sin 2\pi(x/\lambda)$ compared to read head gap $= 2g$. As the tape moves with velocity v, a location x on tape is located at $x' = x + vt$ relative to the head.

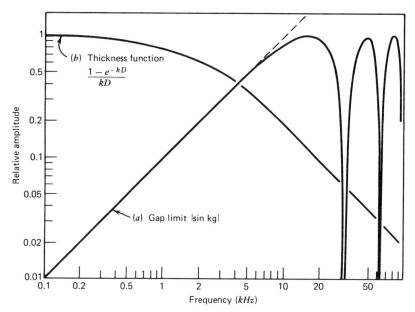

Figure 7.18 Two functions of amplitude versus playback frequency, calculated for a tape velocity of 3.75 ips (9.5 cm/s). Curve a: gap limit for an ideal read head with a gap of 3 μm; curve b: thickness function for oxide of thickness $D = 8$ μm assuming uniform $B_i(y)$.

7.18 as a function of frequency for the case $v = 3.75$ ips (9.5 cm/s) and gap $2g = 3$ μm. For these values $kg = 9.89478 \times 10^{-5} f$ rad. The region of interest is below the first maximum at $f = 16$ kHz, where the amplitude is about 4 dB less than the extrapolated value of kg. The maximum occurs at the frequency where the gap $2g$ is equal to $\lambda/2$ of the recorded sinusoid.

A rather more elegant derivation of the same gap limitation has been done in the research literature [11] using the concept of transfer functions. There is an analogy with electric circuit analysis in the frequency domain, where the output spectral response of a network is given by the input spectrum multiplied by $G(\omega)$, the transfer function of the network

$$V_0(\omega) = V_i(\omega)G(\omega). \qquad (7.15)$$

For the case of magnetic reproduction the domain of interest is that of reciprocal wavelength or spatial harmonics $k = 2\pi/\lambda$. The input spectrum from the tape—for example, kB_m from (7.9), can be multiplied by the transfer function for an ideal head

$$G_1(k) = \frac{\sin kg}{kg} \qquad (7.16)$$

to give the output response shown in Fig. 7.18. The Fourier transform derivation of (7.16) is based on the applicability of the reciprocity principle, to be discussed.

Spacing Loss. In his 1951 study on magnetic reproduction, Wallace [12] was the first to establish that the output voltage from a read head is very sensitive to the spacing between the head and the magnetic medium. The effect was particularly pronounced at high frequency and in fact limited the high-frequency response of his system (Fig. 7.19). Wallace's measurements showed a loss described by

$$54.6 \frac{d}{\lambda} \quad \text{dB,} \tag{7.17}$$

where d is the spacing and λ is the recorded wavelength. A spacing of only 0.1λ reduces the output by nearly 6 dB. Equation 7.17 can be

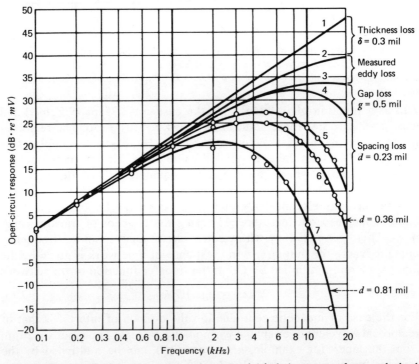

Figure 7.19 Computed (solid curves) and measured (circles) response from a playback head for various effective head-to-media spacings d: cobalt-nickel plated disk, 15.5 ips, 0.1-mA signal, recorded with 55-kHz bias adjusted to give maximum open-circuit response. (After Wallace [12]. Reprinted with permission from the *Bell System Technical Journal*, copyright 1951, The American Telephone and Telegraph Company.)

rewritten as a transfer function

$$G_2(k) = e^{-kd}, \qquad (7.18)$$

which is included below as a component of (7.24). Note that in (7.18) G_2 expressed in decibels is $20\log_{10}(e^{-kd}) = 20(\log_{10} e)(-2\pi d/\lambda) = -54.6 \, d/\lambda$ dB.

There seems to be some justification for believing that the product transfer function $G_1 G_2$, (7.16) and (7.18), belong together in a single description of a read head. Mallinson [11] points out that the Fourier transform of (7.4) is

$$H_x(k, y) = H_g 2g\left(\frac{\sin kg}{kg}\right)e^{-ky}. \qquad (7.19)$$

The similarity of (7.19) to $G_1 G_2$ is the basis for the conjecture.

Effect of Oxide Thickness, D.   A major deterrent to the calculation of the output voltage from a read head is the unknown distribution of $B_x(y)$. Equation 7.8 specifies the sinusoidal variation in the x-direction along the tape; the variation of B_x in the y-direction through the tape oxide is the topic of interest.

Suppose an oxide layer extends between $0 \le y \le D$ above an ideal read head. Consider an incremental area of tape $w\,dy$ located at height y, and assume for simplicity that the flux that reaches the head is

$$\Phi = w \int_{y=0}^{D} B_x(k, y)e^{-ky}\, dy. \qquad (7.20)$$

If B_x is invariant with y, the result of integration is

$$\Phi = wDB_x\left(\frac{1 - e^{-kD}}{kD}\right). \qquad (7.21)$$

After Wallace established (7.17) and (7.18) he did the foregoing analysis, tentatively assuming that the x-component of magnetization was independent of distance into his recording medium (0.3-mil plating of cobalt-nickel alloy). The fraction in (7.21) is plotted in Fig. 7.18 as a "thickness function," which accounts for a relative attenuation of output voltage from short-wavelength recorded signals.

On the other hand if B_x is nonuniform and increases in proportion* to y, the integral (7.20) takes the form

$$\int_{y=0}^{D} ye^{-ky}dy, \qquad (7.22)$$

---

*The model is based on a vector field argument. Figure 7.10 shows $H_x \approx \eta(ni/\pi r)\sin\theta$, where $\sin\theta = y/r$, along a contour of constant $H \approx H_c$.

which leads to a different thickness function

$$\left[\frac{1 - e^{-kD}(kD + 1)}{(kD)^2}\right]. \tag{7.23}$$

Bertram [15] carried out the analysis above, and presented experimental data that matched the calculations very well. His measurements were carried out with both chromium dioxide and γ-Fe$_2$O$_3$ tapes at $v = 4.76$ cm/s, $D = 5\ \mu$m, and gap $2g = 3.5\ \mu$m. The a–c bias was set at the level for optimum long-wavelength response as defined in Fig. 7.14. The main effect of (7.23) is a further attenuation of high-frequency signals, approaching an asymptote of -40 db/decade instead of -20 dB/decade as curve b, Fig. 7.18.

These results seem to explain why the optimum a–c bias for short-wavelength signals is smaller than the optimum bias for long-wave lengths. The exponential dependence e^{-ky} that recurs in (7.18) through (7.23) suggests that 90% of the detected flux change is derived from near the surface of the oxide coating. Specifically, $e^{-ky} = 0.1$ for $y = 0.37\lambda$. But according to (7.22) the magnetization of the tape is recorded more weakly at the surface, increasing with distance into the oxide.

Equation for Read Voltage. Equations 7.10, 7.16, and 7.18 are now brought together into one equation for the output voltage of a read head

$$e \approx \eta N\left(\frac{\mu_r}{\mu_r + 1}\right) WD\left(\frac{\sin kg}{kg}\right) e^{-kd} G_D(k) G_e(\omega) \omega B_m \cos \omega t, \tag{7.24}$$

where e = instantaneous voltage at the playback head
$\quad \eta$ = head efficiency
$\quad N$ = number of turns on the playback head
$\quad \mu_r$ = relative permeability of the head
$\quad WD$ = cross section of the tape oxide under the head (m^2)
$\quad k = 2\pi$ divided by recorded wavelength (in the same units as g)
$\quad g$ = half the gap of the head
$\quad d$ = head-to-tape spacing (in the same units as wavelength)
$\quad G_D(k)$ = dimensionless factor: takes into account the thickness of the
$\qquad\qquad$ oxide and the variation of B_x with thickness for various k
$\quad G_e(\omega)$ = dimensionless factor: accounts for head losses due to eddy
$\qquad\qquad$ currents; see Fig. 7.19 for an example
$\quad \omega$ = reproduced frequency (rads/s)
$\quad \omega t$ = the same argument as kx with $x = vt$, where v is velocity

Equation 7.24 is based on an equation worked out by Wallace from first principles. The main difference is that $G_D(k)$ is left as an unknown in (7.24), whereas Wallace defined $G_D(k)$ as $[1 - \exp(-Dk)]/Dk$.

Equalization. If the output voltage of a tape player is to have a flat frequency response, some frequency compensation is necessary. To a first approximation, a compensation network must compensate for the product of curves a and b of Fig. 7.18 in the frequency range of interest, below the first zero of a. The actual requirements should be determined experimentally for a specific transport, head, and tape.

Reciprocity Principle*. The reciprocity theorem concerns the interchange of excitation and response in linear systems. For a two-port electric network, if a current injected at port 1 elicits a voltage response at port 2 of

$$V_2 = I_1 z_{12}, \tag{7.25}$$

the reciprocity principle states that the ratio of voltage response to current excitation is invariant with interchange of ports, hence

$$z_{12} = z_{21}. \tag{7.26}$$

At first glance the applicability of the reciprocity principle to magnetic recording comes as a surprise and is a credit to the ingenuity of its originators. First, reciprocity is valid only for linear systems. Although the permanent magnet oxide is nonlinear, anhysteretic recording with a–c bias provides a linear response of tape flux to the input current in the head. Second, reciprocity is valid for electrical networks only in the frequency domain where impedance is a valid concept and multiplication of frequency functions yields an output spectrum. Applications to magnetics have been made in the domain of reciprocal space using spatial harmonics, and in the domain of reciprocal time using angular frequency. Third, the magnetic variables for input and response are not immediately obvious. As used by Westmijze, the response is a flux and the excitation is a current. In one "port" definition the tape flux is the output response to an input head current. In the reciprocal port definition, head flux is the output response to an input Amperian current that simulates the residual magnetization of the tape.

For a simple example of these ideas, consider an ideal but physically unrealizable head, which if used as a recording head would produce a field in response to a current I

$$h_x(x) = \frac{NI}{2g} \qquad -g \le x \le g, \qquad \text{all } y, \text{ all } z. \tag{7.27}$$

---

*This section may be omitted on first reading.

The Fourier transform is

$$H_x(k) = \int_{-\infty}^{\infty} h(x)e^{ikx}dx = NI\left(\frac{\sin kg}{kg}\right). \qquad (7.28)$$

If H is in the linear range of anhysteretic response of the tape, the remanent intrinsic induction will be

$$B_{ir} = \mu_0\chi_{an}H. \qquad (7.29)$$

Finally, the remanent flux in a segment of tape of area WD is

$$\Phi = \left[\mu_0 N\chi_{an} WD\left(\frac{\sin kg}{kg}\right)\right]I = T(k)I, \qquad (7.30)$$

where $T(k)$ is the transfer function between tape flux and head current. Now by the reciprocity theorem, an Amperian current I' around the area WD of the tape will induce flux in the head of

$$\Phi' = T(k)I', \qquad (7.31)$$

where $I' = B_x/\mu_0$ amperes per unit length. After substitution of (7.30) and the definition of B_x from (7.8), the flux linkage is found to be

$$\Phi' = N\chi_{an} WD\left(\frac{\sin kg}{kg}\right)B_m \sin kx \qquad (7.32)$$

and the output voltage for a tape of velocity v is,

$$e = N\chi_{an} WD\left(\frac{\sin kg}{kg}\right)\omega B_m \cos \omega t. \qquad (7.33)$$

This final result is similar to (7.24) but is simpler because of the ideal head. The result above illustrates the concept of reciprocity. A practical case involves nonuniformities that require careful attention to integration procedures.

PROBLEMS

1 (Section 7.1.1).   Find the data rate in 8-bit characters/s for data read from $\frac{1}{2}$-in. tape at 75 ips with a packing density of 1600 bits/in.

2 (Section 7.1.1).   A floppy disk rotates at 360 rpm and has a maximum of 13,262 flux reversals per radian. Use the additional information in the text to deduce the data rate, the radius of the smallest track, the radius of the largest track, the number of bits per track, and the total of bits per diskette.

3 (Section 7.3.1). The longitudinal component of H-field near the gap of a record head is given by (7.4). Use it to check the approximate values of the curves in Fig. 7.11.

4 (Section 7.3.1). Derive (7.5) for the contours of constant H_x, starting from (7.4).

5 (Section 7.3.2). Determine the number of ampere·turns required for an audio recording head, to meet the field contour requirement shown in Fig. 7.14. Assume that the total gap is 2 μm and the head efficiency is 0.5; choose reasonable values for d, D, and H_c.

6 (Section 7.4.2). Find the wavelength on tape that corresponds to each of the following combinations of frequency and head-to-tape velocity.

   a. $f = 20\,Hz$ to $20\,kHz$, $v = 1\frac{7}{8}$ ips.

   b. $f = 20\,Hz$ to $20\,kHz$, $v = 7\frac{1}{2}$ ips.

   c. $f = 4.2\,MHz$, $v = 18\,m/s$.

7 (Section 7.4.3). The recording head of Problem 5 is used to play back the specified tape in a cassette player at a speed of $1\frac{7}{8}$ ips. Make three graphs, on log–log paper as in Fig. 7.18, to indicate the separate effects of head gap limit, tape oxide thickness and head-to-tape spacing.

REFERENCES

1. C. E. Lowman, *Magnetic Recording*, McGraw-Hill, New York, 1972.

2. J. C. Mallinson, "Tutorial Review of Magnetic Recording," *Proc. IEEE*, **64**, 196–208 (February 1976). A very comprehensive and readable paper with 188 references.

3. H. W. Sallet, "Magnetic Tape: A High Performer," *IEEE Spectrum*, **14**, 26–31 (July 1977). Gives a tabulation of standards. Compares digital recording codes.

4. D. L. Noble, "Some Design Considerations for an Interchangeable Disk File," *IEEE Trans. Magn.*, **MAG-10**, 571–574 (September 1974). Gives "floppy" disk specifications.

5. B. Gustard and M. Wright, "A New γ-Fe$_2$O$_3$ Particle Exhibiting Improved Orientation," *IEEE Trans. Magn.*, **MAG-8**, 426–427 (September 1972).

6. S. Umeki, S. Saitoh, and Y. Imaoka, "A New High Coercivity Magnetic Particle for Recording Tape," *IEEE Trans. Magn.* **MAG-10**, 655–656 (September 1974). Compares Cobalt absorbed γ-Fe$_2$O$_3$ (Av-1) with chromium dioxide, Co-γ-Fe$_2$O$_3$, and standard γ-Fe$_2$O$_3$.

7. C. D. Mee, *The Physics of Magnetic Recording*, North Holland, Amsterdam, 1964. The standard reference for tape professionals.

8. G. Schwantke, "The Magnetic Tape Recording Process in Terms of the Preisach Representation," *J. Audio Eng. Soc.*, **9**, 37–47 (January 1961).

9. R. O. McCary, "Saturation Magnetic Recording Process," *IEEE Trans. Magn.*, **MAG-7**, 4–16 (March 1971).

10. R. I. Potter, "Digital Magnetic Recording Theory," *IEEE Trans. Magn.*, **MAG-10**, 502–508 (September 1974).

11. J. A. Mallinson, "On Recording Head Field Theory," *IEEE Trans. Magn.*, **MAG-10**, 773–775 (September 1974).

12. R. L. Wallace, Jr., "The Reproduction of Magnetically Recorded Signals," *Bell Syst. Tech. J.*, **30**, 1145–1173 (October 1951).

13. W. K. Westmijze, "Studies on Magnetics Recording," *Philips Res. Rep.*, **8**, 148–157, 161–183, 245–269, 343–366 (1953).

14. H. Neal Bertram, "Long Wavelength AC Bias Recording Theory," *IEEE Trans. Magn.*, **MAG-10**, 1039–1048 (December 1974).

15. H. Neal Bertram, "Wavelength Response in AC Biased Recording," *IEEE Trans. Magn.*, **MAG-11**, 1076–1078 (September 1975).

16. J. A. Geurst, "The Reciprocity Principle in the Theory of Magnetic Recording," *Proc. IEEE*, **51**, 1573–1577 (November 1963).

17. D. E. Speliotis, "Magnetic Recording Materials," *J. Appl. Phys.*, **38**, 1207–1214 (March 1967).

18. F. J. Darnell, "Magnetization Processes in Small Particles of CrO_2," *J. Appl. Phys.*, **32**, 1269–1274 (July 1961).

19. S. Ramo, J. R. Whinnery, and T. Van Duzer, *Fields and Waves in Communication Electronics*, Wiley, New York, 1965, pp 160–161.

8.
Distributed Magnetics

8.1 CONTEXT AND OVERVIEW

This chapter addresses concepts that are fundamental to new and exciting applications of magnetism in distributed geometries. Through the first six chapters the geometry of any magnetic specimen was almost invariably corelike. Any noncorelike shape is defined to be distributed; the geometry of a thin plane has special technical importance. The fundamentals are exposed as components of magnetic energy, including magnetostatic, exchange, and magnetoelastic energies. With the addition of anisotropy energy from Chapter 4, these four energies provide the needed background for subsequent descriptions of domain walls, permalloy thin films, and magnetic bubbles.

The topic of Section 8.2 is magnetostatics, essentially extending the ideas of Section 3.2 to the case of isolated specimens. Magnetostatic effects often tend to obscure or dominate the response of devices. For that reason, the strategy of presentation to now has consisted of three steps.

1. Define an ideal core geometry with no airgap, thereby avoiding the magnetostatic problem and exposing other magnetic properties.
2. Define an ideal permanent magnet with specified poles, thereby permitting H-fields to be calculated using the magnetic Coulomb's law.
3. Model the effect on an ideal core of a short airgap approximated as a reluctance.

None of the three methods is useful for the analysis of isolated permeable specimens, so a fresh approach is required.

Exchange coupling between spins, modeled in Section 8.3, is the basis for bulk magnetic properties such as ferromagnetism below the Curie temperature. In a local region, exchange coupling limits how abruptly the direction of magnetization can be changed and thereby defines the width of the transition (wall) between domains. The magnetic domain, whose existence is fundamental to applied magnetics, now comes to the forefront as the key component of a new technology. Furthermore the walls that divide the domains can exist in a variety of controllable structures.

Magnetostriction and magnetoresistance, described briefly in Section 8.4, are two magnetic phenomena that a designer needs to know about.

A variety of miniature magnetic devices possess the geometry of a planar thin film, commonly using permalloy as the preferred material. Section 8.5 generalizes the derivation from Section 4.3.3 of the easy-axis and hard-axis magnetization curves, then outlines the principles of a thin film memory. The property of a single-domain film for extraordinarily fast reversal is explained by the Landau-Lifshitz equation. Three kinds of domain walls can occur in thin films.

Magnetic bubble technology is a new memory technology based on the controlled movement of tiny magnetic domains. Section 8.6 outlines the operation of a major-loop, minor-loop bubble memory then gives more details of the supporting magnetics. The supporting details include the development of new materials with specified properties, the derivation of performance criteria, and the invention of new devices to meet the requirements of this integrated circuit magnetics.

8.2 MAGNETOSTATICS OF ISOLATED SPECIMENS

The magnetostatic portion of a magnetic design problem can be a formidable obstacle. Roughly speaking there are three engineering strategies or approaches to the magnetostatics problem, although any one method is seldom chosen to the complete exclusion of the others. A magnetic circuit or reluctance approach is especially useful for permanent magnet circuits (Section 3.2.3) and for cores with airgaps (Section 3.3). The same basic approach has also been applied with considerable sophistication to the design of circuits for magnetic bubbles. A second approach is to make field calculations, the topic addressed below. A third viable approach is experimental, depending on the evolution of design principles through a sequence of successive approximations and careful experimental observation of performance.

8.2.1 Types of Field Calculation

It is convenient to define four classes of material magnetostatic problems as involving no poles, specified poles, implied poles, and unknown poles. A toroidal core with no airgap, excited by a field with ϕ-direction symmetry, has no poles and thereby avoids the magnetostatic problem altogether. An isolated specimen in zero field also may have no poles if its domain structure has closure domains (e.g., Fig. 3.18a).

The category of *specified poles* is illustrated by the model for an ideal cylindrical permanent magnet (Section 3.2.1). The problem consists of calculating the field or the potential from pole density distributions that are presumed to be known and specified. In this class of model there is no requirement for self-consistency because the pole distribution is specified. There are probably several cases in which a specified pole model is a reasonable point of departure. The field is found by use of Coulomb's law or Poisson's equation for magnetics.

Implied Poles and Unknown Poles. The intrinsic induction of a magnetic core with an airgap, or of any noncorelike isolated magnetic specimen, responds to a *net* magnetic field. The net internal field H_{in} is the sum of the applied field H_a plus the demagnetizing field H_d that arises from the distribution of poles.

$$\bar{B}_i = \text{some function of } \bar{H}_{\text{in}} = f(\bar{H}_{\text{in}}) = f(\bar{H}_a + \bar{H}_d). \tag{8.1}$$

But the problem is that the pole density is given by the divergence of intrinsic induction

$$\rho = -\bar{\nabla} \cdot \bar{B}_i \qquad \text{Wb/m}^3, \tag{3.26}$$

so that $\bar{H}_d$ is some function of $\bar{B}_i$, as

$$\bar{H}_d = g(\bar{B}_i). \tag{8.2}$$

When (8.2) is substituted into (8.1) the resulting equation is formidable because B_i appears on both sides, functional dependencies f and g are generally unknown, and each vector variable is a function of position.

Fortunately there exists a set of ideal geometrical shapes, ellipsoids, for which the functional dependence g of (8.2) is a simple constant of proportionality if the applied field is uniform. The mathematical tractability of the ellipsoidal models makes that approach extremely useful as an approximation to other specimen geometries. Even for other geometries the agreement is often surprisingly good, which suggests that ellipsoidal distributions of poles may be a natural arrangement of minimum magnetostatic energy. Section 8.2.2 discusses the implied poles and the demagnetizing factors of ellipsoids.

There still remains the problem of solving (8.1) for some nonideal specimen shape, for a nonuniform applied field, and for a sufficient number of internal points to reasonably represent the device of interest. Section 8.2.3 comments on the direction of the research literature in addressing this formidable problem.

8.2.2 Ellipsoids and Demagnetizing Factors

Suppose that a uniform field is applied parallel to an ellipsoidal magnetic sample located in free space. If the ellipsoid is larger than microscopic so that macroscopic field theory applies, it can be calculated that the average induction is uniform internally. The uniformity of the average B_i is a consequence of a uniform demagnetizing field throughout the volume of the ellipsoid, which in turn is a consequence of the surface pole distribution. These facts underlie the special case of (8.2) that follows.

Values of Demagnetizing Factor.   The demagnetizing factor is the constant of proportionality between average magnetization and demagnetizing field along a specimen axis*

$$H_{d_x} = -N_x M_x = -N_x \frac{B_{ix}}{\mu_0} \quad \text{A/m}, \tag{8.3}$$

where N_x is the demagnetizing factor along the x-axis. An ellipsoid has three demagnetizing factors, one for each of its three perpendicular axes, which are related by the very useful equation*

$$N_a + N_b + N_c = 1. \tag{8.4}$$

Equation 8.4 can be used with (8.5) and (8.6) below, if applied with a sense of geometry, to deduce all three N's. For instance, the symmetry of a sphere is a clue to knowing that the demagnetizing field is independent of direction, hence $N_a = N_b = N_c = \frac{1}{3}$. The two most useful ellipsoidal shapes are prolate and oblate spheroids, respectively longer or flattened along the axis we shall call c. Given that the ratio of longest

---

*A common CGS form of (8.3) is

$$H_{d_x} = -4\pi N_x M_x$$

where $4\pi M_x = B_i$ gauss and $0 < N_x < 1$ as defined in (8.4). An alternative CGS convention defines the demagnetizing factor as 4π times the value defined here, hence (8.3) is $H_{dx} = -N_x M_x$ and (8.4) becomes $N_a + N_b + N_c = 4\pi$.

axis to shortest axis $= k$, the demagnetizing factor for the long axis of a prolate spheroid is

$$N_c = \frac{1}{k^2 - 1}\left[\frac{k}{\sqrt{k^2 - 1}}\log_e(k + \sqrt{k^2 - 1}) - 1\right] \qquad (8.5)$$

and for either long axis of an oblate spheroid is

$$N_a = N_b = \tfrac{1}{2}\left[\frac{k^2}{(k^2 - 1)^{3/2}}\arcsin\left(\frac{\sqrt{k^2 - 1}}{k}\right) - \frac{1}{k^2 - 1}\right]. \qquad (8.6)$$

EXAMPLE A

Find the demagnetizing factors for a spheroidal model of a single acicular ferric oxide particle of $0.1 \times 0.5\ \mu$m.

ANSWER.   Using (8.5) with $k = 5$ gives $N_c = 0.0558$, thence (8.4) gives $N_a = N_b = 0.472$.

EXAMPLE B

Find the demagnetizing factors for a spheroid model of a thin disk specimen (as in Figs. 4.15 and 4.16) of diameter 1 cm and thickness $10\ \mu$m.

ANSWER.   Using (8.6) with $k = 10^3$ gives $N_a = N_b = 7.842 \times 10^{-4}$. Hence $N_c = 0.9984$ along the disk axis.

Values of N for the *general* ellipsoid have been worked out and published by Stoner [6] and Osborne [5]. A formula useful for making crude estimates from memory is

$$N_a \approx \frac{1}{a}\left[\frac{abc}{ab + ac + bc}\right], \qquad (8.7)$$

where a, b, c are the lengths along the three axes.

Uses of a Demagnetizing Factor.   The main use of a demagnetizing factor is in estimating the additional field that must be applied to overcome the demagnetizing field, to magnetize an object. The demagnetizing field appears to reduce the effective permeability because the applied field must be larger to achieve the same induction. Consider an ideal linear material described by the special case of (8.1)

$$B_i = \mu_0 \chi H_{in}. \qquad (1.3)$$

If a specimen is cut from this material such that $N = 0.1$ along an axis of

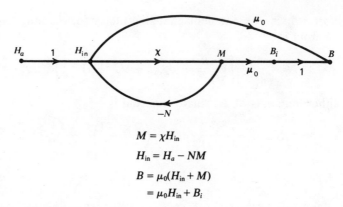

$$M = \chi H_{in}$$
$$H_{in} = H_a - NM$$
$$B = \mu_0(H_{in} + M)$$
$$= \mu_0 H_{in} + B_i$$

Figure 8.1 Signal-flow graph of the equations above illustrate an interpretation of negative feedback, see (8.8).

interest, according to (8.3) the applied field required to achieve an induction of $B_i = 1$ T (10 kG) will need to be larger by $\mu_0 H_a = 0.1$ T (1000 Oe) to overcome the demagnetizing field. The manipulation of (8.3) and (1.3), in Fig. 8.1, gives the results

$$M = H_a \frac{\chi}{1 + \chi N} \tag{8.8a}$$

$$B = H_a \mu_0 \frac{\mu_r}{1 + \chi N}. \tag{8.8b}$$

in which $-\chi N$ is the transfer function of a feedback loop. The fraction of (8.6a) [(8.8b)] is the apparent or effective susceptibility [effective relative permeability], reduced from the bulk value by the feedback factor $(1 + \chi N)$.

EXAMPLE C

Find the applied field H_{az} required to magnetize a sphere of linear ferrite to $B = 0.2$ T, given $\mu_r = 100$. Sketch B, H, and B_i versus z along a line parallel to the uniform applied field and through the diameter of the sphere.

ANSWER. The internal field required to achieve $B = 0.2$ T is $H_{in} = 0.2/\mu_0\mu_r = 1591.5$ A/m (20 Oe). Since intrinsic induction $B_i = 0.99B = 0.198\,T$ and $N = \frac{1}{3}$, the demagnetizing field is $H_d = -52,521$ A/m (-660 Oe), and the applied field is required to be 54,113 A/m (680 Oe). From (8.8), $\chi_{eff} = 2.91$ and $\mu_{eff} = 2.94$ or roughly $1/N$, the limiting value

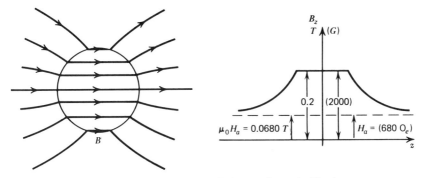

(a) B versus z. (Note that B has no discontinuities.)

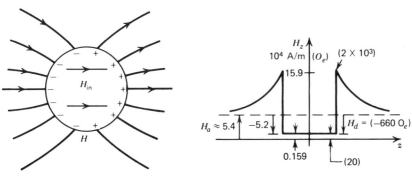

(b) H versus z. (Note that $H_{in} = H_a + H_d$.)

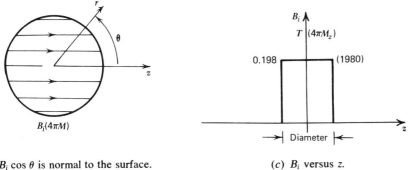

$B_i \cos \theta$ is normal to the surface.
$B_i \sin \theta$ is the tangential component.

(c) B_i versus z.

Figure 8.2 The field quantities B, H, and B_i for Example C, a sphere of $\mu_r = 100$ magnetized to $B = 0.2$ T by a uniform applied field in the positive z-direction. Values are given in both MKS and CGS units.

for $\chi N \gg 1$. The field quantities in Fig. 8.2 include B and H outside the sphere, which is derived subsequently.

Demagnetizing factors are sometimes used to estimate the shape anisotropy of spheroidal specimens. The preferred direction of magnetization for a single-domain particle is along the axis of the smallest demagnetizing factor. Using the notion above, the shape anisotropy for a saturated prolate spheroid has been given as a shape coercivity

$$H_{sh} \approx (N_a - N_c)M_s. \tag{8.9}$$

Equation 8.9 explains why (3.66) is true for the shape anisotropy class of permanent magnets.

EXAMPLE D

Find the theoretical shape anisotropy for the single particle of Example A, given $B_{is} \approx 0.47$ T.

ANSWER. From (8.9) $H_{sh} \approx 155.6$ kA/m (1955 Oe), which is about 5 or 6 times the measured value for tapes and about twice the value of coercivity that has been measured for a single isolated particle.

Derivation of Demagnetizing Factor for a Sphere.* The immediate goal of the following derivation is to show that the demagnetizing field at the center of a uniformly magnetized sphere is $H_d = -M/3$, which will define $N = \frac{1}{3}$ from (8.3).

Figure 8.2c shows the geometry of a sphere magnetized uniformly in the z-direction, from which it can be deduced that the average component of B_i normal to the surface is $B_i \cos \theta$. This defines the surface pole density using (3.28b). On the incremental surface at constant θ defined by

$$dS = 2\pi \imath \sin \theta \cdot \imath d\theta, \tag{8.10}$$

where $\imath$ is the radius of the sphere, the surface magnetic charge will be

$$dQ_m = \bar{B}_i \cdot d\bar{S} = B_i \cos \theta \sin \theta \, 2\pi \imath^2 \, d\theta \tag{8.11}$$

for substitution into the magnetostatic Coulomb's law

$$d\bar{H}(\bar{r}_2) = \frac{\hat{a}_R dQ_m}{4\pi \mu_0 R^2} \tag{3.27}$$

where $\bar{r}_1$ is the source variable, $\bar{r}_2$ is the field point, and $\bar{R} = \bar{r}_2 - \bar{r}_1$. Only the z-component of (3.27) is applicable to the present definition of dQ_m.[†]

---

*This section can be omitted on first reading.

†For $dS = \imath \sin \theta \, d\phi \cdot \imath \, d\theta$ the direction of $d\bar{H}$ is along $\hat{a}_R = -[\cos \theta \hat{a}_z + \sin \theta (\cos \phi \hat{a}_x + \sin \phi \hat{a}_y)]$. Only the z-component survives the ϕ-integration that gives (8.10).

The demagnetizing field at the center of the sphere is the integral of (3.27) with $r_1 = \imath$, $r_2 = 0$, and $R = -\imath$,

$$\bar{H}_d = -\hat{a}_z \frac{B_i}{2\mu_0} \int_{\theta=0}^{\pi} \cos^2 \theta \sin \theta \, d\theta, \tag{8.12}$$

which yields the desired result after integration

$$\bar{H}_d = \hat{a}_z \frac{B_i}{2\mu_0} \left[\frac{\cos^3 \theta}{3} \right]_0^{\pi} = \frac{-\hat{a}_z B_i}{3\mu_0}. \tag{8.13}$$

Potential Method for a Sphere.* The immediate purpose of this section is to provide a more complete analytical solution to support Fig. 8.2. A second purpose is to provide contact with the classical potential method for solving field problems.

Let a magnetic sphere as in Example C have a radius $\imath$ and ideal relative permeability μ_r. Let the applied field be uniform $H_a \hat{a}_z$. We want to be able to solve for the field anywhere in space as the gradient in spherical coordinates of the unknown potential F

$$\bar{H} = -\bar{\nabla} F = -\left[\hat{a}_r \frac{\partial F}{\partial r} + \hat{a}_\theta \frac{1}{r} \frac{\partial F}{\partial \theta} \right], \tag{8.14}$$

where no ϕ-dependence exists for this problem. In this development r is the spherical coordinate variable.

The solution F has the general form

$$F_{\text{outside}} \triangleq F_2 = \left(ar + \frac{b}{r^2} \right) \cos \theta \tag{8.15}$$

$$F_{\text{inside}} \triangleq F_1 = cr \cos \theta, \tag{8.16}$$

where constants a, b, c are to be determined. The solution outside the sphere, in the limit as $r \to \infty$, applying (8.14) to (8.15) gives

$$H_a \hat{a}_z = -(\hat{a}_r a \cos \theta - \hat{a}_\theta a \sin \theta). \tag{8.17}$$

The result of taking the inner product of each side with $\hat{a}_z$ gives the value for the first constant as the negative of the applied field

$$H_a = -a(\cos^2 \theta + \sin^2 \theta) = -a. \tag{8.18}$$

The remaining two constants b, c are related to each other by the boundary conditions at the spherical surface, two equations for the two unknowns.

*This section may be omitted on first reading.

The tangential components of H inside and outside are equal,

$$\frac{1}{r}\frac{\partial F_1}{\partial \theta}\bigg|_{r=\iota} = \frac{1}{r}\frac{\partial F_2}{\partial \theta}\bigg|_{r=\iota}, \tag{8.19}$$

which gives

$$c = -H_a + \frac{b}{\iota^3}. \tag{8.20}$$

The normal components of $B = \mu H$ are also equal,

$$\mu_1 \frac{\partial F_1}{\partial r}\bigg|_{r=\iota} = \mu_2 \frac{\partial F_2}{\partial r}\bigg|_{r=\iota}, \tag{8.21}$$

which gives a second relation

$$\mu_1 c = -\mu_2\left(H_a + \frac{2b}{\iota^3}\right), \tag{8.22}$$

where $\mu_1 = \mu_r\mu_0$ inside the sphere and $\mu_2 = \mu_0$ outside. Solving (8.20) and (8.22) gives

$$b = \frac{H_a \iota^3(\mu_r - 1)}{\mu_r + 2} \tag{8.23}$$

and

$$c = \frac{-3H_a}{\mu_r + 2} = \frac{-3H_a}{\chi + 3}. \tag{8.24}$$

Constant $c = -H_{in} = -H_a/(1 + \chi N)$ in the notation of (8.8), where $N = \frac{1}{3}$ for a sphere; H_{in} may also be written as

$$H_{in} = H_a\left[1 - \frac{\chi}{\chi + 3}\right] = H_a - \frac{M}{3}, \tag{8.25}$$

which identifies the demagnetizing field as $-M/3$ as in (8.3). The final result for the potential is

$$F_2 = -H_a r \cos\theta\left(1 - \frac{\iota^3}{r^3}\frac{\chi}{\chi + 3}\right), \qquad r > \iota \tag{8.26}$$

$$= -r\cos\theta\left[H_a - \frac{M\iota^3}{3r^3}\right]$$

$$F_1 = \frac{-3H_a r \cos\theta}{\chi + 3}, \qquad r < \iota$$

$$= -r\cos\theta\left(H_a - \frac{M}{3}\right). \tag{8.27}$$

EXAMPLE E

Use (8.14) on (8.26) to find the profile of $H(z)$ for $r > \imath$ (Fig. 8-2b).

ANSWER. Find

$$H_z = \frac{-\partial F_2}{\partial r}\bigg|_{r>\imath,\,\theta=0} = H_a[1 + \left(\frac{2\imath^3/r^3)\chi}{\chi+3}\right] = H_a\left[1 + \frac{1.94\imath^3}{r^3}\right]$$

Thus $H = 2.94H_a$ at $r = \imath$; $H = 1.1H_a$ at $r = 2.69\imath$, etc.

Continuum versus Domain Models. In the analytical potential modeling of materials it is usually assumed that the materials are linear, isotropic, and homogeneous. Since magnetic materials as a class have none of these properties, some words of justification for even trying analytical modeling appear to be in order.

The analytical criterion of linearity imposes the constraint, first that the magnetic specimen must not be saturated, that is, not in the magnetic state of a single domain magnetized to saturation parallel to H. Second, the property of linearity is sometimes applicable to a macroscopic model of average B_i in a region of a specimen, even though a detailed local description is lacking. Sometimes specific definitions of linear response can be achieved by using special procedures such as in anhysteretic recording, Section 7.1.3.

The criteria *isotropic* and *homogeneous* seem to be a little less stringent. For many cases of interest the demagnetizing fields are so strong that they tend to dominate the device performance. In such cases a detailed description of the material properties is less important. It should also be recognized that very similar spatial distributions of poles can be made to occur by several very different physical processes. Some of the processes were listed in Section 3.2.1, which also described how surface poles may actually be volume poles that are located very near the specimen surface.

What all this seems to mean may be summarized as follows. The field-theory-related analysis is a continuum type of model. The continuum model cannot always be physically interpreted point by point within the region of interest, but must be interpreted as some sort of average of the magnetic parameter in a region that surrounds the mathematical point of interest. The magnetic state of a device usually consists physically of an aggregation of domains, which is inherently discrete instead of being a continuum. In magnetostatic permeable devices that have been studied in detail, the domains are often found to respond to a range of values of H-field in a manner that yields a continuum-like distribution of poles. The rigorous, self-consistent modeling of local response is a research subspecialty called micromagnetics [42, 43], which is beyond our scope of interest.

8.2.3 Field Calculations by Computer

Field calculations must be done by computer methods unless two conditions are met: (a) the applied field must be uniform, and (b) the specimen shape must be ellipsoidal, so that the demagnetizing field will be an elementary function of the induction. The second condition is very restrictive, since very few devices actually use ellipsoids, although it is common to use an ellipsoidal approximation to other specimen shapes.

The dilemma of this topic is that on one hand, computational procedures for magnetic devices are becoming very widely used, making the subject very timely and relevant. On the other hand, devices differ so dramatically that the common principles of approach are almost inaccessible to a general introduction to the topic.

In a recent review article Colonias [7] observed that numerical methods for calculating magnetic fields were almost nonexistent 20 years ago but have developed rapidly as computers have become available. He defined two general approaches that are widely used for the numerical solution of electromagnetic field problems; they are computationally similar, and both require the solution of many simultaneous equations. Both approaches substitute for the continuous problem an approximation at a discrete number of points, then solve the set of equations for the approximate solution. The system of equations may be solved by iteration or by elimination.

One approach formulates the field problem by differential equations, which are then approximated by a set of difference equations between discrete points. The difference equations may be linear or nonlinear. Various relaxation schemes are used to assure that the iteration of the equations will converge to a solution.

The second general approach formulates the field problem by integral equations, which are then made discrete on a finite element mesh. The finite element method depends on the formulation of a functional, then finding its maximum or minimum by a variational method. Elimination methods are used to solve the system of equations.

With either approach the number of internal points, hence the accuracy, is usually limited by computation costs. A variety of numerical innovations and clever approximations have been devised to achieve computability, to reduce computer costs, and/or to improve accuracy. One gains the impression that in most cases the innovative approximations are specific to the class of device being simulated. The literature in this area may be consulted for further details [7].

Introduction to the Method of Fourier Series. This method is applicable to a number of devices that involve a nonuniform applied field as well as nonellipsoidal specimen shapes. The analytical problem is that the distribution of M must be known before the demagnetizing field can be calculated. However $M = \chi H_{in}$ cannot be known until the demagnetizing field has been determined. The self-consistency dilemma is resolved by expressing M in the form of a Fourier series. It is then possible to find the demagnetizing field as a Fourier series in which each harmonic of H_d is defined by the corresponding harmonic of M. The problem then becomes deterministic, since the harmonics of M, the only unknown quantities, can be found from the harmonics of the applied field.

The first example models a response to a nonuniform applied field, adapted from a paper by Dove [8].

Consider a uniaxial Permalloy thin film of thickness T as described in Section 4.3.3, where the x-coordinate is defined as the easy axis. A distance d above the plane of the film, a wire carries current I parallel to the easy axis of the film (Fig. 8.3). The field applied along the y- or hard axis of the film is therefore

$$H_y = H \cos \alpha = \frac{Id}{2\pi(d^2 + y^2)} \qquad \text{A/m}, \qquad (8.28)$$

as sketched in Fig. 8.4. The nonuniform applied field induces a nonuniform rotation of B_i from the easy axis, but the y-component of induction has a functional dependence different from (8.28). This is because B_{i_y} responds to the sum of H_y plus the demagnetizing field that results from its own nonuniform distribution.

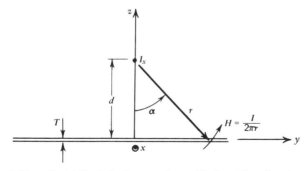

Figure 8.3 A thin uniaxial film is in the x–y plane with the x-direction along its easy axis. A wire at height d above the film carries current I in the x-direction, thereby applying a nonuniform field to the film (8.28).

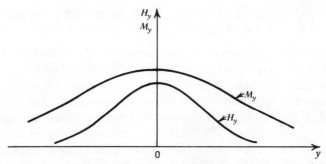

Figure 8.4 The nonuniform applied field H_y induces a nonuniform rotation of M, assuming $H_y < H_k$, but M_y drops off more slowly than H_y as $|y|$ increases.

Let the y-component of intrinsic induction be expressed as a Fourier series

$$B_i(Y) = B_0 + \sum_{n=1}^{\infty} B_n \cos \frac{2\pi n Y}{\lambda} \qquad (8.29)$$

over some arbitrary interval $-\lambda/2 < Y < \lambda/2$. The sine series is omitted because of the even symmetry of the problem. Ignoring the z-component of divergence and assuming no variation of induction over the film thickness, the volume density of poles for this one-dimensional case is

$$\rho = \frac{-dB_i}{dY} = \sum_{n=1}^{\infty} \frac{2\pi n}{\lambda} B_n \sin \frac{2\pi n Y}{\lambda} \qquad \text{Wb/m}^3. \qquad (8.30)$$

It is convenient to use the magnetic Coulomb's law (3.27) in the form

$$dH(y) = \frac{l}{2\pi\mu_0 R}, \qquad l = \rho T \, dY, \qquad (8.31)$$

where l is a line density of poles (Wb/m) and $R = y - Y$. The notation Y is being used to indicate the incremental pole location; y is the point where the field is to be calculated. The total demagnetizing field at y is the integral of the contributions from all the poles. After interchanging summation and integration, use of (8.30) in (8.31) leads to

$$H_d(y) = \int_{Y=-\infty}^{\infty} dH_y = \frac{T}{\lambda\mu_0} \sum_{n=1}^{\infty} nB_n \int_{-\infty}^{\infty} \frac{\sin(2\pi n Y/\lambda) \, dY}{y - Y}. \qquad (8.32)$$

On physical grounds we know the integral must be finite, and in fact*

$$\int_{-\infty}^{\infty} \frac{\sin(ax) \, dx}{\beta - x} = -\pi \cos(a\beta) \qquad [a > 0]. \qquad (8.33)$$

---

*Integral 3.722-6, page 406 of Gradshteyn and Ryzhik, [9].

After using (8.31), (8.32) becomes

$$H_d(y) = - \frac{\pi T}{\mu_0 \lambda} \sum_{n=1}^{\infty} n B_n \cos \frac{2\pi n y}{\lambda},$$ (8.34)

which gives the demagnetizing field as a function of the unknown harmonics of B_i. It follows that

$$H_a + H_d = \frac{B_i}{\mu_0 \chi},$$ (8.35)

where the applied field is represented by the series

$$H_a = h_0 + \sum_{n=1}^{\infty} h_n \cos \frac{2\pi n y}{\lambda}$$ (8.36)

and susceptibility $\chi = (B_{i_{\text{sat}}}/\mu_0 H_k) = M_s/H_k$.

If B_i and H_d, defined by (8.29) and (8.34), are substituted into (8.35), the result is

$$H_a = \frac{B_0}{\mu_0 \chi} + \sum_{n=1}^{\infty} \frac{B_n}{\mu_0} \left(\frac{1}{\chi} + \frac{\pi T n}{\lambda} \right) \cos \frac{2\pi n y}{\lambda},$$ (8.37)

which can be matched term by term with (8.36) as

$$h_n = \frac{B_n}{\mu_0} \left(\frac{1}{\chi} + \beta_n \right), \qquad \beta_n = \frac{\pi T n}{\lambda}.$$ (8.38)

The nth harmonic of B_i is therefore defined as

$$B_n = h_n \frac{\mu_0 \chi}{1 + \chi \beta_n}, \qquad n = 0, 1, 2, \ldots,$$ (8.39)

which is the principal result of interest.

The fraction of (8.39) is like a low-pass filter function that couples the harmonics of H_a to B_i. The equation is very similar to (8.8) for an ellipsoid in a uniform applied field, where dimensionless parameter β_n has a role analogous to that of a demagnetizing factor.

In the original research [8] that pioneered this approach, the harmonics of H in (8.36) were found by evaluating the usual integrals of the function in (8.28). Each corresponding harmonic B_n was then calculated by using (8.39), and finally the harmonic amplitudes were summed to yield the spatial distribution of $B_i(y)$. The calculated distribution was found to agree very well with experimental observations of the local magnetization using a small-spot Kerr effect optical probe.

The general magnetostatic problem requires that the intrinsic induction be self-consistent with the demagnetizing field that results from it. In the example above the self-consistency was established by representing the harmonics of the demagnetizing field as a function of the unknown harmonics of B_i, permitting both components of the solution to be found at once without iteration. Furthermore it is interesting that there exists an analytical solution for B as a function of H, expressed in (8.39) as a transfer function in the spatial frequency domain. There is an evident analogy with electrical network theory in which the output frequency function is found by the multiplication in the frequency domain of the input function times the network transfer function. Equation 8.32 can be thought of as a form of convolution in the spatial domain, but that point of view has not been widely exploited in the literature.

The Fourier series modeling approach has also been applied to a set of magnetostatic problems that consist of arrays of discrete rectangular magnetic elements rather than one magnetic sheet of infinite extent, as in the above example. The geometry is represented as a multiplying factor $U(x, y, z)$, where $U = 1$ represents a point inside the specimen and otherwise $U = 0$. The equation for magnetic equilibrium along the x-axis then becomes

$$M_x(x) = \chi U[H_{ax}(x) + H_{dx}(x)], \qquad (8.40)$$

where M, H_a, H_d, and U are all functions in the domain of spatial frequency, as Fourier series. Equation 8.40 is clearly more complicated than (8.38) and requires a computer to solve the set of equations. At the time of this writing, one-dimensional variations of average M have been calculated for periodic arrays of permeable I-bars in response to uniform and nonuniform applied fields. The rectangular shape of an I-bar (Fig. 3.18a) is computationally tractable and is similar to the shapes of permalloy elements that are used to control the movement of magnetic bubble domains (see Section 8.6.2). Calculations using Fourier series methods have yielded several practical results that compare reasonably with experimental measurements and with other methods of calculation. Calculated results include the distribution profile of the average magnetization along the bar, the static equilibrium position of a bubble under the bar, and the effective field that acts on the bubble. The results take into account the relevant variables of geometry of sizes and spacings, the bubble-to-bar interactions, and the bar-to-bar interactions. The references may be consulted for further details [44–47].

8.2.4 Magnetostatic Energy

The general category of magnetostatic energy has several components that are interrelated in ways that seem subtle at first glance. It is useful to recognize three distinct components:

1. The interaction energy between a permanent magnet and an applied field, W_{pm}.
2. The demagnetizing energy of a magnetized body, W_{dm}.
3. The energy required to magnetize a permeable medium, W_{mm}.

The MKS unit for energy E is the joule, the product of B (T or Wb/m^2) times H (A/m) times volume V (m^3). It is also convenient to define energy density W (J/m^3). In all three cases we choose to represent the material property by the intrinsic induction B_i and the applied field by H.

Potential Energy of a Permanent Magnet. The interaction energy of a permanent magnet of volume V and local induction $\bar{B}_i$ with an applied field $\bar{H}_a$ is given by

$$E_m = -\int_V \bar{B}_i \cdot \bar{H}_a dv \approx -V\bar{B}_i \cdot \bar{H}_a = -\bar{j} \cdot \bar{H}_a, \tag{8.41}$$

where $\bar{j}$ is the magnetic moment (Wb·m). The energy expression may be compared with the torque equation given in Chapter 2,

$$\bar{T} = \bar{j} \times \bar{H}_a \qquad \text{N·m}. \tag{2.3}$$

It is common to omit the volume integration from (8.41) and define magnetostatic energy density

$$W_{pm} = -\bar{B}_i \cdot \bar{H}_a = -B_i H_a \cos \theta \qquad \text{J/m}^3, \tag{8.42}$$

where θ is the angle between $\bar{B}_i$ and $\bar{H}_a$. The negative sign means that the magnetostatic energy is a minimum when B_i and H_a are parallel, which is a stable orientation that develops zero torque.

Bozorth [3] describes (8.42) as the work per volume required to transport a specimen of fixed magnetic moment from a location of zero field to a location where $H = H_a$. The negative of (8.42) is the work required to move the specimen in the opposite direction. The latter energy consists of two components (Fig. 8.5),

$$B_i H_a = \int_0^{H_a} B_i \, dH + \int_0^{B_i} H_a dB_i. \tag{8.43}$$

The first integral represents the (negative of the) work required to transport a previously unmagnetized specimen of variable B_i in from a location of zero field. The second integral represents the energy required to magnetize the specimen, which is discussed later. Equation 8.43 is given merely as a matter of perspective for (8.42), the equation of more importance to us.

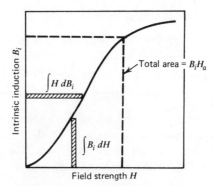

Figure 8.5 Illustration of components of magnetostatic energy, (8.43). (Adapted from *Ferromagnetism* by Richard M. Bozorth © 1951 by Litton Educational Publishing, Inc., by permission of Van Nostrand Reinhold Company.)

Finally, in the special case of a collection of magnetized particles where the field that acts on each particle is due to the others, a self-energy factor of $\frac{1}{2}$ is required

$$W_m = -\tfrac{1}{2}\bar{B}_i \cdot \bar{H} \qquad \text{J/m}^3. \tag{8.44}$$

Demagnetizing Energy. This is a special case of (8.44) with

$$H = H_d = \frac{-NB_i}{\mu_0}, \tag{8.45}$$

where N is the demagnetizing factor along the specimen axis of induction. Substituting (8.45) into (8.44) yields

$$W_{dm} = \frac{1}{2\mu_0} NB_i^2 \qquad \text{J/m}^3, \tag{8.46}$$

which shows that the criterion of minimum energy requires the minimum value of N. This explains why the natural direction of magnetization is along the longest axis of a specimen, as in Example B. Equations 8.45 and 8.46 are rigorously valid only for ellipsoidal specimens and are qualitatively valid for other shapes.

The total demagnetizing energy of a body is the integral over the volume of the body of the special case of (8.44). The total demagnetizing energy thereby evaluated is equal to the field energy in the rest of the system, outside the body but due to the presence of the body.

Energy of Magnetization for a Permeable Body. Let a permeable magnetic specimen of volume $V = Sl$ be excited by a current-carrying coil. It is assumed that the geometry of the specimen is such that the demagnetizing effects are negligible, and it is further assumed that the coil is closely coupled to the specimen. Under these assumptions an incremental change of current di will increase the field by dH, thereby inducing a flux change and a proportional voltage e in excess of the voltage with no specimen present. The electrical power for the time dt does work on the specimen

$$ei\, dt = dW\, V \qquad J \tag{8.47}$$

that can be found by substituting for e and i

$$\left(nS\frac{dB_i}{dt}\right)\frac{Hl}{n}\, dt = H\, dB_i\, V = dW\, V.$$

After canceling V and integrating both sides, the energy density is

$$W_{mm} = \int_0^{B_i} H\, dB_i \qquad J/m^3, \tag{8.48}$$

which is part of (8.43).

The average intrinsic induction of a permeable material is proportional to applied field $B_i = \mu_0 \chi H$ so that (8.48) becomes

$$W_{mm} = \mu_0 \chi \int H\, dH = \tfrac{1}{2}\mu_0 \chi H_a^2 = \tfrac{1}{2}B_i H_a, \tag{8.49}$$

which is the result of interest. The positive sign of (8.49), in contrast with (8.42), means that work was done on the material to bring it to a magnetized state, the additional work required to build up the current when the specimen is there. The factor of $\tfrac{1}{2}$ results from the proportionality of B_i and H. For this condition of linearity, both components of (8.43) have equal value, but it would not be true in general. Stratton [2] gives the interpretation that (8.49) is the energy density of magnetization if induction B_i results from fixed sources that would cause a field H_a in the absence of the specimen. The following example illustrates.

EXAMPLE F

Find the values of the components of magnetostatic energy for the permeable sphere of Example C, which has $\mu_r = 100$, $B = 0.2\,T$, and field quantities as in Fig. 8.2.

ANSWER. Using (8.44) with $B_i = 0.198\,T$ and $H_a = 54.113 \times 10^3\,A/m$ yields $W_m = 5357.2\,J/m^3$, which includes the energy of the stray field set up by the sphere plus the energy required to magnetize the sphere itself. The former, given by (8.46) with $N = \tfrac{1}{3}$, is $W_{dm} = 5199.6\,J/m^3$. The energy of magnetization is given by (8.49) using $H_{in} = H_a + H_d$, where H_d has a negative value; hence $H_{in} = 1591.5$ A/m and $W_{mm} = 157.6$ J/m^3.

EXAMPLE G

Find the expressions for the components of magnetostatic energy for the uniaxial thin film of Section 4.3.3 if $H_a = H_k$ along the hard axis, the y-direction.

ANSWER.   The demagnetizing factor in the plane of the film is assumed to be negligible. The magnetic state of the film is further assumed to be a single domain as a permanent magnet, yet with rotatable χ. With $H_y = H_k = 2K/B_{is}$, angle $\phi = 90°$ in (4.44) and $\theta = 0°$ in (8.42), yielding $W_{pm} = -2K$. The energy of magnetization $W_{mm} = K$ using (8.49) the mechanism of which is $W_k = K$ using (4.34).

8.3 EXCHANGE COUPLING

The local effect of coupling between magnetic moments has been postponed to this point to permit the development of a background of supporting concepts. Chapter 2 modeled intrinsic induction at the atomic level and deduced the number of uncompensated spins per atom to account for the bulk value of saturation induction. That there must exist some sort of cooperative coupling within the system of magnetic moments was argued, modeled as positive feedback in Section 4.2.2. The coupling energy per atom was given approximately by kT_c, Boltzmann's constant times the Curie temperature in kelvins.

Local Interpretation of the Heisenberg Model.   The mechanics for the cooperative coupling was identified in Section 4.2.3 as exchange coupling between spins, modeled by the Heisenberg model

$$E_{ex} = -2X\bar{S}_1 \cdot \bar{S}_2. \qquad (4.22)$$

If (4.22) is treated as a classical inner product between two vectors of magnitude S, the equation becomes

$$E_{ex} = -2XS^2 \cos \phi \approx -2XS^2 \left(1 - \frac{\phi}{2!}\right), \qquad (8.50)$$

where ϕ is the small angle between spins and the parenthesis term is the small-angle approximation for $\cos \phi$. The change in coupling energy as a function of ϕ is thus

$$\Delta E_{ex} \approx XS^2\phi^2, \tag{8.51}$$

which is the final result. Exchange coupling requires neighboring spins to be very nearly parallel. Angle ϕ is therefore very small; we see that the exchange energy varies with the square of the angle. Section 8.3.1 gives a different formula that is much more widely used.

8.3.1   Direction Cosine Model for Exchange Energy

The usual equation for exchange energy density is

$$W_{ex} = A[(\nabla\alpha_1)^2 + (\nabla\alpha_2)^2 + (\nabla\alpha_3)^2] \qquad J/m^3, \tag{8.52}$$

which is attributed to Landau and Lifshitz (Ref. 11, Ch. 5). Kittel and Galt [10] have derived (8.52) from (8.51) by expressing ϕ in direction cosines, expanding them in a Taylor series, and summing over nearest neighbors in a body-centered cubic lattice.

For comparison with (8.51), exchange constant $A = 2XS^2/a$, where a is the lattice constant. However A is regarded as a fundamental parameter in its own right which is determined by measurement. Typical values are in the range of 10^{-11} J/m (10^{-6} erg/cm). To use (8.52), the direction of magnetization must be expressed by the α's, which are direction cosines in the Cartesian coordinate system.* The vector gradient operator ∇ can be in whatever coordinate system is appropriate. Finally, each $(\nabla\alpha_i)^2$ term is found by the dot product operation

$$(\nabla\alpha_i)^2 = \bar{\nabla}\alpha_i \cdot \bar{\nabla}\alpha_i. \tag{8.53}$$

EXAMPLE H

Rewrite (8.52) for the case where $\bar{M}$ is in the x–y plane at an angle ϕ with the x-axis, where ϕ can vary with x and y.

ANSWER. $M_x = M \cos\phi$, $M_y = M \sin\phi$, $M_z = 0$,   thus $(\alpha_1, \alpha_2, \alpha_3) =$ $(\cos\phi, \sin\phi, 0)$. In the x–y plane $\bar{\nabla} = (\hat{a}_x\partial/\partial x + \hat{a}_y\partial/\partial y)$, so use of (8.53) on α_1, for example, gives $(\bar{\nabla}\cos\phi)^2 = \sin^2\phi[(d\phi/dx)^2 + (d\phi/dy)^2]$. After a similar operation on α_2 the final result is

$$W_{ex} = A\left[\left(\frac{d\phi}{dx}\right)^2 + \left(\frac{d\phi}{dy}\right)^2\right] \qquad J/m^3, \tag{8.54}$$

where $d\phi/dx$ is in rads/m.

*Defined in Fig. 4.17.

EXAMPLE I

Rewrite (8.52) for the case of a small magnetic structure called a Bloch line [48] in which the components of M in cylindrical coordinates are $(M_r, M_\phi, M_z) = (0, M \sin \theta, M \cos \theta)$, where θ is the angle between M and the z-axis. The ϕ-component of M closes upon itself around a circular path of radius r; for small values of r, θ decreases so that M_z increases.

ANSWER. The components of M in Cartesian coordinate are $M_x = -M \sin \phi \sin \theta$, $M_y = M \cos \phi \sin \theta$, $M_z = M \cos \theta$, which defines the direction cosines. The gradient operator in cylindrical coordinates is $\bar{\nabla} = [\hat{a}_r \, \partial/\partial r + \hat{a}_\phi (1/r) \, \partial/\partial \phi]$, neglecting variations in z. After carrying out (8.53), we have

$$W_{\text{ex}} = A\left[\left(\frac{d\theta}{dr}\right)^2 + \frac{\sin^2 \theta}{r^2}\right] \qquad \text{J/m}^3. \tag{8.55}$$

8.3.2 Domain Wall Width

The description of domain wall motion (Section 5.4.2) pointed out that a wall possesses a small but finite width that corresponds to a transition region between domains. We are now in a position to estimate the width and the energy of such a wall modeled as a tradeoff of exchange and anisotropy energies.

The idealized wall in Fig. 8.6 is drawn as an expanded view of Fig. 5.17 where θ, the angle between the local induction and the positive z-axis, increases by π rad across the width of the wall in the x-direction. Since no variation occurs as a function of y or z, the exchange energy density within the wall is

$$W_{\text{ex}} = A\left(\frac{d\theta}{dx}\right)^2 \tag{8.56}$$

as a simpler version of (8.54). For the case of a 180° wall we would expect the anisotropy energy density to be uniaxial, modeled reasonably by

$$W_k = K \sin^2 \theta \qquad \text{J/m}^3. \tag{8.57}$$

As a simple approximation, valid for many cases, we neglect any other energies and find the total energy of the wall as the volume integral of the sum $W_{\text{ex}} + W_k = W_t$

$$E = \iiint W_t \, dV = y_0 z_0 \int (W_{\text{ex}} + W_k) \, dx \qquad \text{J}, \tag{8.58}$$

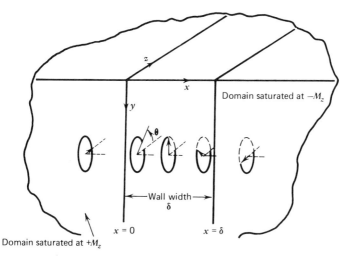

Figure 8.6 Static domain wall in which the angle of local M, relative to the z-axis, increases from 0 to π through the wall width δ. Such a wall is called a 180° Bloch wall.

where $y_0 z_0$ is the large cross section of the specimen.

To solve the integral we need to know how angle θ varies with x. The simplest assumption to give us a feel for the problem is

$$\theta = \frac{\pi}{\delta} x \qquad 0 \le x \le \delta, \qquad (8.59)$$

where the origin is at the edge of the wall. Substituting into (8.58) divided by the area yields

$$\gamma_t = \frac{E}{y_0 z_0} = \frac{K\delta}{\pi} \int_0^\pi \sin^2 \theta \, d\theta + A\left(\frac{\pi}{\delta}\right)^2 \int_0^\delta dx \qquad \text{J/m}^2,$$

which is easily integrated, since $\sin^2 \theta = \frac{1}{2}(1 - \cos 2\theta)$. The result is the energy per area of domain wall

$$\gamma_t = \frac{K\delta}{2} + \frac{A\pi^2}{\delta}. \qquad (8.60)$$

If the wall width δ were very large, the exchange energy would be small because $d\theta/dx = \pi/\delta$ rads/m. However the anisotropy energy would be large because of the large volume where a component of B_i points in the hard direction. But if δ were extremely small, the exchange energy would be large. The value of δ for minimum energy is

$$\delta = \sqrt{2} \, \pi \sqrt{\frac{A}{K}} \qquad \text{m}, \qquad (8.61)$$

which can be determined from

$$\frac{d\gamma_t}{d\delta} = 0 = \frac{K}{2} - \frac{A\pi^2}{\delta^2},$$

for which the two components of (8.60) are equal. Substituting (8.61) into (8.60) gives the minimum wall energy

$$\gamma_t = \sqrt{2}\,\pi\sqrt{AK} \qquad J/m^2. \tag{8.62}$$

Equations 8.61 and 8.62 are the results we were after, slightly off value because of the simplifying assumption of (8.59).

A more rigorous derivation of wall energy would omit the assumed relation of (8.59), and would try to deduce the actual functional relation between θ and x. The correct function would have equal components of exchange and anisotropy energy at every point through the wall width, rather than merely equal average values as in Fig. 8.7. The function can be deduced by setting (8.56) equal to (8.57)

$$A\left(\frac{d\theta}{dx}\right)^2 = K\sin^2\theta,$$

and after some manipulation

$$dx = \sqrt{\frac{A}{K}}\frac{d\theta}{\sin\theta}. \tag{8.63}$$

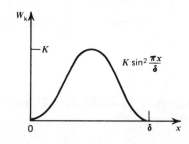

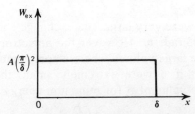

Figure 8.7 Anisotropy and exchange energy density components for the fictitious wall angle $\theta = (\pi/\delta)x$. The analysis has equalized the areas under the curves, but the instantaneous values are not matched.

After integration

$$x = \sqrt{\frac{A}{K}} \ln \tan \frac{\theta}{2} \quad \text{m,} \qquad (8.64)$$

where the origin of x is now taken at the midpoint of the wall where $\theta = \pi/2$. Since the two components of wall energy in (8.58) are known to be equal, the total is

$$\gamma_t = 2 \int_{\theta=0}^{\pi} K \sin^2 \theta \, dx = 4\sqrt{AK} \quad \text{J/m}^2, \qquad (8.65)$$

where (8.63) has been used to get the final result. The so-called exact solution (8.65) is about 10% lower than (8.62).

EXAMPLE J

Show that $\sqrt{A/K}$ has dimensions of length and that $\sqrt{AK}$ has dimensions of energy per area. Find values of γ_t and δ for a permalloy with induced anisotropy.

ANSWER. The dimensions of A and K are J/m and J/m^3, respectively; thus $\sqrt{A/K}$, $\sqrt{AK}$ have dimensions of length, energy per area respectively. Using values $A \approx 10^{-11}$ J/m, $K \sim 200$ J/m^3; and using $\delta = \pi\sqrt{A/K}$ yields 0.7 μm; using $\gamma_t = 4\sqrt{AK}$ yields 1.7×10^{-4} J/m^2 (0.17 erg/cm^2). This value of energy per area is low because induced anisotropy is small compared with magnetocrystalline values. For the same reason δ is large, the order of 2500 atoms across, which is less than 0.1 degree of angle change between neighbors.

The foregoing analysis suggests that the spin system will turn more tightly in a region of high anisotropy, so the wall width may be of the order of hundreds of atoms. We may also deduce the concept of critical size from the wall width parameter $\Delta = \sqrt{A/K}$. If a particle is smaller than Δ, it may be too small to support a domain wall and will therefore exist as a single magnetic domain. The small oxide particles in magnetic tape are examples of particles that are designed to exist as single domains.

8.4 MAGNETIC PHENOMENA

This brief section points out two interesting second-order magnetic effects that have been used for applications. When a substance is magnetized by reorientation of induction, both its length and its electrical resistance may change by slight amounts.

8.4.1 Magnetostriction, and so Forth

Magnetostriction is the change of length of a specimen due to its state of magnetization, also called the Joule effect. Conversely, a stress applied to a specimen can change its magnetic properties, a phenomenon called the Villari effect. Furthermore, the twisting of a ferromagnetic rod due to the combination of a circular and longitudinal field is called the Wiedemann effect. The general set of topics relating changes in magnetization to mechanical deformations or stresses comprises what are called magnetomechanical effects. This is a subject entirely different from the "magnetomechanical factor" g' (Chapter 2). It is also different from the "form effect," which is a slight distortion of a short magnetized specimen due to the compressive force of the two poles.

In some cases these effects can be very troublesome. For instance, in permalloy thin film technology it is important to use an alloy of zero magnetostriction (about 0.82 Ni, 0.18 Fe). Otherwise, bending of the substrate can cause a shift of the apparent easy axis. As a second example, a component of transformer acoustic noise is attributed to magnetostriction.

Several uses have been found for magnetomechanical effects. For instance, ultrasonic transducers using the magnetostriction effect of nickel rods have been used in various products such as sonar depth finders for ships and tooth-cleaning tools for dentists. As another example, the inverse Wiedemann effect is sometimes used to measure the torque transmitted through a shaft from a motor to its load. Finally, digital memory elements have been developed using a magnetostriction delay line.

These various effects are all related to the same physical processes, introduced below. Only the rudimentary ideas can be exposed here; more comprehensive treatments are available in Cullity [11], Chikazumi [1], and Bozorth [3].

Elementary Definitions

1. *Strain.* A fractional change in length of a body is called a strain $\Delta l/l = \lambda$. The notation λ implies that the strain is induced by a change of induction, whereas ϵ is a stress-induced strain. The order of magnitude of λ is 10^{-5} for iron and nickel.
2. *Stress.* The force applied to a body, normalized to the cross-sectional area, is called the stress σ. MKS units for stress are N/m^2, which is also the same as energy density J/m^3. English units are psi (lb/in.^{2}). Hooke's law gives stress proportional to strain $\sigma = C\epsilon$, where

C is the elastic stiffness constant, or Young's modulus, which has the same units as stress. Hooke's law is inaccurate for magnetic materials because of magnetostriction and its complications. Hooke's law becomes a tensor equation for single crystals with anisotropic constants.

3. *Modulus of elasticity (Young's modulus).* For nonmagnetic materials, the elastic stiffness constant $C = \sigma/\epsilon$ is the ratio of stress to strain, as above. For a magnetic material C may vary over a range of 2 depending on the annealing temperature of the specimen, the temperature of the measurement, and the level of induction. For instance, Bozorth shows graphical data for nickel as varying from $12–24 \times 10^3 \text{ kg/mm}^2$,* and for iron as $18.5–21.5 \times 10^3 \text{ kg/mm}^2$. In the case of iron, most of the variation was due to temperature. Using the notation E instead of C for the varying modulus of elasticity, the so-called ΔE effect for magnetic materials has been studied by materials physicists. This is essentially a measure of $E = \sigma/(\epsilon \pm \lambda)$. In a final relationship that is relevant to ultrasonic transducers, the velocity of sound is given as

$$v = \left(\frac{C}{\rho}\right)^{1/2} \tag{8.66}$$

where ρ is the mass per volume density.

Unconstrained Magnetostriction. When a magnetic body is free to move, its length may change with the direction of magnetization. Positive magnetostriction means that the length of the body increases in the direction of magnetization; negative magnetostriction means that its length decreases. The volume is essentially constant, so the transverse magnetostriction has the opposite sign

$$\lambda_\perp \approx -\tfrac{1}{2}\lambda_\parallel, \tag{8.67}$$

a concept illustrated by Fig. 8.8.

A systematic study of magnetostriction soon requires careful attention to the physics and notation of single crystals. For single crystals of pure iron and nickel, cubic structures, the saturation magnetostriction along the [100] and [111] axes is evidently a fundamental material property. Values given in Table 8.1 were compiled from several sources for comparison. Bozorth [3] gives the most comprehensive compilation of data.

---

*$20.4 \times 10^3 \text{ kg/mm}^2$ is the same stress as $2 \times 10^{12} \text{ dynes/cm}^2$, $2 \times 10^7 \text{ N/cm}^2$, $2 \times 10^{11} \text{ N/m}^2$, and $29 \times 10^6 \text{ psi}$.

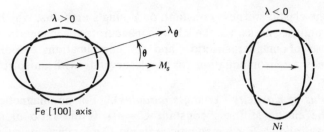

Figure 8.8 Magnetostriction figures giving an (exaggerated) indication of the change in shape of a specimen that would be spherical if randomly demagnetized.

The saturation magnetostriction along any other axis can be calculated by the "two constant" equation for magnetostriction in a cubic crystal

$$\lambda_s = \tfrac{3}{2}\lambda_{100}(\alpha_1^2\beta_1^2 + \alpha_2^2\beta_2^2 + \alpha_3^2\beta_3^2 - \tfrac{1}{3})$$
$$+ 3\lambda_{111}(\alpha_1\alpha_2\beta_1\beta_2 + \alpha_2\alpha_3\beta_2\beta_3 + \alpha_3\alpha_1\beta_3\beta_1), \qquad (8.68)$$

where the α's are the direction cosines of the magnetization relative to the crystal axes and the β's are the direction cosines of the direction of observation of change of length relative to the crystal axes.

The saturation magnetostriction for polycrystalline materials involves some sort of averaging over all crystallite directions. A commonly used

Table 8.1 Saturation magnetostriction data at room temperature for iron and nickel single crystals

Crystals	Source	Saturation Magnetostriction (ppm)	
		λ_{100}	λ_{111}
Nickel	b	−46	−24
Nickel	c	−46	−25
Iron	a	20.7	−21.2
Iron	b	21	−21

[a] From Tebble and Craik (Ref. 4, Ch. 4: data by Hall (1959).
[b] After Cullity [11].
[c] From Bozorth [3]: data by Masiyama (1928), analysis by Becker and Döring.

equation is

$$\lambda_p = \frac{2\lambda_{100} + 3\lambda_{111}}{5}. \tag{8.69}$$

Cullity [11] derives this equation and gives an alternative, together with the underlying assumptions for each. He gives commonly accepted experimental values for polycrystalline iron and nickel as $\lambda_p = -7 \times 10^{-6}$ and -34×10^{-6}, respectively. The value of λ observed at an angle relative to M is given by

$$\lambda_\theta = \tfrac{3}{2}\lambda_p(\cos^2 \theta - \tfrac{1}{3}). \tag{8.70}$$

The only values of λ that have been described at this point are the values for a magnetically saturated specimen. How the magnetostrictive elongation will vary with intrinsic induction is a question with no unique answer, depending as it does on the initial configuration of domains. For instance, in Fig. 8.9 the demagnetized state (a) would be expected to undergo no magnetostrictive change of length at saturation state (c) because the reversal process involves only 180° wall motion. There is no change of direction of B_i to the x-axis, only a change of polarity. On the other hand, the demagnetized state (b) would be expected to undergo a total change of $3\lambda_s/2$ in the x-direction, from $-\lambda_s/2$ at (b) due to (8.67), to

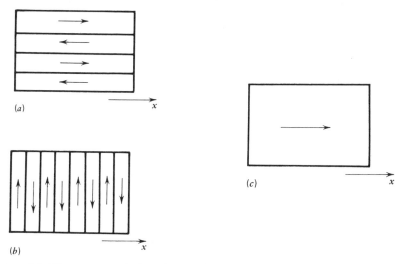

Figure 8.9 The magnetostrictive change of length of a specimen on going from an unsaturated state, (a) or (b), to a saturated state (c) depends on the initial domain configuration.

$+\lambda_s$ at state (c). Chikazumi [1] gives analyses and data for several examples of single crystals.

Magnetization with Stress. If a magnetic body is constrained so that it is unable to undergo magnetostrictive elongation, the resulting stress will alter the internal energy of the body as a function of induction, thereby changing the apparent anisotropy. Furthermore, if an external tension is applied to a single crystal in a direction defined by direction cosines γ_i relative to the crystal axes, there is developed a magnetoelastic energy density given by

$$W_{me} = -\tfrac{3}{2}\lambda_{100}\sigma(\alpha_1^2\gamma_1^2 + \alpha_2^2\gamma_2^2 + \alpha_3^2\gamma_3^2)$$
$$- 3\lambda_{111}\sigma(\alpha_1\alpha_2\gamma_1\gamma_2 + \alpha_2\alpha_3\gamma_2\gamma_3 + \alpha_1\alpha_3\gamma_1\gamma_3). \qquad (8.71)$$

As also in (8.68), this equation simplifies quickly if any direction cosine is along a [100]-axis.

The magnetoelastic energy density for a polycrystalline specimen is

$$W_{me} = -\tfrac{3}{2}\lambda_p\sigma \cos^2\phi \qquad \text{J/m}^3, \qquad (8.72)$$

where ϕ is the angle between B_{is} and tensile stress σ. If the product $\lambda_p\sigma$ is positive, the orientation is $\phi = 0$ for minimum magnetoelastic energy. On the other hand if $\lambda_p\sigma$ is negative, the minimum magnetoelastic energy occurs at $\phi = 90°$. Negative $\lambda_p\sigma$ means either a negative λ_p and tensile stress or positive λ_p and compressive stress.

Equations (8.71) and (8.72) can be added to anisotropy equations (4.31) and (4.34), respectively, to gain a quantitative appreciation of the influence of stress on magnetic properties.

8.4.2 Magnetoresistance

In 1857 Lord Kelvin found that the electrical conductivity of nickel and iron changed as the material was magnetized. For most magnetic substances the resistance is seen to increase if the measurement current is in the same direction as the applied field but decreases in the transverse direction to the field. The same observation is true regardless of the sign of the magnetostriction constants for the material, although otherwise there is some similarity between magnetoresistance and magnetostriction.

A physical process that causes resistance change by definition is a process that affects the scattering of conduction electrons. The anisotropy of magnetoresistance, increasing ρ in the direction parallel to M_{sat} and decreasing ρ in the transverse direction, seems to suggest an anisotropy of the magnetic orbitals. Figure 8.10 shows an intuitive

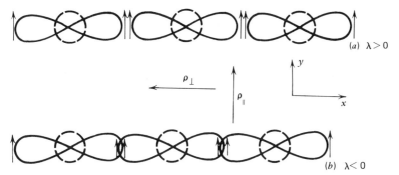

Figure 8.10 Plausible orientation of orbitals of the ferromagnetic spin system. Attraction between spins with no overlap in (a) could account for $\lambda > 0$; with overlap in (b) could account for $\lambda < 0$. In either case it is assumed that conduction electrons will be scattered more in the y-direction than in the x-direction, to qualitatively account for the anisotropy of electrical resistivity of magnetized specimens.

spin-orbital arrangement for a cubic crystal that may provide a plausible interpretation for both magnetostriction and magnetoresistance. The figure is a conjecture that has not been reviewed.

For single crystals the change in saturation resistivity is described by exactly the same geometrical dependence as (8.68), with $\Delta\rho$ substituted for each λ and the subscripts left intact. Values for $\Delta\rho$ at room temperature are listed in Table 8.2.

There has been considerable interest in magnetoresistance for the detection of magnetic fields, especially since about 1970. The usual sensor for magnetic bubbles uses a magnetoresistance detector in one arm of a Wheatstone bridge. The stray field from a bubble passing through the detection circuit biases the magnetoresistor to unbalance the bridge. The purpose of the bridge is to null out the static voltage drop across the quiescent magnetoresistor, to be able to detect a resistance

Table 8.2 Magnetoresistance coefficients for single crystals of nickel and iron at room temperature

Crystals	$\dfrac{\Delta\rho_{100}}{\rho}(\%)$	$\dfrac{\Delta\rho_{111}}{\rho}(\%)$
Nickel	4.3	1.9
Iron	0.102	0.395

After Chikazumi [1], page 422.

change of 2 or 3%. Magnetoresistors have also been used in magnetic tape read heads, in power supply current monitors, and in magnetometers. Anhysteretic techniques seem to be useful for improving resolution at low fields. Further information on general material properties is in Cullity [11], Bozorth [3], or Chikazumi [1]. The recent research literature may be consulted for application information.

8.5 THIN PERMALLOY FILMS

Overview. The technology of thin magnetic films was established in a flurry of research activity that was most vigorous from about 1955 to 1970. Groups with expertise in thin film technologies are now widely distributed throughout industry. Thin film magnetic properties are well documented in books on the topic by Prutton [12] and Soohoo [13], a booklet by Middelhoek, [18], and in perhaps a thousand technical papers. A bibliographical listing of papers published through 1963 has been tabulated by Chang and Feth [14]. Annual digests were produced subsequently of all papers published each year, organized by various research topics [15].

Thin films proved to be very fruitful devices for research into general properties of magnetism and magnetic materials. Vacuum technology and evaporation-deposition methods added a new, broader accessibility than the classical metallurgical heavy equipment such as the rolling mill. A second motivation for the work was a race to replace the magnetic core technology of memory for digital computers. Several successful thin film memory arrays were built, but the technology never did achieve broad acceptance in the memory market. Plated wire memories are still available for special applications such as equipment to be used by the military or in space, where radiation hardness is important.

One key property of a thin film that makes it attractive and useful is derived from its very thinness relative to length or width. The demagnetizing field is typically very small in the plane of the film, so that a single-domain magnetic state can exist. The single-domain possibility means that a film can retain a magnetized state, therefore possesses the capability of data storage.

EXAMPLE K

Find the demagnetizing factors and the in-plane demagnetizing field for a thin film modeled as an oblate spheroid (8.6) with $k = 10^5$.

ANSWER. For large k, (8.6) is approximately $N_a = N_b \approx \pi/4k = 7.85 \times 10^{-6}$ for this case. Thus $N_c = 0.99998 \approx 1.0$. Given $B_i = 1$ T, (8.3) becomes $H_d = -N/\mu_0 = -(\pi/4k)(10^7/4\pi) = -(10^7/16k) \approx -6$ A/m (0.08 Oe). Such a small H_d, $H_d \ll H_c$, means that a single domain will not demagnetize itself.

The large demagnetizing factor of unity in the direction normal to the film means that B_i is confined to lie in the plane of the film, for minimum magnetostatic energy. Furthermore, if the film thickness has a value of $\sqrt{A/K}$ or less, we can be certain that no more than one domain can exist through the film thickness. However the possibility of domains in the lateral directions is not excluded.

The following metallurgical properties are usually expected of Permalloy thin films: the films usually are polycrystalline with composition in the range 80% nickel, 20% iron by weight, which has low magnetostriction. (The average polycrystalline magnetostriction constant crosses through zero at about 82% Ni.) At that composition the saturation induction is $B_{is} \approx 1$ T. If the films are annealed in an H-field to induce a uniaxial anisotropy, the anisotropy constant is in the range $K \sim 160$ J/m³ (1600 ergs/cc), and if so $H_k \sim 320$ A/m (~ 4 Oe). The magnetization curves for an ideal thin film were calculated in Section 4.3.3 (Fig. 4.18). In practice the easy-axis coercivity H_c may be in the range of about half H_k, but this parameter is particularly susceptible to fabrication variation from batch to batch. (The lower coercivity can be attributed to dispersion of the easy axis. "Dispersion" implies that the film easy axis is a statistical average of the local easy axes of the individual crystallites, each of which in fact may be a few degrees off.)

In summary, the dominant characteristic of a Permalloy thin film is a uniaxial anisotropy in the plane. As shown in Fig. 4.18, the uniaxial property is revealed by a magnetization curve that is square loop for H-fields applied along the easy axis, and is linear if the input field is applied along the hard axis. The response of a single-domain film to a general vector input field is best explained by the switching astroid.

8.5.1 Switching Astroid

A switching astroid is a geometrical figure that defines the locus of inflection field conditions for a uniaxial thin film. Consider a uniaxial thin film in the x–y plane with the easy axis along the x-coordinate. An applied field can be resolved into two components

$$\bar{H}_a = \hat{a}_x H_x + \hat{a}_y H_y$$

and plotted as a vector from the origin to a point such as 1 of Fig. 8.11 where the axes are normalized to H_k,

$$h_x = \frac{H_x}{H_k} \quad \text{and} \quad h_y = \frac{H_y}{H_k}. \tag{8.73}$$

The uniaxial film is represented by the astroid

$$h_x^{2/3} + h_y^{2/3} = 1, \tag{8.74}$$

which has the property that its slope $dh_y/dh_x = \tan \phi$, where ϕ is the angle between the easy axis and B_i. A tangent to the astroid drawn to point 1 represents the response of the film. If the applied field is small enough that its vector lies inside the astroid, two solutions are possible, depending on the initial state of the film, $\phi = 0$ or π. However if the applied field vector lies outside the astroid as point 2, only one solution is possible.

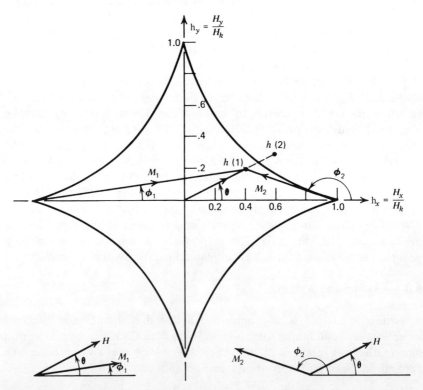

Figure 8.11 A switching astroid and its use to construct the ideal static response to a vector applied field.

EXAMPLE L

Describe the path in relation to the switching astroid traced by the two magnetization curves of Fig. 4.18.

ANSWER
(a) Along the x-axis.
(b) Along the y-axis of Fig. 8.11.

EXAMPLE M

Use Fig. 8.11 to predict the value of easy-axis switching field H_x, if a d–c field $H_y = 0.2251H_k$ biases the film.

ANSWER.   The film will switch at $H_x = \pm \frac{1}{2}H_k$, confirmed by (8.74).

EXAMPLE N

Find the two responses ϕ_1 and ϕ_2 to the applied field $(h_x, h_y) = (0.4, 0.2)$.

ANSWER.   The graphical construction should agree with calculated values $\phi_1 = 8.19°$, $\phi_2 = 159.58°$.

Derivation of Astroid Equation.   The derivation begins with the identical assumptions as in (4.33) and (4.34), page 178. However instead of seeking the energy minimum defined in (4.35), we seek a solution to the closely related inflection condition

$$\frac{\partial W_t}{\partial \phi} = 0 \qquad \frac{\partial^2 W_t}{\partial \phi^2} = 0, \tag{8.75}$$

where

$$W_t = -B_i(H_x \cos \phi + H_y \sin \phi) + K \sin^2 \phi, \tag{8.76}$$

which is the same as (4.38) rewritten for convenience.
   On applying (8.75) and (8.73), the derivatives of (8.76) become

$$h_x \sin \phi - h_y \cos \phi + \sin \phi \cos \phi = 0 \tag{8.77}$$

$$h_x \cos \phi + h_y \sin \phi + \cos^2 \phi - \sin^2 \phi = 0. \tag{8.78}$$

If (8.77) is multiplied by $\sin \phi$ and the product is added to (8.78) times $\cos \phi$, the result is $h_x = -\cos^3 \phi$. Similarly, $h_y = \sin^3 \phi$. Taking the cube roots and applying the trigonometric identity, $\cos^2 \phi + \sin^2 \phi = 1$, yields the final result, (8.74).

Concept of a Thin Film Memory. A uniaxial film can be magnetized to either polarity to represent the binary states 0, 1. In the memory organization of Fig. 8.12, a pulse of read current in the word line produces a hard-axis field $H_\perp > H_k$ at every bit position. The magnetization at each bit position rotates into the hard position, from orientation 1 to 2 in Fig. 8.12, thereby changing the flux that links each bit line. The time derivative of each flux linkage is the output read voltage of the bit line; the polarity of each signal depends on the original direction of magnetization stored at the particular bit location.

The rewrite sequence is best understood by reference to the switching astroid, Fig. 8.11. At the trailing edge of a pure hard-axis pulse $H_y > H_k$ with no easy-axis component, the field vector would collapse down the y-axis to cause the film segment to break up into a demagnetized state of many domains. A "tipping" field of $\pm H_x$ can control the fall-back polarity to retain the single-domain magnetic state. In Fig. 8.13, the tipping field is from currents pulses I_1, I_2, which overlap the read current. The polarity of each current is controlled by local bit circuitry in response to the polarity of the read signal. The current amplitude can be less than the read current, but must be large enough to overcome effect of angular dispersion of the film plus any angular misalignment.

Switching by Rotation. The fast switching speed of magnetic films, in addition to the single-domain capability, is a second property that

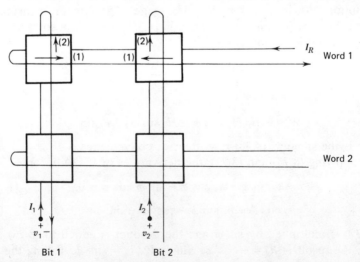

Figure 8.12 Four bits to show the organization of a word-addressed thin film memory. The film easy axes are parallel to the word lines.

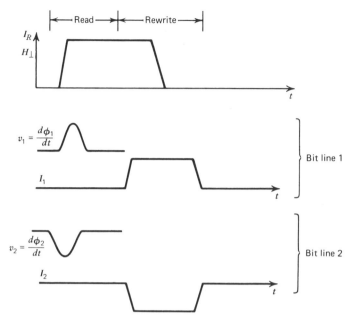

Figure 8.13 Waveforms of a read-rewrite cycle for the film memory of Fig. 8.12.

stimulated interest in their potential for digital memory applications. It is interesting to see how the fast switching speed is believed to occur as a two-mode process. Assuming a step function of applied field, it can be shown from the Landau-Lifshitz equation that the initial motion of B_{is} is a precession about the applied field, $d\theta/dt$ of Fig. 8.14. But the initial precession is out of the plane of the film, thereby giving rise to a demagnetizing field H_z. The motion of fast flux reversal $d\phi/dt$ is actually a precession of B_{is} about the demagnetizing field.

EXAMPLE O

If a magnetic film undergoes 180° reversal by rotation in about 3 ns, find the value of field about which B_{is} precesses.

ANSWER. Assume $\omega = d\phi/dt \approx 1 \text{ rad/ns} = 10^9 \text{ s}^{-1}$. For $\omega = \gamma H$, the average $H = 10^9/2.21 \times 10^5 = 4.5 \times 10^3 \text{ A/m}$ (57 Oe). For a demagnetizing factor $N_z = 1$, $H_z = -B_{iz}/\mu_0$, so the normal component of B_{is} is $B_{iz} = 57 \times 10^{-4} \text{ T}$. If the saturation induction $B_{is} = 1 \text{ T}$, angle θ of Fig. 8.14 exceeds 90° by $0.325° = \sin^{-1} 5.7 \times 10^{-3}$ on the average.

The two components of precession of B_{is} can be identified by manipula-

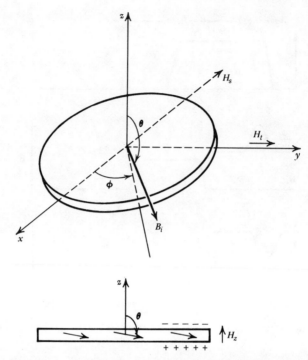

Figure 8.14 Geometry for calculation of flux reversal. A step-function switching field $H_x = -H_s$ and transverse d-c field $H_y = H_t$ are applied to a magnetic thin film in the $x - y$ plane, the x-axis is the easy axis. The initial precession $d\theta/dt$ about the applied field establishes a demagnetizing field H_z. The reversal $d\phi/dt$ is a precession about H_z.

tion of the Landau-Lifshitz equation as interpreted by Smith [16]

$$\frac{d\bar{B}_{is}}{dt} = \gamma\bar{\tau} + \alpha\gamma\frac{\bar{B}_{is}}{B_{is}} \times \bar{\tau}, \tag{5.67}$$

where $\bar{B}_{is} = \hat{a}_r B_{is}$ in spherical coordinates. It is convenient to define the torque as $\bar{\tau} = -\bar{r} \times \bar{\nabla}W$, where energy density

$$W = K[1 - \sin^2\theta\cos^2\phi] + H_s B_{is}\sin\theta\cos\phi - H_t B_{is}\sin\theta\sin\phi$$

$$+ \frac{B_{is}^2}{2\mu_0}\cos^2\theta \qquad \text{J/m}^3. \tag{8.79}$$

Equation (8.79) is the same as (8.76) with $H_x = -H_s$ and with the addition of a fourth term to include the demagnetizing energy, (8.46). For the sake of completeness the first three terms also include the effect of $\sin\theta$ dependence, which will shortly be deleted as negligible, since $\theta \approx 90°$. The time derivative of $\bar{B}_{is}$ has only rotational components according to the Landau-Lifshitz model that the spins rotate as free vectors, thus

$$\frac{d\bar{B}_{is}}{dt} = \hat{a}_\theta B_{is} \frac{d\theta}{dt} + \hat{a}_\phi B_{is} \sin \theta \frac{d\phi}{dt}. \tag{8.80}$$

The first term on the right-hand side of (5.67) is

$$\gamma\bar{\tau} = \gamma\left[\hat{a}_\theta \frac{1}{\sin \theta} \frac{\partial W}{\partial \phi} - \hat{a}_\phi \frac{\partial W}{\partial \theta} \right] \tag{8.81}$$

and the second term is

$$\alpha\gamma \frac{\bar{B}_{is}}{B_{is}} \times \bar{\tau} = \alpha\gamma\left(\hat{a}_\theta \frac{\partial W}{\partial \theta} + \hat{a}_\phi \frac{1}{\sin \theta} \frac{\partial W}{\partial \phi} \right). \tag{8.82}$$

After collection of like components from the three equations above, the Landau-Lifshitz equation becomes

$$B_{is} \sin \theta \frac{d\phi}{dt} = -\gamma \frac{\partial W}{\partial \theta} + \frac{\alpha\gamma}{\sin \theta} \frac{\partial W}{\partial \phi} \tag{8.83}$$

and

$$B_{is} \frac{d\theta}{dt} = \frac{\gamma}{\sin \theta} \frac{\partial W}{\partial \phi} + \alpha\gamma \frac{\partial W}{\partial \theta}. \tag{8.84}$$

Equations (8.83) and (8.84) will yield the desired results after some manipulation. The ϕ-derivative of (8.79) is

$$\frac{\partial W}{\partial \phi} = H_k B_{is} \sin \theta[\sin \theta \cos \phi \sin \phi - h_t \cos \phi - h_s \sin \phi] \tag{8.85}$$

where the term in brackets will be denoted as $\acute{u}$.
The θ-derivative of (8.79) is approximately

$$\frac{\partial W}{\partial \theta} \approx -\left(\frac{B_{is}^2}{\mu_0} \right) \sin \theta \cos \theta, \tag{8.86}$$

under the assumption that H_k, H_s, and H_t are all negligible compared with B_{is}/μ_0.
After substituting (8.85) and (8.86) into (8.83) and (8.84), the components of precession become

$$\frac{d\phi}{dt} = \gamma\left(\frac{B_{is}}{\mu_0} \right) \cos \theta + \alpha\gamma \frac{H_k\acute{u}}{\sin \theta}$$

$$\frac{d\theta}{dt} = \gamma H_k\acute{u} - \alpha\gamma\left(\frac{B_{is}}{\mu_0} \right) \cos \theta \sin \theta.$$

Finally, we recognize the demagnetizing field due to the precession out of the plane as

$$H_z = -\left(\frac{B_{is}}{\mu_0}\right)\cos\theta \qquad (8.87)$$

and omit $\sin\theta$ which equals unity, for the final results

$$\frac{d\phi}{dt} = -\gamma H_z + \alpha\gamma H_k\acute{u} \qquad (8.88)$$

$$\frac{d\theta}{dt} = \gamma H_k\acute{u} + \alpha\gamma H_z, \qquad (8.89)$$

where $\acute{u}$ is the bracketed portion of (8.85). Initially $\sin\theta = 1$, $H_z = 0$, and $\acute{u} = -h_s h_t$, assuming that $\sin\phi = h_t$. Assuming damping factor $\alpha \ll 1$, we expect that initially θ begins to increase past 90°, then ϕ begins to increase as H_z builds up.

A complete solution is given in Fig. 8.15, calculated for $\alpha = 0.01$. When the calculated voltage waveform is compared with experimental measurements, the agreement is moderate. The reversal times are generally comparable, and an oscillatory character is common, but the leading edges of experimental signals usually lack the long delay. The status of thin film switching, both theory and experiment, has been reviewed by Hagedorn [17].

8.5.2 Domain Walls in Thin Films

The width and energy per area of a domain wall were calculated (Section 8.3.2) under the assumption of minimum energy equally distributed between anisotropy and exchange. The neglect of magnetostatic energy in the derivation implies that the specimen thickness, the y-direction in Fig. 8.6, must be large as compared with the wall width,

$$y_0 \gg \delta. \qquad (8.90)$$

The derivation of Section 8.3.2 is therefore for a Bloch wall in bulk material. For thin films (8.90) is no longer true, and magnetostatic energy must be taken into consideration. Two additional types of domain wall occur in thin ferromagnetic films. One type was first predicted by Néel on theoretical grounds in 1955 and bears his name. The second type, a cross-tie wall, was first discovered experimentally.

A rigorous treatment of domain walls is beyond the scope of this book, but it is easy to show the qualitative distinction between the types of walls. Consider a thin film in the x–y plane with one domain wall

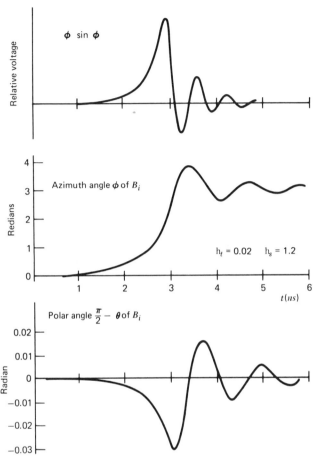

Figure 8.15 Calculated solution of thin film switching using the Landau-Lifshitz equation ($\alpha = 0.01$).

through which the local induction makes a 180° change of direction. In principle a wall is a result of changing either angle θ or ϕ. Let the x-axis be defined as the easy axis of the film so that $|B_i|$ and the wall between the domains are in the x-direction. Inside a Bloch wall, the polar angle θ is the variable (Fig. 8.16) so that B_{is} has a z-component within the wall. Inside a Néel wall, the azimuthal angle ϕ is the variable (Fig. 8.17), thus B_{is} has a y-component within the wall. If the walls are approximated with elliptical crosssections, the demagnetizing energy density is

$$W_{dm} = \frac{N}{2\mu_0} B_i^2 \qquad \text{J/m}^3, \qquad (8.46)$$

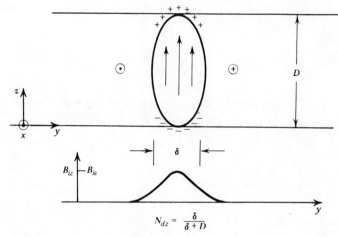

Figure 8.16 Cross-section view of elliptical model for a Bloch wall in a film where $D > \delta$.

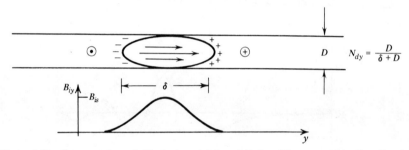

Figure 8.17 Cross section of elliptical model for a Néel wall in a very thin film, $D < \delta$.

where the demagnetizing factors are

$$N_{dz} = \frac{\delta}{(\delta + D)} \qquad \text{for Bloch wall} \qquad (8.91)$$

$$N_{dy} = \frac{D}{(\delta + D)} \qquad \text{for Néel wall} \qquad (8.92)$$

for a film of thickness D and wall width δ. Similar reasoning led Néel to recognize the high energy density for a Bloch wall in the thin film limit, $D \ll \delta$, and to propose the type of wall with static rotation of magnetization in the plane of the film (i.e., with ϕ as the angle that varies).

Middelhoek [18] has estimated the approximate energy per area for Bloch and Néel walls as a function of film thickness D with results given in Fig. 8.18. His method consisted of adding a term for demagnetizing

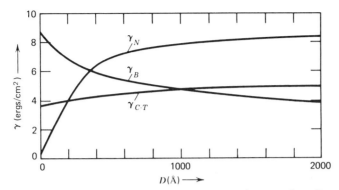

Figure 8.18 Surface energy of a Bloch wall, a Néel wall, and a cross-tie wall as a function of the film thickness: $A = 10^{-6}$ erg/cm, $M_s = 800$ G, $K = 1000$ ergs/cc. (After Middelhoek [19], reprinted with permission.]

energy per area to the approximate equation for γ_t (8.60) and solving for a value of δ that lets the derivative equal to zero. The term he used to approximate the demagnetizing energy per area was (8.46) multiplied by δ, with N defined by either (8.91) or (8.92).

As shown in Fig. 8.18, a Néel wall is calculated to have lower energy in very thin films and a Bloch wall has lower energy in thick films. It is interesting that Middelhoek's calculation of the energy per area of a Bloch wall in the limit of a very thick film is the same as the energy per area of a Néel wall in the limit of a very thin film, (8.65), omitting magnetostatic energy in both cases. For intermediate values of film thickness the cross-tie wall has a lower energy than either of the others.

The relative trend of the curves in Fig. 8.18 has been confirmed experimentally by data such as Fig. 8.19. The lowest energy wall is the type most likely to occur at a specific film thickness. In 80–20 nickel-iron permalloy films, cross-tie walls are most likely in the thickness range from about 25 to 80 nm (250–800 Å).

Cross-Tie Memory. A proposed digital storage system uses cross-ties on a domain wall to represent data, where the presence of a cross-tie represents a binary "1". Figure 8.20 is an example of cross-tie walls with a nonuniform distribution of cross-ties. The minimum spacing of cross-ties is about 4 μm.

A cross-tie wall consists of Néel wall segments of alternate polarity, where polarity is defined in Fig. 8.21. Néel wall structure is more complicated than indicated by the simple models used up to now. A 180° Néel wall appears to consist of a tightly wound inner core where the magnetization turns 90° within a short distance, bounded by a "tail"

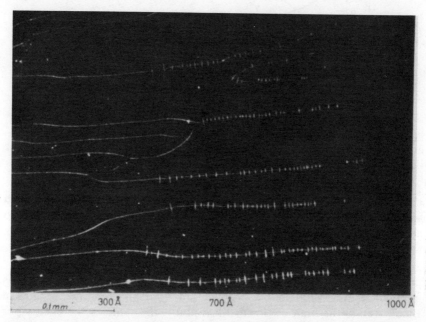

0.1mm   300 Å   700 Å   1000 Å

Figure 8.19 Domain walls observed in a tapered film of 80 Permalloy using the dark-field Bitter technique. The bright walls at the thin end are Néel walls, the Bloch walls at the thick end are hard to see. The cross-tie walls in the middle are very distinctive. (From Methfessel et al., [20], reprinted with permission.)

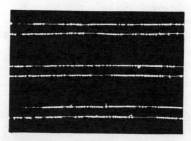

Figure 8.20 Cross-tie walls placed on thin film using a bifilar winding. (From Schwee et al., Naval Ordnance Lab. Technical Report 73–185, White Oak, Silver Spring, Md., (1 October 1973), reprinted with permission.)

420

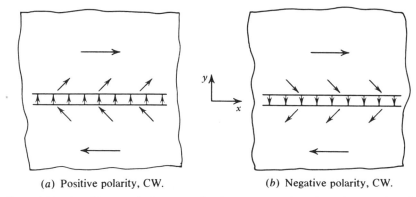

(a) Positive polarity, CW.   (b) Negative polarity, CW.

Figure 8.21   An arbitrary polarity convention for two clockwise Néel walls. Polarity refers to the y-axis orientation of the magnetization within a wall that runs in the x-direction, the film easy axis. Clockwise or counterclockwise chirality (CW, CCW) describes the wall polarity in relation to the domains on either side of the wall.

region on each side of the core where the remaining 45° transition is more gradual.

The polarity of a Néel wall is related to "high-energy" and "low-energy" wall conditions in the following way. If a small hard-axis field is applied, $H_y \ll H_k$, the magnetization will rotate toward the hard axis by an angle

$$|\phi| = \sin^{-1}\frac{H_y}{H_k}$$

in each domain. Actually the rotation occurs in the majority of each domain far away from the wall. The positive wall of Fig. 8.21 would then have a total rotation of $180° - 2\phi$ and would therefore possess lower energy. Correspondingly, the total rotation of the high-energy negative wall would be $180° + 2\phi$.

Figure 8.22 shows how Néel wall segments of alternate polarity make up a cross-tie wall. At every point of wall reversal there is a special magnetic structure, a circular Bloch line occurs at one end of a reversed section and at the other end there occurs a cross-tie. The Bloch line, described briefly in Example I (Section 8.3.1), occurs at the reversal where the clockwise flux paths of the two wall components mesh together in a compatible closed-flux structure. The cross-tie arises at the opposite reversal, to accommodate the mismatched end of CW components. The cross-tie is a Néel side wall, decreasing from a maximum of 90° at its junction with the main wall. Schwee and Watson [22] give a more detailed description of models that have been used for the cross-tie wall and its components.

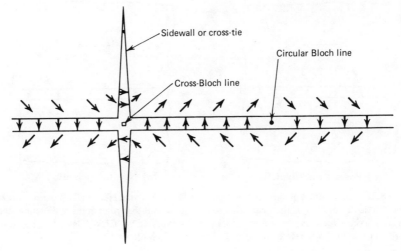

Figure 8.22 Representation of a cross-tie wall. The positive section could have been created by a local pulse $+H_y$ of sufficient amplitude to reverse the negative wall.

The Bloch line is a small (radius ~5 nm), stable structure [48] that moves very easily when driven by a hard-direction field. A mobility of 6 m²/A·s has been measured. Movement of the Bloch line changes the wall polarity, and high-energy wall is changed to low-energy wall as the Bloch line moves past.

The cross-tie is relatively sluggish by comparison. The following steps have been proposed for effecting its motion in data propagation: move the Bloch line to the right, nucleate a new cross-tie in the desired location by reversing the wall, and annihilate the old cross-tie.

In summary, the cross-tie memory development stores data by encoding the wall polarity, then causes the polarity structure to be propagated along a fixed domain wall. The memory organization is serial, as a shift register. Data readout is by a magnetoresistance bridge. At the time of writing, all individual components of the system have been designed and have operated successfully. It will be interesting to see how the system progresses.

8.6 MAGNETIC BUBBLE TECHNOLOGY

Magnetic "bubble" is the colloquial name of a cylindrical magnetic domain. Early studies of bubble properties were made optically using orthoferrites, with bubble diameters in the range of tens to hundreds of microns. The crystals are transparent to red light; use of polarized light allows the domains to be readily seen (Faraday effect) through a microscope. The responsiveness of the domains to field perturbations earned for them the name "magnetic bubbles." Streams of bubbles can be moved along specified tracks in a serial-access, shift register type of memory organization. Bubble technology is vying for acceptance as a bulk storage medium.

Cylindrical domains were first reported in 1960 [40] and were first proposed for memory applications in about 1966. A great many magnetic materials are capable of sustaining bubble domains statically, in the specimen geometry of a thin layer. The material requirements are essentially that the anisotropy be strong and uniaxial, and normal to the plane of the layer. In addition, the magnetization must be weak; more accurately, the demagnetizing field normal to the layer $H_{dm} = -NB_{is}/\mu_0 \approx -B_{is}/\mu_0$ must be less than anisotropy field H_k. The ratio

$$\frac{H_k}{H_{dm}} = Q > 1 \tag{8.93}$$

defines a material parameter Q, which must be greater than unity if the material is to be capable of sustaining bubbles [27]. Essentially this means that the layer is dominated by strong anisotropy that orients the magnetization normal to the plane of the layer. By contrast, thin permalloy films discussed in Section 8.5 are dominated by strong demagnetizing fields so that B_{is} lies in the plane of the film. A typical magnetic garnet may have anisotropy constant $K \approx 900 \, \text{J/m}^3$ or $H_k \sim 9 \times 10^4 \, \text{A/m}$ (1100 Oe), compared with $B_{is}/\mu_0 \approx 0.02/\mu_0 = 16 \times 10^3 \, \text{A/m}$ ($4\pi M_s = 200 \, \text{G}$). The corresponding parameters for a Permalloy film are $B_{sat} = 1 \, \text{T}$, some 50 times larger, and H_k some 300 times smaller.

A magnetic bias is required for bubbles to exist in the layer (Fig. 8.23). The value of field is somewhat less than that required to saturate the material completely, and the polarity of the field is opposite that of the bubble. The total range of bias is around 25% from strip-out to collapse. Strip-out is the limiting form of bubble instability at low field, in which the cylindrical bubble suddenly elongates into a snake. As the bias field is increased, the bubble diameter gradually becomes smaller until the bubble suddenly collapses at the high-field point of instability. These limits define the range of bias conditions within which bubble systems are designed to work.

Bubble motion can be controlled by the design of a local minimum of bias field (Fig. 8.24) that can be moved along in space. The bubble is attracted toward the point of minimum magnetostatic energy (8.41) (point p of Fig. 8.24a) by a force proportional to the gradient of the

No external
magnetic field

(a)

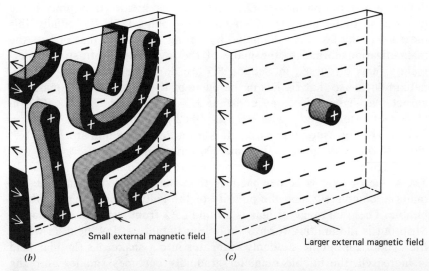

Small external magnetic field

(b)

Larger external magnetic field

(c)

Figure 8.23 Influence of an external bias field on the magnetic state of a bubble layer. With no magnetic field (a), the specimen is demagnetized with equal volume domains of positive and negative orientation. With a field applied normal to the layer and in a negative sense (into the paper), as in (b), the negative domains grow and the positive domains shrink. For a larger field (c) the positive domains shrink to stable cylinders. (Diagrams from "Magnetic Bubbles," by Andrew H. Bobeck and H. E. D. Scovil. Copyright © June 1971 by Scientific American, Inc. All rights reserved.)

magnetostatic energy. It has been shown theoretically that the bubble velocity is

$$v = \frac{m}{2}\left(|\Delta H_z| - \frac{8H_c}{\pi}\right), \tag{8.94}$$

where m is the mobility of a straight wall, H_c is wall coercivity, and ΔH_z is the change in bias field across the bubble diameter d, given approximately by

$$\Delta H_z \approx -d\left(\frac{\partial H_z}{\partial x}\right).$$

In (8.94) the velocity is zero unless the term in parentheses is positive, the velocity is then in the direction of the steepest derivative of H_z.

A field gradient for driving bubbles can be established by a conductor overlay that is driven by current, or alternatively by a magnetic overlay that is excited by an applied field (Fig. 8.24b). These two practical schemes are called *current access* and *field access* drive methods. In today's technology, field-accessed elements are used to provide the routine propagation of bubbles along the storage track; current access is often used to actuate auxiliary functions such as bubble transfer gates.

Figure 8.25 is a once-widely used field-access overlay configuration, driven by a rotating field. Three sets of T–I bars are shown for five orientations of drive field. Each field orientation partially magnetizes the overlay along a major axis, thus causing magnetic poles that attract the bubbles. The convention of Fig. 8.24b is used here in which the negative top surface of the bubble is attracted to the positive pole of the overlay. The direction of propagation can be reversed either by reversing the

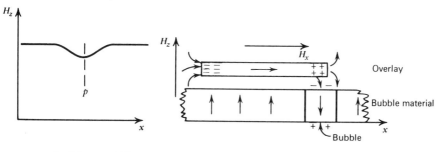

(a) Local minimum of bias.   (b) Local minimum caused by magnetic overlay.

Figure 8.24 Bubble motion can be caused by creating a local minimum bias field that can be moved.

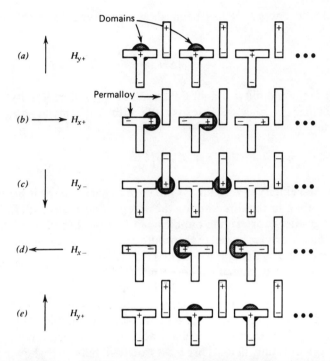

Figure 8.25 Propagation of bubbles with field-accessed T-bar overlay elements. The drive field rotates clockwise in the x–y plane, causing the bubble pattern to move to the right. (From Perneski [26]. Copyright © 1969 by The Institute of Electrical and Electronics Engineers, Inc. Reprinted, with permission, from IEEE Transactions on Magnetics, Sept. 1969, Vol. MAG-5, p. 556.)

sense of field rotation or by using an opposite overlay structure with T-elements that point up instead of down.

The usual bubble memory is serially accessed with some sort of major-loop, minor-loop organization, Fig. 8.26 gives one example. The implementation of such a memory uses not only bubble propagation elements but also configurations for the generation, replication, sensing, and transfer gating of bubbles. The scheme of Fig. 8.26 represents the first commercial bubble memory, which became available a few months before this writing. It has a nominal capacity of 92K bubbles of 5-μm diameter, organized in 144 storage loops (plus spares) of 641 bits each. The rotating field for propagation is achieved by x-direction and y-direction coils that are driven by currents phased 90° apart, in this case triangular current waveforms at 100 kHz. A nondestructive read is accomplished by removing, sensing, and replacing a set of bubbles as

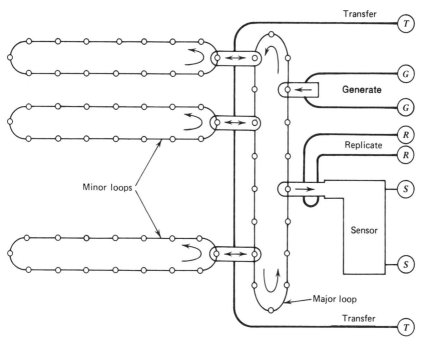

Figure 8.26 Concept of major-loop, minor loop memory organization. The minor loops hold the data; the major loop assembles the data for reading or distributes the data for storage. (Generate, replicate, and transfer gates are current controlled, whereas the propagation is field controlled.)

follows. A pulse of current on the transfer line, at the right time, amplitude, and duration, will parallel-transfer the top bit (bubble or no bubble) from each minor loop into the major loop at a particular phase of the rotating drive field.

As the drive field continues to rotate, the assembled string of bubbles is moved around the major loop in synchronism with the just-vacated voids that are moved around the minor loops. As each bit of the assembled string passes the replicate gate, a proper current pulse makes a copy of each passing bubble into the sensor circuit, which generates an output signal pulse. After 640 cycles of the drive field, all the bubbles will have been propagated completely around the major loop, ready to be inserted back into their original sites by a transfer-in pulse during the next cycle. Other memory functions, such as a destructive read or a store, will use the replicate/annihilate gate in its second mode of operation to destroy each passing bubble. Other bubble memory organizations have been proposed, but at the time of writing, most published architectures are some type of major-loop, minor-loop scheme.

8.6.1 Bubble Materials

Three types of materials have received the most attention as bubble technology has emerged: orthoferrites, garnets, and amorphous gadolinium-cobalt alloy. These three materials represent early exploratory development, present technology, and a research material for possible future use, respectively.

Amorphous gadolinium-cobalt is an interesting material because the bubbles are less than $1 \, \mu$m in diameter, presenting the potential for extremely high density memory. Realization of this potential requires, among other issues, a technology for making very small propagation structures, and the solution of some serious material problems.

Rare earth orthoferrites were used for the first studies of magnetic bubbles. Their chemical formula is $RFeO_3$, where R is a rare earth element such as dysprosium, erbium, gadolinium, holmium, lutetium, samarium, terbium, yttrium, or ytterbium. All these compositions have been studied, in addition to various fractional combinations of two rare earths. The crystal structure is orthorhombic, a distorted cube, and the spin system is almost antiferromagnetic. Significantly, the condition for bubble existence, (8.93), is met by a slight canting of the antiferromagnetic axes that results in a small net moment (Fig. 8.27).

In his early theoretical work on bubble stability [32], Thiele defined optimum values for bubble diameter d and specimen thickness h (thus bubble height) as

$$d = 2h = 8l, \qquad (8.95)$$

where l is a material length parameter. The definition of l is ($\gamma_w/4\pi M_s^2$ in CGS)

$$l = \frac{\gamma_w}{2 W_{dm}} = \frac{\mu_0 \gamma_w}{B_{is}^2} \qquad (8.96)$$

where $\gamma_w = 4\sqrt{AK}$ is the energy of a 180° wall as defined by (8.65) and W_{dm} is the demagnetizing energy of a thin layer with $N = 1$, (8.46). The bubbles observed in orthoferrites have diameters in the range of 50–250 μm (2–10 mils), which meant that large chips would be required to

Figure 8.27 Canted antiferromagnetism for rare earth orthoferrites. Angle ϕ is about 0.5°.

store a few thousand bits. Furthermore, by (8.95) the optimum thickness of orthoferrites is in the range of 25–125 μm (1–5 mils), which is an awkward thickness to produce. It is difficult to cut and polish such a thin layer from a single crystal, but it is also difficult to grow such a thick layer without defects. Figure 8.28 summarizes the state of bubble materials in early 1969.

Bubble Garnets. One of the remarkable accomplishments of bubble technology has been the development of specific materials that sustain

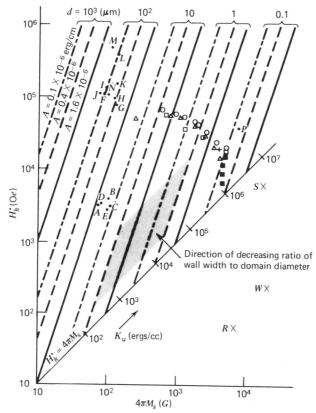

Figure 8.28 Anisotropy field H_k versus demagnetizing field $4\pi M_s$ for bubble materials (log scale). The region of bubble existence is above the diagonal line, (8.93). Lines of constant bubble diameter are shown for three values of exchange constant A, from (8.95) and (8.96). Letters and data points are materials that were studied. The gray region defines the authors' concept of an ideal material that did not yet exist. (Graph from Gianola et al. [27]. Copyright © 1969 by The Institute of Electrical and Electronics Engineers, Inc. Reprinted, with permission, from IEEE Transactions on Magnetics, Sept. 1969; Vol. MAG-5, p. 559.)

small, highly mobile bubbles. A great many combinations and structures of materials were investigated initially, but magnetic garnets have dominated since the breakthroughs of about 1970. At this writing the best bubble materials are rare earth garnet layers grown by liquid-phase epitaxy (LPE) on nonmagnetic substrates at a rate of order $1 \mu m/min$. The most widely used substrate is GGG, gadolinium gallium garnet $(Gd_3Ga_5O_{12})$, which can be grown in large single crystals that are almost entirely free of defects. The rapid success of the effort to develop bubble garnets was greatly aided by the experience in solid-state laser technology with neodymium-doped yttrium-aluminum-garnet (YAG) crystals.

Garnets have the basic formula $A_3B_5O_{12}$; for example YIG, yttrium-iron-garnet, is $\{Y_3\}[Fe_2](Fe_3)O_{12}$. The unit cell of garnet is a cube of about 1.24 nm (12.4 Å) and consists of eight formula units. In contrast with ferrite, which has only two lattice sites (Section 4.2.4), garnets have three sites: {dodecahedral}, [octahedral], and (tetrahedral) identified for YIG using parentheses notation. Each type of site is an interstice surrounded by oxygen ions. The physically larger dodecahedral sites are favored by rare earth ions, whereas the octahedral and tetrahedral sites are favored by iron and other ions of similar size. The magnetic moments of the octahedral sites are aligned parallel, opposite to the alignment of the tetrahedral sites. In YIG, for example, the net moment is due to one iron ion per formula unit (5 Bohr magnetons for the Fe^{3+} ion) because the Y-ion has no magnetic moment.

EXAMPLE P

Bubble garnets require a saturation induction of about 0.02 T. How many Bohr magnetons per formula unit does this correspond to?

ANSWER. The volume of a unit cell is $(1.24 \times 10^{-9})^3 \, m^3$, so $0.02 = nj_B/(1.24 \times 10^{-9})^3$, where $j_B = 1.165 \times 10^{-29}$ Wb·m from (2.8). So $n = 3.27$ Bohr magnetons per unit cell or about 0.41 per formula unit.

One breakthrough that led to the selection of garnets was the discovery by Bobeck et al. [28] that a strong anisotropy was induced by the growth process, to satisfy the requirement of (8.93). The magnetization, the temperature dependence of magnetization and other properties, and the lattice constant all can be controlled by varying the garnet chemistry. Varnerin [29] attributes the simplicity and adaptability of the garnet system to four properties.

1. *Structure.* The garnets are cubic and have no anisotropic properties.

2. *Ease of substitution.* The chemical formula is readily altered; the site preferences are well understood scientifically and are easily controlled.

3. *Wide range of magnetic properties.* The compensation temperature is controllable by rare earth substitution (dodecahedral sites), and magnetization is adjustable by substitution into tetrahedral sites (Fig. 8.29).

4. *High degree of chemical and structural compatibility.* The same garnet structure exists for a wide variety of magnetic properties— permitting, for instance, the epitaxial growth of a magnetic layer onto a nonmagnetic substrate.

Hundreds of plausible chemical combinations of bubble garnets have been studied. At the time of writing, a typical combination for the technology of 5-μm-diameter bubbles is $\{Y_{1.32}Sm_{0.38}Lu_{0.92}Ca_{0.38}\}$

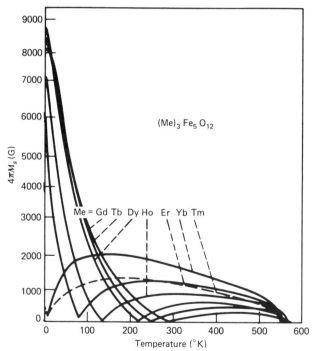

(*a*) Substitution of rare earth elements with higher atomic number lowers the compensation temperature. This widens the range of operating temperatures but increases the magnetization.

Figure 8.29 Tailoring garnet composition for bubble devices. (Adapted from Neilsen [30].)

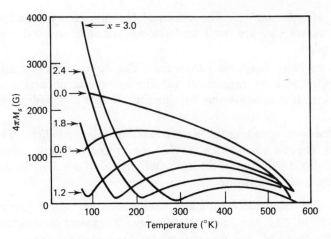

(b) Partial substitution of Gd for Y in YIG, $(Gd_{3-x}Y_x)Fe_5O_{12}$, adjusts both compensation temperature and magnetization.

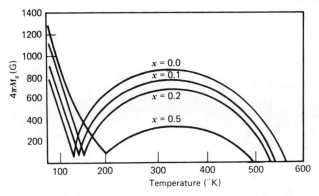

(c) Partial substitution of Al for Fe in YIG, $(Gd_{1.5}Y_{1.5})$-$(Fe_{5-x}Al_x)O_{12}$, adjusts magnetization while maintaining compensation temperature fairly constant.

Figure 8.29   (Cont'd).

$(Fe_{4.08}Ge_{0.92})O_{12}$, but further refinements will probably continue to be made. It is interesting to note that the design goal for temperature stability is to match the bubble garnet to the permanent magnet material that supplies the z-axis bias field, rather than to achieve zero variation with temperature.

Bubble Stability. The earliest experimental observations of magnetic bubbles concerned the range of bias field, normal to the plane of material, required for their existence. At too small a field the bubble suddenly elongates or strips out, but at too large a field the bubble suddenly disappears.

Consider a layer of bubble material of thickness h in the x–y plane, magnetized upward everywhere except in a bubble of radius r, hence $\bar{B}_{is} = \pm \hat{a}_z B_s$, where the minus sign is inside the bubble, and omitting subscript i for simplicity. The bias field H_a is positive in the z-direction and the bubble is modeled as a right circular cylinder with zero wall width. Relative to the case of no bubble, the total energy is the sum of wall energy plus the magnetostatic energy of the bubble in the applied field plus the demagnetizing energy of the bubble

$$E_t = \gamma_w 2\pi r h + 2B_s H_a \pi r^2 h - E_{dm} \qquad \text{J.} \qquad (8.97)$$

In (8.97) γ_w is wall energy per area. The second term is given by (8.41), where the induction of the bubble is a change of $-2B_s$ relative to the case of no bubble. The term E_{dm} in principle is the integral of (8.44) over all space, which is not easily obtained. It is central to this formulation that a larger bubble corresponds to more wall energy and more applied energy but less demagnetizing energy. For stable equilibrium the first derivative of E_t is zero

$$\frac{\partial E_t}{\partial r} = \gamma_w 2\pi h + 4\pi B_s H_a r h - \frac{\partial E_{dm}}{\partial r} = 0. \qquad (8.98)$$

At this point Bobeck [31] chose to divide by $4\pi B_s r h$ to give an equation in H:

$$\frac{\partial E_t / \partial r}{4\pi B_s r h} = \frac{\gamma_w}{2r B_s} + H_a - \frac{\partial E_{dm} / \partial r}{4\pi B_s r h}. \qquad (8.99)$$

The left-hand side of (8.99) is the total equivalent field that acts on a bubble to define its size, which is zero under equilibrium conditions. The first term on the right is an equivalent field H_w due to the wall, which has a $1/r$ dependence, assuming that the unknown γ_w is a material constant independent of r. The second term is the applied bias field $H_a = H_{bias}$, which is independent of r and is controlled by the investigator. The third term on the right is the average z-component demagnetizing field for a bubble, for which Bobeck worked out an analytical solution H_D. At equilibrium (8.99) becomes

$$H_w + H_{bias} = H_D, \qquad (8.100)$$

which is shown in Fig. 8.30. For well-chosen values of H_{bias} there are two intersections at r_a, r_b in Fig. 8.30 that satisfy (8.100), where r_b is the stable solution. A stable solution occurs at the energy minimum, where

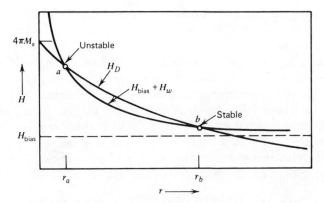

Figure 8.30 Equilibrium conditions for the existence of a stable bubble of radius r_b. (From Bobeck [31]. Reprinted with permission from the *Bell System Technical Journal*, copyright 1967, The American Telephone and Telegraph Company.)

not only $\partial E_t/\partial r = 0$ but also $\partial^2 E_t/\partial r^2 > 0$. The latter condition can be interpreted in Fig. 8.30 such that the slope dH/dr must be less negative for the curve $(H_w + H_{bias})$ than the curve for H_D at the stable intersection b. Using this approach, Bobeck recognized the existence of an optimum thickness for bubble layers because the ratio $2r/h$ is the only geometrical parameter in the calculation of H_D. Furthermore, by measuring the actual bubble radius r_b as a function of H_{bias} he was able to deduce values for wall energy γ_w for orthoferrites of different compositions.

Using a more analytical method than Bobeck, Thiele [32] divided (8.98) by $B_s^2 2\pi h^2/\mu_0$ to give the following equilibrium condition:

$$\frac{\mu_0 \gamma_w}{B_s^2 h} + \frac{\mu_0 H_a}{B_s} \frac{2r}{h} = \frac{\mu_0 (\partial E_{dm}/\partial r)}{B_s^2 2\pi h^2} \tag{8.101a}$$

$$\frac{l}{h} + \frac{H_a}{H_{dm}} \frac{d}{h} = F\left(\frac{d}{h}\right). \tag{8.101b}$$

In the first term l is the material length parameter by (8.96) and in the second term $H_{dm} = B_s/\mu_0$ is a demagnetizing field for the material (not the same as Bobeck's H_D for the bubble). On the right-hand side F is an equivalent force function that tends to expand the bubble because of its own demagnetizing field, plotted in Fig. 8.31 as a function of (diameter/height) for the bubble. Thiele's function F is exactly d/h times Bobeck's function $(H_D/4\pi M_s)$. Thiele continued his analysis to work out the optimum bubble dimensions $d = 2h = 8l$, as well as theoretical values for the critical bias fields for bubble strip-out and for bubble collapse. The critical fields can be shown by a graphical construction on Fig.

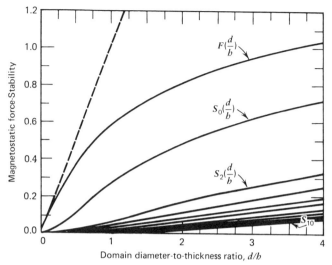

Figure 8.31 The magnetostatic radial force function and the stability functions S_0–S_{10} for an isolated magnetic bubble. (After Thiele [32], reprinted with permission.)

8.31, using his force function F and two stability functions S_0 and S_2. Both functions S_0 and S_2 were obtained from second derivatives of the energy equation (8.97), where S_0 defines the radial instability (bubble collapse) and S_2 defines an instability of the bubble shape (elliptical metastability of bubble strip-out).

The graphical construction consists of plotting (8.101b) onto Fig. 8.31,—detailed in Fig. 8.32. Thiele's construction begins with the given value $l/h = 0.3$, which defines the intercept point W on the ordinate axis. The line from W drawn tangent to function F at point C defines the condition for bubble collapse, the critical diameter d_0 ($d/h = 1.16$) and the critical applied field H_{col}. The line drawn horizontally from W intersects S_0 at C' (which implies d_0), and intersects S_2 at R' (which implies d_2, the critical diameter for bubble strip-out). The critical field H_{s-o} for bubble strip-out is defined by the slope of the line from point W that intersects function F at R, which corresponds to the critical diameter d_2. A stable bias condition is exemplified by the construction WS, which intersects function F at an unstable point U and at the stable point S, where $d/h = 2$. At $d/h = 2$ the operating point S' is equally far from curves S_0 and S_2, so the bubble is at a point of greatest stability. Again, as specified by (8.101b), it is the slope of the line from W to S that defines the bias field.

The static stability of bubbles is well understood by workers in the

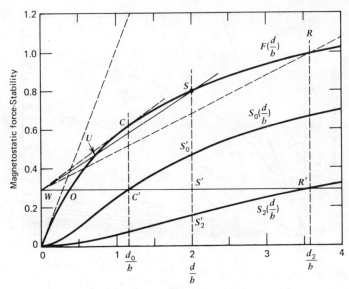

Figure 8.32 Graphical construction of (8.101*b*) for $l/h = 0.3$, $d = d_0$, $d = d_2$, and $d = 2h$. (After Thiele [33]. Reprinted with permission from the *Bell System Technical Journal*, copyright 1971, The American Telephone and Telegraph Company.)

field. The criterion $d/h = 2$ is not always carefully followed; a thicker layer $d/h = 1$ increases the stray field from the bubble to make its detection easier.

8.6.2 Bubble Propagation

A bubble to which a sufficient nonuniform bias field is applied will tend to move toward the region of smaller field with a velocity given by

$$v = \frac{m}{2}\left(|\Delta H_z| - \frac{8H_c}{\pi}\right), \tag{8.94}$$

as explained previously. Materials for high-velocity bubble memory applications must have small coercivity H_c; furthermore the wall mobility m should exceed some minimum value. Wall mobility is a critical material parameter that is measured for each bubble garnet composition. Typical acceptable values are in the range 0.025–0.25 m²/A·s (200–2000 cm/s·Oe).

Wall mobility is related to memory operation in the following way. Suppose that a bubble memory is specified to operate at a drive-field frequency, $f = 250$ kHz. For periodic propagation elements of period λ

(Fig. 8.25), the required velocity is $v = f\lambda$. Bubble-bubble interaction sets a practical propagation period of about 4 bubble diameters

$$\lambda \approx 4d, \qquad (8.102)$$

so the average bubble velocity is 5 m/s for the technology of 5-μm bubbles. For a representative value of mobility $m = 0.05$ m^2/A·s (400 cm/s·Oe), neglecting H_c in (8.94), the drive field across the bubble is required to be $\Delta H_z \approx 200$ A/m (2.5 Oe). This value of field is representative of the drive requirements to be met by propagation elements.

Field Access Elements. A great many overlay designs have been successfully operated in bubble memories. The most widely used versions are T-bars, Y-bars, single chevrons, multiple chevrons, and the half-disk (Fig. 8.33). Each type of element is activated by a rotating field to cause bubble motion. Qualitatively all designs work similarly being partially magnetized by the applied field to create a periodic array of poles that move along as the field rotates. The devices are similarly fabricated of about 0.3 μm-thick Permalloy, not directly on the bubble garnet but separated from it by perhaps 0.3 to 1.0 μm. The element design parameters of thickness, separation, width, and length, as well as the gap

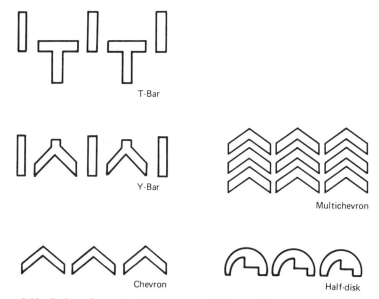

Figure 8.33 Styles of overlay design most widely used for bubble propagation. The direction of propagation is from left to right in every case, assuming clockwise rotation of the drive field.

between elements, involve tradeoffs for any design type that must be carefully evaluated in detail. Three comprehensive papers in the IEEE Transactions on Magnetics (May 1976) address the problem of device modeling and design: George and Hughes (pp. 137–147, 148–159) and Almasi and Lin (pp. 160–202). A Fourier series method of calculation was described in Section 8.2.3.

The greatest-distinction among the elements of Fig. 8.33 are as follows. The multiple chevron propagates an elongated bubble that is stripped out vertically across the multielements. This provides redundancy for immunity to material defects, but at a sacrifice of chip area. The half-disk is a recent innovation that makes it easier for a small bubble to cross the gaps between elements. When the rotating field is oriented straight down, poles are developed on both sides of the gap. This allows the bubble to strip across with no potential barrier. Future systems using somewhat smaller bubbles will probably use half-disk propagation elements, or some variant. Research continues on the problem of propagating extremely small bubbles.

Evaluation. The methods of evaluating the design of bubble domain devices are ultimately experimental and quite varied. The early designs of propagation elements for orthoferrite bubbles were derived from simply looking through a microscope to see what the bubble did. At the other extreme, rather sophisticated measurement studies are now routinely done to establish long-term performance statistics with different patterns of bubbles. Intermediate between the two extremes is a type of test that defines the operating margins for bias field and for rotating field (Fig. 8.34).

For a preliminary understanding of failure mechanisms, recall that a free bubble will collapse at a large bias field that exceeds H_{col} and that for $H_B \approx H_{col}$ the bubble radius has its minimum value r_0. Furthermore, a free bubble will strip out (or run out) at the smaller bias field $H_{s\text{-}o}$, for which the bubble radius is maximum at r_2. A bubble under a field-access element sees a net bias field that is the sum of the bias field plus the field from the element $\beta_{zx}H_x$ plus an interaction field H_{bp}

$$H_{net} = H_B + \beta_{zx}H_x + H_{bp}, \qquad (8.103)$$

which must lie between limits such as

$$H_{s\text{-}o} < H_{net} < H_{col}. \qquad (8.104)$$

In (8.103) the parameter β_{zx} specifies the z-axis field due to the in-plane rotating field H_x. It has a negative sign, since $H_{net} < H_B$, and β undoubtedly varies with the azimuth angle ϕ of the rotating field. The

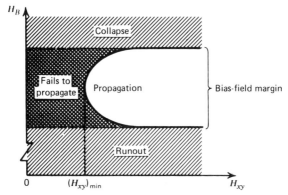

Figure 8.34 The allowed range of values for bias field H_B and for rotating field H_{xy}. This format is widely used to show the results of measured system performance. (From Almasi and Lin [34]. Copyright © 1976 by the Institute of Electrical and Electronics Engineers, Inc. Reprinted, with permission, from IEEE Transactions on Magnetics, May 1976, Vol. MAG-12, p. 165.

effective field H_{bp} is due to the interaction between the bubble and the permeable overlay. It is also negative with a value that varies with bubble position.

The field margin limit (8.104) can be rewritten as a limit on bubble radius

$$r_2 > r > r_0. \qquad (8.105)$$

Since in practice the bubble propagation performance is somewhat sensitive to bubble size, the measured margins may be less than the range implied by (8.104) or (8.105).

Dynamic Effects. When bubble memories are operated at different frequencies and the field margins are plotted as in Fig. 8.34, considerably less margin is found at high frequency. Although there are many exceptions, the performance of present technology deteriorates at frequencies above 0.3 to 1 MHz. At one time, moreover, attempts to push bubbles to high velocity caused a permanent change of their characteristics; that is, the bubbles would undergo a dynamic conversion to become "hard bubbles." The latter problem may have delayed bubble technology for a year, to research the problem and to develop a satisfactory cure.*

*The most popular scheme of hard-bubble suppression uses an extra processing step of ion implantation to develop a thin, stressed garnet surface layer. Other methods include deposition of a very thin permalloy on the garnet surface, or the epitaxial growth of a second magnetic garnet.

Considerable research on domain wall velocity still continues in an effort to extend the data rate for bubble memories. It seems that the equation for wall mobility

$$m = \frac{\gamma\sqrt{A/K}}{\alpha} \qquad (5.76)$$

is merely an approximation for low-drive fields, below the limiting value of wall velocity. Limiting values of wall velocity have been measured in several different materials, and two plausible mechanisms have been given.

The Walker limit for wall velocities in garnet arises as a precession angle limitation of the torque required to overcome damping losses, (see Ref. [16] of Chapter 5). Alternatively, the Slonczewski limit arises because a more complicated wall structure develops, with a corresponding increase in wall inertia [41]. The wall precession model of Section 5.4.2 is inapplicable to bubble walls for two reasons:

1. The intrinsic induction for garnets is 2 orders of magnitude smaller than for ferromagnets. As a result, demagnetizing fields such as the Becker field are not very strong.
2. A bubble wall is a closed cylindrical surface, in contrast to a planar wall. Unless hard-bubble suppression techniques are used, extremely fast velocities may cause bubble walls to acquire twists and kinks because of spin precession. The result is a complicated wall configuration, analogous to the cross-tie wall, but in cylindrical geometry.

The final word on bubble velocity limitations still seems unclear, and extraordinarily high velocities continue to be reported from time to time.

8.6.3 Memory System Components

The concept of a major-loop, minor-loop organization for a serially accessed bubble memory is illustrated in Fig. 8.26. The realization of such a system requires not only propagation but also components for generation, for replication, for bubble transfer, and for bubble detection.

Generation. The earliest type of bubble generator used the principle of maintaining a resident seed bubble from which a new bubble is split off once every rotation of the drive field. Figure 8.35 presents an extension of that principle to permit current control. In this design the resident bubble is driven around the square by a counterclockwise rotating field. As the phase angle ϕ of the rotating field increases from $-90°$ to $0°$, part of the resident bubble is attracted from the protrusion to bridge across

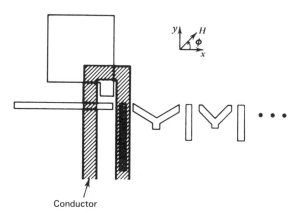

Figure 8.35 A normally on bubble generator that can be inhibited by current through the conductor. (From Bosch et al. [35]. Copyright © 1973 by The Institute of Electrical and Electronics Engineers, Inc. Reprinted, with permission, from IEEE Transactions on Magnetics, Sept, 1973, Vol. MAG-9, p. 482.)

into the propagation circuit. As the phase angle continues to increase, the extension from the seed bubble is cut loose to form a new bubble. The generation can be prevented by a clockwise current in the hairpin conductor.

Replication.   Replication is a variation of bubble generation in which a bubble in one propagation track is duplicated into an adjacent track. The replicator circuit in Fig. 8.36 consists of two propagate paths and a conductor loop. A current pulse in the proper phase will cause a bubble in either track to strip across into both tracks. The two ends of the

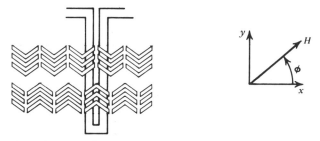

Figure 8.36 A replicate gate in chevron technology. A bubble in either channel can be stretched into the other by applying a current pulse at the time the bubble is under the conductor. The replication is completed by a second current pulse of opposite polarity. (From Bobeck et al. [36]. Copyright © 1973 by the Institute of Electrical and Electronics Engineers, Inc. Reprinted, with permission, from IEEE Transactions on Magnetics, Sept. 1973, Vol. MAG-9, p. 477.)

elongated bubble then are propagated in opposite directions, stretched across the conductor region until cut by a short current pulse of the opposite polarity. The design must ensure that the two multichevron propagation channels "zig and zag" in phase, so that a bubble in either track will be under the conductor loop when the rotating field is at H_y (i.e., when $\phi = 90°$). The direction of bubble propagation is to the right in the top track and to the left in the bottom track for a counterclockwise sense of field rotation, assuming the convention of a negative bubble as defined in Fig. 8.24b. The direction of propagation is controlled by the phase of the gap in the general zig-zag structure.

Transfer. A bubble transfer gate is used to control whether a single bubble moves from one propagation track into another—for instance, from a minor storage loop into the major read-out loop of a memory. A practical example of a current-controlled transfer gate is the dollar-sign transfer gate (Fig. 8.37), so called because of the shape of the Permalloy transfer element, which has a rounded protrusion from each side. As described earlier, bubble propagation is caused by a gradient of the z-axis bias field that causes the bubble to move toward the lower field. When a bubble is at the transfer location of a gate, either of two gradients can act on it. The normal gradient would keep the bubble moving along its normal propagation path, or alternatively a transfer gradient would move the bubble into the new path. The inventors of the dollar-sign transfer [37] have described it as a combination of two simpler configurations as follows. In a configuration where the control current flow is parallel to the major loop, the control current tends to increase the transfer field gradient but does not decrease the normal gradient. Alternatively, in a configuration with the conductor perpendicular to the major loop, the control current has little effect on the transfer gradient but decreases or blocks the normal field gradient. In the present case, both field gradients are affected by the current that flows at an angle of 45° to the major loop. Is the current direction shown correctly in Fig. 8.37?

Detection. In the early days of bubble technology a great variety of bubble detection methods were investigated, including inductive sensors, Hall effect devices, and optical methods. Magnetoresistance detectors are almost universally used at this time, usually in a multichevron configuration that forms one leg of a resistance bridge circuit. The field from a single bubble is very localized, so that bubbles are temporarily stretched into very long strips for ease of detection. The elongation, perpendicular to the propagation path, is done gradually over several cycles by increasing the number of parallel chevron elements. The

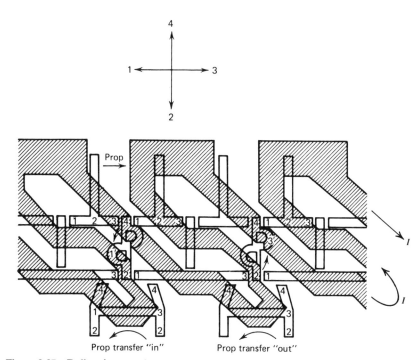

Figure 8.37 Dollar-sign transfer gate for transferring between major loop (top), and minor loops (bottom). The hashed-line area is the conductor, which is located underneath the Permalloy pattern (i.e., between the Permalloy and the bubble garnet). Transfer "in" ("out") is shown on the left (right) of the structure. Numbers corresponding to the phase of *H* have been added to the original figure to indicate the bubble propagation sequence. (Adapted from Smith, Kish, and Bonyhard [37]. Copyright © 1973 by The Institute of Electrical and Electronics Engineers, Inc. Reprinted, with permission, from IEEE Transactions on Magnetics, Sept. 1973, Vol. MAG-9, p. 287.

incremental voltage due to a bubble acting on a magnetoresistor is

$$v = I\Delta R = Jl\Delta\rho \qquad \text{V,} \qquad (8.106)$$

where J is current density and l is the length of the magnetoresistance element that undergoes a change of resistivity $\Delta\rho$. A stretched bubble uses a longer detector, therefore causes a larger output voltage. The maximum current density is limited by considerations mentioned in Section 3.1.3, such as electromigration failure of the conductor.

Considerable attention has been given to fabrication methods that require as few photolithography masks as possible; thus the detectors are usually made of the same material and at the same time as the other permalloy overlay elements. Figure 8.38 shows some designs for detec-

(a) An elementary detector.   (b) Chevron detector structures.

Figure 8.38 Permalloy chevron elements, interconnected for use as magnetoresistance detectors for bubbles. (From Bobeck et al. [36]. Copyright © by The Institute of Electrical and Electronics Engineers, Inc. Reprinted, with permission, from IEEE Transactions on Magnetics, Sept. 1973, MAG-9, p. 475.)

tors that consist of interconnected multichevron propagation elements, illustrating the elementary concept of a transition region to stretch the bubble before it is detected (a), and two configurations of practical detector elements, each of which consists of more than 300 interconnected chevrons (b).

8.7 SUMMARY COMMENTS

The range and scope of magnetic bubble technology provide a measure of the status of applied magnetics at the time of writing. Several ancillary technologies have laid significant scientific and technological foundations on which the bubble technology has been built. The supporting technologies include, as a minimum, the art and science of growing large, defect-free single crystals; the development of garnet chemistries that yield specific magnetic properties, and the realization of these compositions in thin layers by liquid-phase epitaxy; permalloy thin film technology; and multiple-mask integrated circuitry using high-resolution photolithography.

But how is the magnetic bubble related to the history of prior magnetic technologies? We can make several general observations that seem to be broadly applicable, not only to bubbles but also to several other areas of magnetics:

1. The technology depends on the response of magnetic materials to

applied magnetic fields and/or other stimuli, and on the innovative use of certain details of that response.

2. The details of the magnetic response have extended our understanding of magnetic processes.
3. The technology was developed in conjunction with the development of new magnetic materials.
4. The new materials are used in specific geometries that are well suited to the material and to the application.

The practice of electrical engineering is rich with innovative applications of magnetism, some of which have been described in this book. The descriptions represent an attempt to expose the physics of the magnetic processes as well as the electrical results, while also giving specific values for physical parameters that relate the two. One never gets the whole story in magnetism, but I hope that this work will be a useful point of departure.

PROBLEMS

1 **(Section 8.2.2).**   Work out expressions (8.8) for M/H_a and B/H_a for an ellipsoidal sample of an ideal linear magnetic material, assuming that $B_i = \mu_0 \chi H_{in}$, $H_{in} = H_a + H_d$ and $H_d = -NB_i/\mu_0$.

2 **(Section 8.2.2).**   Show the equivalence of (8.8b) to the expression $(1 - 1/\mu_{eff}) = (1 - N)(1 - 1/\mu_r)$.

3 **(Section 8.2.2).**   A manufacturer of radio core linear magnetic materials supplies his components as cylindrical rods of dimensions 0.6 cm diameter × 1.8 cm long. Make a graph of the effective relative permeability of such a specimen as a function of the intrinsic relative permeability of the material. Assume for that purpose that the rod, if excited by a uniform field, may be approximated by an inscribed prolate spheroid. What can you say about the response to the excitation of a short coil around the center of the rod?

4 **(Section 8.2.2).**   Suppose the sphere of Fig. 8.2 is a permanent magnet of $B_i = 0.198\,T$ with zero applied field. How should the figure be modified to describe the new situation?

5 **(Section 8.2.2).**   Make a more detailed numerical plot of H versus z in Fig. 8.2b, with particular attention to the field just outside the sphere. Assume that the axis of interest passes through the center of the sphere.

6 **(Section 8.2.3).**   The fraction in (8.39), if divided by μ_0, is the

transfer function M_n/h_n. For a thin film of thickness $T = 100$ nm and hard-axis (rotational) susceptibility $\chi = 2 \times 10^3$, make a log–log graph of the transfer function for $n = 10$–10^4. Assume that $k = 2\pi/\lambda$ has a value of 200 rads/m. How does the transfer function explain Fig. 8.4?

7 (Section 8.3.1). Work out the details that lead to (8.54) of Example H and (8.55) of Example I.

8 (Section 8.3.1). In the one-dimensional model of a 180° domain wall, do the following:

a. Plot a few points using (8.64) to show how wall angle varies with distance.

b. Develop a definition for wall width δ by extrapolating $dx/d\theta$ in the center of the wall.

9 (Section 8.4.1)

a. Assuming in (8.68) that the magnetostriction is measured in the same direction as the magnetization, solve for the saturation magnetostriction of a cubic crystalline material along each of the following axes: [100], [111], [110].

b. Use (8.70) to derive (8.67).

10 (Section 8.5). A significant but second-order effect in polycrystalline magnetic films is the dispersion of the easy axis. A ripple model of this effect is given by Middelhoek [18, pp. 46–56]. Study the reference material and be prepared to describe the results orally.

11 (Section 8.5). Suppose a magnetic thin film has been deposited on a glass substrate, which can be bent slightly to subject the film to a uniaxial stress. Using (8.72) to model the magnetostriction, prescribe how to stress the film to increase the apparent H_k:

a. If the film has a positive magnetostriction constant λ.

b. If the film has a negative magnetostriction constant λ.

12 (Section 8.5.1)

a. Plot a graph of one quadrant of the switching astroid using (8.74).

b. Show that the astroid slope $dh_y/dh_x = \tan \phi$.

c. Find the value of the constant C in the equation for the particular hyperbola $h_x h_y = C$, which is just tangent to the astroid at $h_x = h_y$.

13 (Section 8.5.1). Angular dispersion of the easy axis of a polycrystalline permalloy thin film can be qualitatively represented by a group of astroids, plotted to share a simple common origin but with their easy axes aligned at slightly different angles. Make a sketch to

represent a polycrystalline film with a dispersion angle α_{90} of about 5°. (This means that 0.9 of the film has 5° or less angular dispersion.) Use your sketch to explain why currents I_1 and I_2 in Fig. 8.13 overlap the read current waveform.

14 (**Section 8.5.1**). Explain the role of the transient field H_z in thin film reversal by the rotation process.

15 (**Section 8.5.2**). Use (8.65) to calculate the energy per area of a domain wall, given the physical data (CGS) in the legend of Fig. 8.18. Recognizing that (8.65) does not include magnetostatic energy, how is it applicable to Fig. 8.18?

16 (**Section 8.5.2**). At $t = 0$ a field $\bar{H} = H\hat{a}_x$ is applied to the two thin films of Fig. 8.21, causing each Néel wall to move parallel to itself. Explain the direction of motion and the polarity of the Becker field for each case.

17 (**Section 8.5.2**). Make sketches to indicate the probable local orientation of intrinsic induction in the immediate vicinity of each type of Bloch line (Fig. 8.22). Note .that (8.55) is thought to be a valid equation for exchange energy for each of the two types of Bloch line.

18 (**Section 8.6**). Consider a wafer of magnetic bubble garnet of $B_{is} = 0.02$ T, diameter = 5 cm and thickness = 5 μm = 5×10^{-4} cm. Use (3.36a) for a cylindrical magnet to calculate the h-field at a point 1-μm above the surface of the center of the wafer, for each of the following cases:

a. The entire wafer is magnetically saturated in the positive z-direction; that is, the top surface has a positive pole.

b. The wafer is magnetized as in (a) except for one cylindrical region of 5 μm diameter in the center, directly under the field point, which is magnetized in the negative z-direction.

Hint. The field change from (a) is like superposing an isolated cylinder of $B_{is} = 0.04$ T, twice the background value.

19 (**Section 8.6**). Refer to the bubble memory data that accompany Fig. 8.26 and estimate the times required to execute a nondestructive read of the following bubble locations.

a. The desired data in the minor loops will propagate to the transfer gate during the next cycle of rotating field.

b. The desired data are in a minor loop location that passed by the transfer gate one cycle ago.

20 (**Section 8.6.1**). Find the material length parameter for a bubble material if exchange constant $A = 4 \times 10^{-12}$ J/m, $B_{is} = 0.02$ T, and the

material has a Q of 5. What diameter bubble would you expect from this material?

21 (Section 8.6.1). A bubble garnet for a commercial bubble memory has been characterized [39] as follows: $h = 5.3\,\mu$m, $l = 0.55\,\mu$m, $\gamma_w = 0.21$ erg/cm^2, $Q = 4.6$, $K = 8956$ erg/cc, $4\pi M = 218$ G, $\lambda = 22.5\,\mu$m, $m = 509$ cm/s·Oe, and $f = 10^5$ Hz.

a. Check the consistency of the data (CGS) using MKS values, (8.96).

b. Find the value of exchange constant A.

c. Find the value of damping factor α in (5.76).

22 (Section 8.6.1). Using Thiele's method, make a graphical construction as in Fig. 8.32 for the bubble material of Problem 21, and deduce theoretical values for the critical bias fields and the critical bubble radii.

23 (Section 8.6.1) Using the material data of Problem 21 as a point of departure, what specifications would you suggest for a material to sustain bubbles of 1.5 μm diameter?

24 (Section 8.6.2). Find the net drive field ΔH_z that is required to be developed across the bubble in the system of Problem 21, assuming that material coercivity is negligible.

25 (Section 8.6.2). Make sketches similar to Fig. 8.25* to illustrate the bubble propagation of the Y-bar and the half-disk elements (Fig. 8.33). (*Maybe you can devise a simpler way to show this.)

26 (Section 8.6.3). Make sketches of bubble position, as a function of the phase of H, to illustrate the workings of the bubble generator (Fig. 8.35) and the replicate gate (Fig. 8.36).

27 (Section 8.6.3). Can you devise a configuration of bubble generator, in contrast to Fig. 8.35, that normally generates no bubbles until it is enabled by control current?

28 (Section 8.6.3). Study the dollar-sign transfer gate (Fig. 8.37) in enough detail to deduce the sequence of bubble positions. Make a sketch of the side view, to show the "conductor-first" pattern deposition sequence. Use your sketch as an aid in determining the effects of control current on the normal field gradient and on the transfer field gradient.

REFERENCES*

1. S. Chikazumi, *Physics of Magnetism*, Wiley, New York, 1964. Chapter 10, "Magnetostatic Energy," emphasizes magnetostatic energy and the product (poles × potential) in addition to B_iH.

2. J. A. Stratton, *Electromagnetic Theory*, McGraw-Hill, New York 1941. Sections 2.14–2.18 present a general field theoretic view of magnetostatic theory.

3. R. M. Bozorth, *Ferromagnetism*, Van Nostrand, New York, 1951. See pages 729–731 for an explanation of the energy of magnetization.

4. W. F. Brown, Jr., *Magnetostatic Principles in Ferromagnetism*, North Holland, Amsterdam, 1962. An advanced book for further study.

5. J. A. Osborne, "Demagnetizing Factors of the General Ellipsoid," *Phys. Rev.*, **67**, 351–357 (1945).

6. E. C. Stoner, "Demagnetizing Factors for Ellipsoids," *Phil. Mag.* **36**, No. 7, 803–821 (1945).

7. J. S. Colonias, "Calculation of Magnetic Fields for Engineering Devices," *IEEE Trans. Magn.*, **MAG-12**, 1030–1035 (November 1976). A review paper quoted in Section 8.2.3. Also see other papers on computer simulation in the same *Transactions*. At least two recent international conference on computation exist, see *Proceedings of the International Conference on the Computation of Magnetic Fields*, (*COMPUMAG*), Rutherford Laboratory, Oxford, England, March 31–April 2, 1976. Also *Proceedings of the International Conference on Numerical Methods in Electric and Magnetic Field Problems* (ICCAD), Genoa, Italy, May–June 1976.

8. D. B. Dove, "Demagnetizing Fields in Thin Magnetic Films," *Bell Syst. Tech. J.*, **46**, 1527–1559 (September 1967).

9. I. S. Gradshteyn and I. M., Ryzhik, *Tables of Integrals, Series and Products*, Academic Press, New York 1965.

10. C. Kittel and J. K. Galt, "Ferromagnetic Domain Theory," in *Solid State Physics*, vol. 3, F. Seitz and D. Turnbull, Editors, Academic Press, New York, 1956, p. 439.

11. B. D. Cullity, *Introduction to Magnetic Materials*, Addison-Wesley, Reading, Mass., 1972.

12. M. Prutton, *Thin Ferromagnetic Films*, Butterworths, London, 1964.

13. R. F. Soohoo, *Magnetic Thin Films*, Harper & Row, New York, 1965.

14. H. Chang and G. C. Feth, "Bibliography of Thin Magnetic Films," *IEEE Trans. Commun. Electron.* (November 1964).

15. *Magnetism and Magnetic Materials: 19xx Digest, A Survey of the Technical Literature of the Preceding Year*, Academic Press, New York and London. Published each year (from about 1963 to 1969) with the cooperation of the AIP-IEEE Conference on Magnetism and Magnetic Materials.

*A bracketed notation [C], [S], or [C, S] following a citation indicates that the referenced paper is reprinted by Chang [23], Smith [24], or both.

16. D. O. Smith, in *Magnetism*, Vol. 3, G. T. Rado and H. Suhl, Editors, Academic Press, New York, 1963, Chap. 10, p. 465.

17. F. B. Hagedorn, "Review of Thin Film Switching," *IEEE Trans. Magn.*, **MAG-4**, 41–44 (March 1968).

18. S. Middelhoek, *Ferromagnetic Domains in Thin Ni–Fe Films*, Thesis, University of Amsterdam, 1961. Also issued as IBM Technical Report TR 00.1390, January 1966.

19. S. Middelhoek, "Thin Films," in *Magnetic Properties of Materials*, Inter-University Electronics Series, Vol. 13, Jan Smit, Editor, McGraw-Hill, New York, 1971, Chap. 8, pp. 269–339.

20. S. Methfessel, S. Middelhoek, and H. Thomas, "Domain Walls in Thin Magnetic Ni–Fe Films," *J. Appl. Phys.*, **31**, 302S–304S (1960).

21. L. J. Schwee, "Stability Conditions for Néel Walls and Cross-Tie Walls, in Thin Magnetic Films," *AIP Conf. Proc.*, **10**, p. 2, 996–1000 (1973).

22. L. J. Schwee and J. K. Watson, "A New Model for Cross-Tie Walls Using Parabolic Coordinates," *IEEE Trans. Magn.*, **MAG-9**, 551–554 (September 1973).

23. Hsu Chang, Editor, *Magnetic Bubble Technology: Integrated Circuit Magnetics for Digital Storage and Processing*, IEEE Press, New York, 1975. Selected reprints of 46 significant papers, 216 pages of editorial interpretation, some 70 pages of bibliography and patent disclosures (699 pages).

24. Alan B. Smith, Editor, *Bubble Domain Memory Devices*, Artech House, Dedham, Mass., 1974. Selected reprints of 37 significant papers with editorial comments and additional references (258 pages).

25. A. H. Bobeck and H. E. D. Scovil, "Magnetic Bubbles," *Sci. Amer.*, **224**, 78–90 (June 1971) [C, S].

26. A. J. Perneski, "Propagation of Cylindrical Magnetic Domains in Orthoferrites," *IEEE Trans. Magn.*, **MAG-5**, 554–557 (September 1969) [C, S].

27. U. F. Gianola, D. H. Smith, A. A. Thiele, and L. G. Van Uitert, "Material Requirements for Circular Magnetic Domain Devices," *IEEE Trans. Magn.*, **MAG-5**, 558–561 (September 1969) [S].

28. A. H. Bobeck et al., "Magnetic Properties of Flux Grown Uniaxial Garnets," *IEEE Trans. Magn.*, **MAG-7**, 461–463 (September 1971).

29. L. J. Varnerin, "Approaches for Making Bubble-Domain Materials," *IEEE Trans. Magn.*, **MAG-7**, 404–409 (September 1971).

30. J. W. Nielsen, "Properties and Preparation of Magnetic Materials for Bubble Domains," *Metall. Trans.*, **2**, No. 3, 625–633 (March 1971).

31. A. H. Bobeck, "Properties and Device Applications of Magnetic Domains in Orthoferrites," *Bell Syst. Tech. J.*, **46**, 1901–1925 (October 1967).

32. A. A. Thiele, "Theory of the Static Stability of Cylindrical Domains in Uniaxial Platelets," *J. Appl. Phys.*, **41**, 1139–1145 (1 March 1970).

33. A. A. Thiele, "Device Implications of the Theory of Cylindrical Magnetic Domains," *Bell Syst. Tech. J.*, **50**, 727–775 (March 1971) [C].*

34. G. S. Almasi and Y. S. Lin, "An Analytical Design Theory for Field-Access Bubble Domain Devices," *IEEE Trans. Magn.*, **MAG-12**, pp. 160–202, May 1976. Figure 8.34

was taken from this comprehensive paper, which considers failure mechanisms in some detail, including the replicate generator Fig. 8.35.

35. L. J. Bosch et al., "1024-Bit Bubble Memory Chip," *IEEE Trans. Magn.*, **MAG-9**, 481–484 (September 1973). Figure 8.35 was taken from this paper.

36. A. H. Bobeck et al., "Evolution of Bubble Circuits Processed by a Single Level Mask," *IEEE Trans. Magn.*, **MAG-9**, 474–480 (September 1973). Figures 8.36 and 8.38 were taken from this paper.

37. J. L. Smith, D. E. Kish, and P. I. Bonyhard, "Dollar-Sign Transfer for Magnetic Bubbles," *IEEE Trans. Magn.*, **MAG-9**, 285–289 (September 1973). Figure 8.37 and related discussion were adapted from this paper.

38. P. I. Bonyhard and J. L. Smith, "68 K-Bit Capacity, 16 μm Period Magnetic Bubble Memory Chip Design with 2 μm Minimum Features," *IEEE Trans. Magn.*, **MAG-12**, 614–617 (November 1976). Describes the evolution of the half-disk propagation element.

39. R. A. Naden, W. R. Keenan, and D. M. Lee, "Electrical Characterization of a Packaged 100K-Bit Major/Minor Loop Bubble Device," *IEEE Trans. Magn.*, **MAG-12**, 685–687 (November 1976).

40. C. Kooy and U. Enz, "Experimental and Theoretical Study of the Domain Configuration in Thin Layers of $BaFe_{12}O_{19}$, " *Philips Res. Rep.*, **15**, 7–29 (February 1960).

41. J. C. Slonczewski, "Dynamics of Magnetic Domain Walls," *AIP Conf. Proc.*, *No. 5*, 170–174 (1972).

42. William Fuller Brown, Jr., *Micromagnetics*, Wiley-Interscience, New York, 1963.

43. S. Shtrikman and D. Treves, "Micromagnetics," in *Magnetism*, Vol. 3, G. T. Rado and H. Suhl, Editors, Academic Press, 1963. Chap. 8, pp. 375–414.

44. Y. S. Lin, "Analysis of Permalloy Circuits for Bubble Domain Propagation," *IEEE Trans. Magn.* **MAG-8**, 375–377 (September 1972).

45. D. B. Dove, J. K. Watson, E. Huijer, and H. R. Ma, "A Simplified Fourier Series Method for the Calculation of Magnetostatic Interactions in Bubble Circuits," *AIP Conf. Proc.*, **29**, Magnetism and Magnetic Materials-1975, 44–45 (1976).

46. E. Huijer, D. B. Dove, and J. K. Watson, "Magnetostatic Effects in I-bars: A Unifying Overview of Domain and Continuum Results," *IEEE Trans. Magn.* **MAG-16** (January 1980).

47. E. Huijer, D. B. Dove, and J. K. Watson, "Fundamentals of Modeling I-bars and Bubbles Using Fourier Series," submitted to *IEEE Trans. Magn.*

48. E. Feldtkeller and H. Thomas, "Struktur und Energie von Blochlinien in Dünnen Ferromagnetischen Schichten", *Phys. konders. Materie*, **4**, 8 (1965).

Author Index

Numbers in *italics* indicate chapter references.

Subject Index

Numbers in **boldface** refer to the Table of Contents that precedes each chapter; page numbers of references that follow each chapter are in *italics*.